VECTOR
CALCULUS

VECTOR

CALCULUS

B. W. LINDGREN   *Department of*

Mathematics, University of Minnesota

THE MACMILLAN COMPANY

COLLIER-MACMILLAN LIMITED, LONDON

Fifth Printing, 1969

Library of Congress catalog card number: 64-10969

The Macmillan Company
Collier-Macmillan Canada, Ltd., Toronto, Ontario

Printed in the United States of America

PREFACE

This book is intended as a text for a short course in the elements of vector analysis in three dimensions. Its name was chosen to emphasize the fact that it is not a book on the analysis of problems in mechanics and electromagnetics using vector methods, but is a presentation of the mathematics—the algebra and calculus—of vectors.

A mathematics course based on this book would ordinarily follow the usual first course in differential and integral calculus, which is assumed as a prerequisite. It reviews the notions of limit, continuity, derivative, and integral from elementary calculus, and introduces more advanced topics—line integrals, surface integrals, Jacobians, and directional derivatives—in a setting of "real" problems. This motivated introduction to advanced topics makes them perhaps a bit more palatable when they are encountered in more detail in a course in advanced calculus. Thus, my aim has been to teach some useful mathematics associated with certain physical problems, rather than to study those physical problems by means of mathematical techniques for whose adequate development there is hardly room at this stage of the student's career.

I am grateful to Professors Fulton Koehler and Richard Juberg for valuable suggestions which have added to the accuracy and usefulness of the book.

B. W. LINDGREN

CONTENTS

vii

1 VECTOR ALGEBRA

THE physical sciences abound with "quantities" whose effects depend on the directions in which they act as well as on their magnitudes or amounts. For instance, a force of ten pounds pushing an object in one direction will produce a result different from that of a force of ten pounds pushing in another direction. A displacement or motion of an object two miles in a southerly direction will give it a position different from that given by a motion of two miles in a northwesterly direction. Such quantities are called *vector quantities*, and it is clearly not sufficient to represent them mathematically by a single number. Both a number (for the amount or magnitude) *and* a direction are necessary.

In the examples cited the "direction" is an orientation in the "space" of our experience, for which the solid geometry of Euclid is the mathematical model. Although the notion of vector can be usefully extended and applied to mathematical spaces of higher dimension, this book will treat the three-dimensional case (and incidentally the one- and two- dimensional cases) and will consider only applications in which vectors represent actual physical magnitudes and directions.

1.1   *Basic definitions*

Mathematically, a *vector* is a combination of a direction or orientation in three-dimensional geometry and a (non-negative) magnitude. Various symbols are used to denote vectors. In this book, a boldface letter, such as **V**, will denote a vector. Other symbols used, especially when writing by

1

hand, are a letter with a small arrow above it: $\overrightarrow{V}$, and an underlined letter: $\underline{V}$. The *length* or *magnitude* of the vector **V** will be denoted by $|\mathbf{V}|$, or occasionally by V.

A vector quantity and the mathematical vector which represents it have no *location*—do not refer to any particular point of application (of the force or displacement, say). Yet it is convenient to represent a vector as a *directed line segment*, with the understanding that two directed line segments have the same magnitudes and same directions denote the same vector and are equivalent. The directed line segment from P to Q will be symbolized either $\overrightarrow{PQ}$ or (P, Q), where P is called the initial point and Q

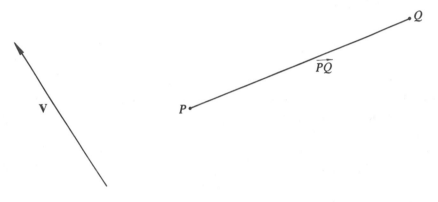

Figure 1.1.   Vectors.

the terminal point; and it will be the practice to say that the vector being represented *is* $\overrightarrow{PQ}$, although it should be kept in mind that any other directed line segment equal in length and direction to $\overrightarrow{PQ}$ could be used to indicate this length-direction pair. In particular, when definitions are given in terms of the geometric representation by directed segments, the results must be shown to be independent of location.

Another point to be noted is that in representing (say) a force vector **F** as a directed line segment $\overrightarrow{PQ}$, there is implicit a choice of a unit of measurement, and that a change in scale would alter the representation accordingly.

It will be seen that some combinations of forces or displacements result in *no* net force or displacement, and to complete the representation of vector quantities it is convenient to define a *zero vector*—a vector with zero length and unspecified direction. This is not quite the same kind of element as a vector of positive length, but it can be included as a vector so long as special rules for operating with it are given. These rules, of course, will not require the assignment of a direction to the zero vector, since the direction is immaterial. The zero vector will be denoted by **0**.

In studying geometry and space motion with vector methods it is convenient to associate with each point in space a vector from an arbitrarily chosen reference point or *origin* out to the point in question. This assignment is unique, and the vector serves to identify the point. In Fig.

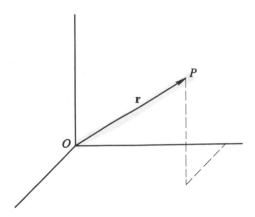

Figure 1.2.   Position vector.

1.2 there is shown a point P, an origin O, and the vector $\overrightarrow{OP}$, which is called the *position vector* of P. The vector $\overrightarrow{OP}$ locates the point P, and the point P defines the vector. Thus, the set of all points in space can be identified with the set of all vectors issuing from a fixed reference point. Even the reference point itself is so identified—by the zero vector. (Notice that in the figure there are drawn "axes." These are shown simply to give some pictorial indication of a reference frame, rather than to suggest that rectangular coordinates are pertinent or necessary.)

The symbol **r** will be used rather consistently to denote the position vector $\overrightarrow{OP}$ of the point P. In following the motion of a point particle whose position is the varying point $P(t)$ it will be sufficient to consider the function $\mathbf{r}(t)$, that is, the position vector of P considered as a function of time. This notion of vector function, or vector-valued function, is defined in a manner analagous to that in which an ordinary real-valued function $f(t)$ is defined, except that the range of values of the function is a set of vectors rather than a set of real numbers.

EXAMPLE 1.1   Consider the parallelogram $ABCD$, shown in Fig. 1.3. The

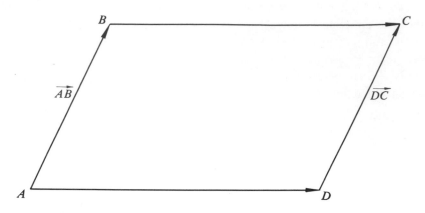

Figure 1.3.   (See Example 1.1).

following relations hold:

and
$$\overrightarrow{AB} = \overrightarrow{DC},$$
$$\overrightarrow{BC} = \overrightarrow{AD},$$

expressing the fact that opposite sides of a parallelogram are equal and parallel.

EXAMPLE 1.2   A sphere is defined as the set of points P lying at a fixed distance a from a certain point. The sphere of radius a and center at the origin O can be defined as the set of points P whose position vectors $\mathbf{r}$ have length a:

$$|\mathbf{r}| = a.$$

This is the vector form of the equation of the given sphere; it is a condition satisfied by those points P on the sphere and not satisfied by any point which is not on the sphere.

1.2   *Vector addition and subtraction*

It is often the case with quantities described by a combination of a magnitude and a direction that two such quantities combine according to a "parallelogram law" to yield a resultant quantity of the same type. This resultant behaves in some respects like a sum of ordinary numbers, and the terms *sum* and *addition* are used. One might even restrict the term *vector quantity* to quantities which *do* combine in this way, about to be defined and described.

The *sum* of two vectors (P, Q) and (Q, R), that is, $\overrightarrow{PQ}$ and $\overrightarrow{QR}$, is defined to be the vector (P, R) or $\overrightarrow{PR}$:

$$\overrightarrow{PQ} + \overrightarrow{QR} = \overrightarrow{PR}.$$

(See Fig. 1.4.) In this definition one vector is assumed to issue from the terminal point of the other. But there is no loss of generality in this, since

for any two vectors **U** and **V** the vector **V** can be replaced by a vector **V'** equal to it (in length and direction) but issuing from the terminal point of **U**. Indeed, the sum does not depend on the locations of the line segments used in its construction. In Fig. 1.5 are shown two computations of the sum **U** + **V**, one in which **V'** issues from the terminal point of **U**, and one in which **U** is replaced by an

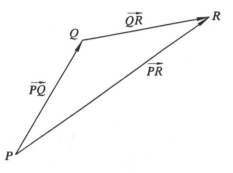

Figure 1.4.   Vector addition.

equivalent **U'** and **V** by an equivalent **V''** issuing from the terminal point of **U'**. Clearly, **U'** + **V''** = **U** + **V'** = **U** + **V**.

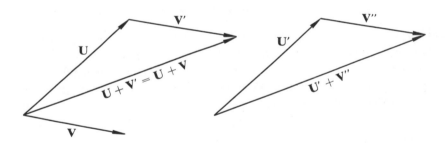

Figure 1.5

The definition of addition includes as a special case the following, worth special mention:

$$\overrightarrow{PQ} + \mathbf{0} = (P, Q) + (Q, Q) = \overrightarrow{PQ}.$$

It also covers the case in which the summands are parallel; if $\overrightarrow{PQ}$ is parallel to $\overrightarrow{QR}$, then the sum $\overrightarrow{PR}$ is parallel to them both. It has a length equal to the sum of the lengths, if $\overrightarrow{PQ}$ and $\overrightarrow{QR}$ point the same way, and a length equal to the difference of the lengths, if $\overrightarrow{PQ}$ and $\overrightarrow{QR}$ point in opposite directions.

In Fig. 1.6 there is drawn the sum $\mathbf{U} + \mathbf{V}$ as well as the sum $\mathbf{V} + \mathbf{U}$; the latter can be obtained by taking a vector $\mathbf{V}''$ equal to $\mathbf{V}$ but issuing

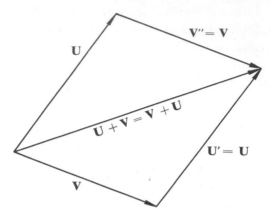

Figure 1.6.   Addition is commutative.

from the initial point of $\mathbf{U}$ and a vector $\mathbf{U}'$ equal to $\mathbf{U}$ but issuing from the terminal point of $\mathbf{V}$. It is clear that these sums are equal:

$$\mathbf{U} + \mathbf{V} = \mathbf{V} + \mathbf{U}.$$

That is, vector addition is *commutative*. It is also clear that the common sum is the diagonal of a parallelogram defined by the vectors $\mathbf{U}$ and $\mathbf{V}$ (or vectors equal to them) as adjacent sides. (This accounts for the name "parallelogram law" used to describe the above rule for adding vectors.)

The magnitude and direction of a sum can be obtained analytically from the magnitudes and directions of the summands with the aid of some trigonometry. Observe that when $\mathbf{U}$ and $\mathbf{V}$ issue from the same point, the sum $\mathbf{U} + \mathbf{V}$, issuing from that point, lies in the plane determined by $\mathbf{U}$ and $\mathbf{V}$. Observe also that since the sum is the third side in a triangle having $\mathbf{U}$ and $\mathbf{V}$ as two sides, its length is not larger than the sum of the lengths of those sides:

$$|\mathbf{U} + \mathbf{V}| \leq |\mathbf{U}| + |\mathbf{V}|.$$

This is known as the *triangle inequality*. [Notice that the plus sign on the left denotes vector addition, whereas the plus sign on the right denotes addition of real numbers.]

Having added together vectors $\mathbf{U}$ and $\mathbf{V}$ to obtain $\mathbf{U} + \mathbf{V}$ one can add to this sum a third vector $\mathbf{W}$, to obtain $(\mathbf{U} + \mathbf{V}) + \mathbf{W}$. This is exactly the same as the vector $\mathbf{U} + (\mathbf{V} + \mathbf{W})$:

$$(\mathbf{U} + \mathbf{V}) + \mathbf{W} = \mathbf{U} + (\mathbf{V} + \mathbf{W}),$$

a fact which is described by saying that vector addition is *associative*. To see this, let $\mathbf{U} = \overrightarrow{PQ}$, $\mathbf{V} = \overrightarrow{QR}$, and $\mathbf{W} - \overrightarrow{RS}$:

$$(\overrightarrow{PQ} + \overrightarrow{QR}) + \overrightarrow{RS} = \overrightarrow{PR} + \overrightarrow{RS} = \overrightarrow{PS} = \overrightarrow{PQ} + \overrightarrow{QS} = \overrightarrow{PQ} + (\overrightarrow{QR} + \overrightarrow{RS}).$$

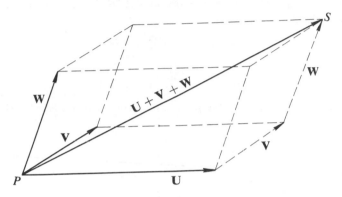

Figure 1.7.   Sum of three vectors.

Because of this property it is not essential that parentheses be used in indicating the sum of three vectors, and one writes simply $\mathbf{U} + \mathbf{V} + \mathbf{W}$. Figure 1.7 exhibits this sum as the diagonal of a parallelepiped. (The six possible "paths" from P to S along the edges of the parallelepiped correspond to the six possible orders of the summands.)

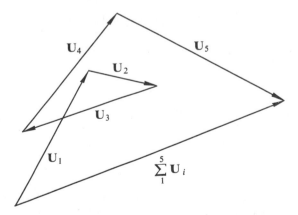

Figure 1.8.   Sum of five vectors.

Sums of any finite numbers of vectors are defined by induction. The sum $\mathbf{U}_1 + \mathbf{U}_2 + \cdots + \mathbf{U}_n$ is defined, after choosing $\mathbf{U}_i$ with its initial point at the terminal point of $\mathbf{U}_{i-1}$ ($i = 2, \ldots, n$), as the vector required to close the polygon. (See Fig. 1.8, in which the sum of five vectors is indicated.) The associative law and the triangle inequality are readily extended to the case of n summands by induction. (See Problem 1.8.)

E X A M P L E 1.3   Consider any four points A, B, C, D, shown in Fig. 1.9, as defining a tetrahedron. The relations

$$\vec{AB} + \vec{BC} + \vec{CD} = \vec{AD}$$

and

$$\vec{AB} + \vec{BD} + \vec{DC} + \vec{CA} = \mathbf{0}$$

follow from the definition of addition and are evident geometrically in the figure.

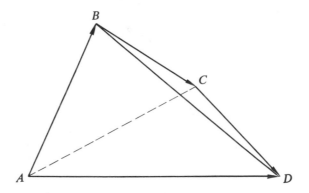

Figure 1.9.   (See Example 1.3.)

Subtraction of vectors is defined so as to be an inverse of addition, as follows:

$$\vec{PQ} - \vec{PR} \equiv \vec{RQ}.$$

With this definition (see Fig. 1.10), it follows that

$$(\vec{PQ} - \vec{PR}) + \vec{PR} = \vec{RQ} + \vec{PR}$$
$$= \vec{PR} + \vec{RQ} = \vec{PQ}.$$

That is, $\mathbf{U} - \mathbf{V}$ is the vector which when added to $\mathbf{V}$ yields $\mathbf{U}$. It is the vector needed to close up the triangle formed with $\mathbf{U}$ and $\mathbf{V}$ as sides issuing from a common vertex.

A special case of the above definition of subtraction is the following:

$$\mathbf{U} - \mathbf{U} = \overrightarrow{PQ} - \overrightarrow{PQ} = \overrightarrow{QQ} = \mathbf{0}.$$

Conversely, if $\mathbf{U} - \mathbf{V} = \mathbf{0}$, then $\mathbf{U} = \mathbf{V}$, which follows upon addition of $\mathbf{V}$ to each side of $\mathbf{U} - \mathbf{V} = \mathbf{0}$.

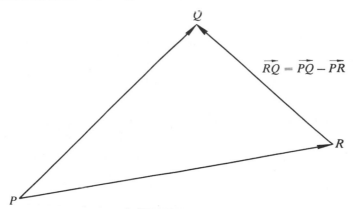

$$\overrightarrow{RQ} = \overrightarrow{PQ} - \overrightarrow{PR}$$

Figure 1.10.   Subtraction of vectors.

The vector $-\mathbf{U}$ is defined as a vector equal in length to $\mathbf{U}$ but pointing in exactly the opposite direction:

$$-\overrightarrow{PQ} = \overrightarrow{QP}.$$

Then if $\overrightarrow{PQ} = \mathbf{U}$ and $\overrightarrow{PR} = \mathbf{V}$,

$$\mathbf{U} + (-\mathbf{V}) = \overrightarrow{PQ} + (-\overrightarrow{PR})$$
$$= \overrightarrow{PQ} + \overrightarrow{RP} = \overrightarrow{RQ} = \mathbf{U} - \mathbf{V}.$$

Subtracting $\mathbf{V}$ is equivalent to adding $-\mathbf{V}$, and so subtraction can be considered as a special case of addition.

A combination of displacements is represented accurately by vector addition. For, a displacement of a particle from point A to the point B is represented by the vector $\overrightarrow{AB}$, and from the point B to the point C by the vector $\overrightarrow{BC}$. The net total displacement is from A to C, represented by $\overrightarrow{AC}$, which is precisely the vector sum of $\overrightarrow{AB}$ and $\overrightarrow{BC}$. This will be seen subsequently to imply that velocities, accelerations, and (by Newton's laws) forces also combine according to the parallelogram law.

Problems

1.1.   If the vector $\mathbf{U}$ is ten units long and points east, and the vector $\mathbf{V}$ is five units long and points northeast, determine the length and direction of the vectors $\mathbf{U} + \mathbf{V}$ and $\mathbf{U} - \mathbf{V}$.

1.2. Describe the vectors $\mathbf{U} + \mathbf{U} + \mathbf{U}$ and $\mathbf{U} + \mathbf{U} - \mathbf{U}$.

1.3. Show that $(\mathbf{U} - \mathbf{V}) + \mathbf{W} = (\mathbf{U} + \mathbf{W}) - \mathbf{V}$.

1.4. Explain how $\mathbf{U}_1 + \cdots + \mathbf{U}_n$ is defined for any positive integer n using induction.

1.5. Given any four arbitrary points in space, A, B, C, and D, show that $\overrightarrow{AD} - \overrightarrow{AB} = \overrightarrow{CD} - \overrightarrow{CB}$.

1.6. Let $\mathbf{r}_1$ and $\mathbf{r}_2$ denote the position vectors of P_1 and P_2, respectively. Interpret $\mathbf{r}_1 - \mathbf{r}_2$ geometrically.

1.7. Use the triangle inequality to show that $|\mathbf{U} - \mathbf{V}| \geq \big||\mathbf{U}| - |\mathbf{V}|\big|$, and interpret this geometrically.

1.8. Show by induction that $|\mathbf{U}_1 + \cdots + \mathbf{U}_n| \leq |\mathbf{U}_1| + \cdots + |\mathbf{U}_n|$.

1.3   *Multiplication by scalars*

An ordinary real number is termed *scalar* to distinguish it from a vector. Similarly, a physical quantity (temperature, for instance) having magnitude without direction is called a scalar quantity to distinguish it from a vector quantity, which has both magnitude and direction.

It is convenient and natural to call the vector $\mathbf{U} + \mathbf{U}$ by the name $2\mathbf{U}$, and $\mathbf{U} + \mathbf{U} + \mathbf{U} + \mathbf{U} + \mathbf{U}$ by the name $5\mathbf{U}$. The vector $2\mathbf{U}$ is a vector in the same direction as $\mathbf{U}$ but twice as long; the vector $5\mathbf{U}$ is also in the same direction as $\mathbf{U}$, but five times as long. In this spirit $k\mathbf{U}$, where k is a positive scalar, is defined to be a vector in the direction of $\mathbf{U}$, k times as long as $\mathbf{U}$. The symbol $k\mathbf{U}$ is then defined for any real number k by the rules

$$0\mathbf{U} = \mathbf{0},$$
$$(-k)\mathbf{U} = -(k\mathbf{U}).$$

This operation between the scalar k and the vector $\mathbf{U}$ which yields the vector $k\mathbf{U}$ is called *multiplication*. It satisfies the following properties:

$$(ab)\mathbf{U} = a(b\mathbf{U}),$$
$$|a\mathbf{U}| = |a||\mathbf{U}|,$$
$$(a + b)\mathbf{U} = a\mathbf{U} + b\mathbf{U},$$
$$k(\mathbf{U} + \mathbf{V}) = k\mathbf{U} + k\mathbf{V}.$$

The last two properties are *distributive laws;* of these, the first is a consequence of the definition of the sum of parallel vectors, and the second is a

result of the proportionality of corresponding sides of similar polygons.
(See Fig. 1.11.)

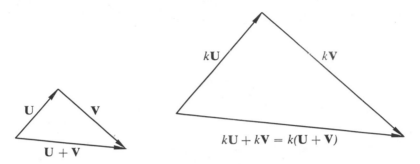

Figure 1.11.   A distributive law.

Division by a nonzero scalar is automatically defined, of course, along
with the definition of multiplication. Division by k is simply multiplication
by $1/k$.

EXAMPLE 1.4   A vector whose length is one unit is called a *unit vector*.
Given an arbitrary vector **V** of positive length a unit vector in the same direction
can be constructed by dividing the vector by its length: $\mathbf{V}/|\mathbf{V}|$. For the length
of this vector is

$$\left| \frac{1}{|\mathbf{V}|}\, \mathbf{V} \right| = \frac{1}{|\mathbf{V}|}|\mathbf{V}| = 1. \qquad \textit{Normalizing the Vector}$$

Thus, for example, if **V** has length five, $\tfrac{1}{5}\mathbf{V}$ has length one.

A combination of the vectors **U** and **V** of the form $a\mathbf{U} + b\mathbf{V}$ is called a
linear combination of them. When **U**, **V**, and $a\mathbf{U} + b\mathbf{V}$ issue from a common
point, the combination $a\mathbf{U} + b\mathbf{V}$ lies in the plane defined by the vectors
U and **V**, no matter what values the multipliers a and b have, if **U** and **V**
define a plane. Conversely, it can be seen that if **U** and **V** are not zero and
not parallel, any vector **W** in the plane of **U** and **V** can be represented as a
linear combination of them. This is evident from the geometrical construction shown in Fig. 1.12; the tip of **W** is projected parallel to **V** onto **U**,
and parallel to **U** onto **V**, to obtain vectors $a\mathbf{U}$ and $b\mathbf{V}$ parallel to **U** and **V**
whose sum is then **W**. Moreover, this representation is unique. For, if **W**
can be written as $a\mathbf{U} + b\mathbf{V}$ and also as $c\mathbf{U} + d\mathbf{V}$, then

$$a\mathbf{U} + b\mathbf{V} = \mathbf{W} = c\mathbf{U} + d\mathbf{V},$$

or

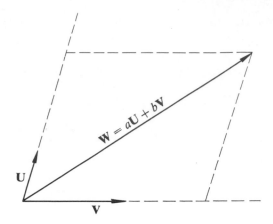

Figure 1.12.

$$(a - c)\mathbf{U} + (b - d)\mathbf{V} = \mathbf{0},$$

which implies that $\mathbf{U}$ and $\mathbf{V}$ are parallel unless $a = c$ and $b = d$ (since it was assumed that neither $\mathbf{U}$ nor $\mathbf{V}$ is the zero vector).

The linear combinations of the form $a\mathbf{U} + (1 - a)\mathbf{V}$ have a special property. Subtracting $\mathbf{U}$ from this vector yields (see Fig. 1.13)

$$a\mathbf{U} + (1 - a)\mathbf{V} - \mathbf{U} = (1 - a)(\mathbf{V} - \mathbf{U}),$$

which is parallel to $\mathbf{V} - \mathbf{U}$ and $1 - a$ times as long. This means that the tip of $a\mathbf{U} + (1 - a)\mathbf{V}$ lies on the segment jointing the tips of $\mathbf{U}$ and $\mathbf{V}$ (or on an extension of this segment). Thus, the particular linear combinations whose coefficients add to one are vectors whose tips are on the line

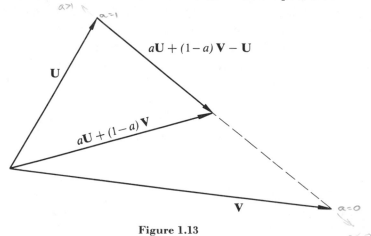

Figure 1.13

determined by the tips of **U** and **V**. Clearly $a = 1$ yields **U** and $a = 0$ yields **V**. Values of a between zero and one correspond to vectors which lie *between* **U** and **V**, and values of a less than zero and greater than one correspond to vectors whose tips lie on the *extension* of the line segment joining the tips of **U** and **V**.

Observe that the end point of the vector $a\mathbf{U} + (1 \quad a)\mathbf{V}$, for $0 \leq a < 1$, lies at a point which is the fraction $1 - a$ of the way from the tip of **U** to the tip of **V**. The midpoint of the segment joining the tips of **U** and **V**, in particular, is the tip of the vector $\frac{1}{2}(\mathbf{U} + \mathbf{V})$.

E X A M P L E 1.5   The ideas just developed can be used to derive anew certain well-known geometrical relationships. Consider, for instance, the parallelogram

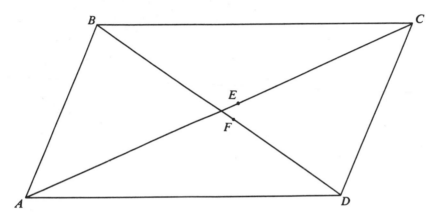

Figure 1.14.   **(See Example 1.5.)**

ABCD in Fig. 1.14. The vector from *A* to *C* is surely twice the vector from *A* to the midpoint *E* of $\overline{AC}$; that is,

$$\overrightarrow{AE} = \tfrac{1}{2}(\overrightarrow{AB} + \overrightarrow{AD}).$$

But this linear combination is a vector from *A* to the midpoint *F* of the line segment $\overline{BD}$ joining the tips of $\overrightarrow{AB}$ and $\overrightarrow{AD}$; that is, *E* and *F* really *coincide*, so the diagonals of a parallelogram bisect each other.

Linear combinations of three vectors are also of interest—sums of the form $a\mathbf{U} + b\mathbf{V} + c\mathbf{W}$. If the vectors **U**, **V**, and **W** are not coplanar (when initiated at the same point), every vector **R** can be expressed as such a linear combination. For, projecting **R** parallel to **W** onto the plane of **U** and **V** determines a vector $c\mathbf{W}$ and a vector **S** in the plane of **U** and **V** which in turn can be expressed as $a\mathbf{U} + b\mathbf{V}$, so that

$$\mathbf{R} = \mathbf{S} + c\mathbf{W} = a\mathbf{U} + b\mathbf{V} + c\mathbf{W}.$$

(See Fig. 1.15.)

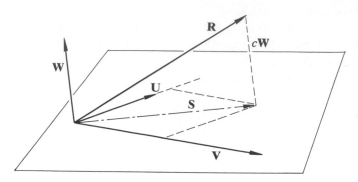

Figure 1.15.   Expressing a vector as a linear combination of three vectors.

Linear combinations $\alpha\mathbf{U} + \beta\mathbf{V} + \gamma\mathbf{W}$ in which the coefficients add to one are again of special significance. For, if $\alpha + \beta + \gamma = 1$, then

$$(\alpha\mathbf{U} + \beta\mathbf{V} + \gamma\mathbf{W}) - \mathbf{U} = \beta\mathbf{V} + \gamma\mathbf{W} - (1 - \alpha)\mathbf{U} = \beta(\mathbf{V} - \mathbf{U}) + \gamma(\mathbf{W} - \mathbf{U}).$$

This shows (see Fig. 1.16) that the tip of $\alpha\mathbf{U} + \beta\mathbf{V} + \gamma\mathbf{W}$ lies in the plane

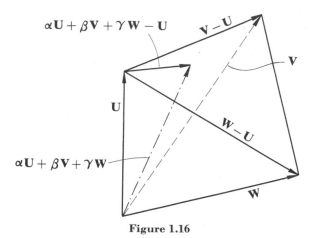

Figure 1.16

defined by the tips of $\mathbf{U}$, $\mathbf{V}$, and $\mathbf{W}$. Thus, linear combinations of this special type generate the plane determined by the end points of $\mathbf{U}$, $\mathbf{V}$, and

W. Further, if the coefficients α, β, and γ are positive, the vector $\alpha\mathbf{U} + \beta\mathbf{V} + \gamma\mathbf{W}$ terminates somewhere inside the triangle determined by the tips of **U**, **V**, and **W**.

Since the expression of an arbitrary vector in terms of three vectors as a linear combination of them generally requires that they be non-coplanar, consider for a moment the significance of the coplanarity of three vectors. If **U**, **V**, and **W** *are* coplanar, one of them can be expressed in terms of the other two (surely, if the three vectors are not all parallel, and even if they are) as a linear combination; say,

$$\mathbf{W} = r\mathbf{U} + s\mathbf{V},$$

or

$$r\mathbf{U} + s\mathbf{V} - \mathbf{W} = 0.$$

That is, there is a linear combination of **U**, **V**, and **W** which is the zero vector, but in which not all coefficients are zero. Conversely, if there is a linear combination $a\mathbf{U} + b\mathbf{V} + c\mathbf{W}$ in which at least one coefficient is not zero, and if this linear combination is the zero vector, then **U**, **V**, and **W** are coplanar. For, if (say) $c \neq 0$, the relation

$$a\mathbf{U} + b\mathbf{V} + c\mathbf{W} = 0$$

implies

$$\mathbf{W} = -\frac{a}{c}\mathbf{U} - \frac{b}{c}\mathbf{V},$$

so that **W** is a linear combination of **U** and **V** and so lies in the plane of **U** and **V**. The term *trivial* is often used to describe the linear combination $0\mathbf{U} + 0\mathbf{V} + 0\mathbf{W}$, and in terms of this the foregoing can be summarized as follows: Three vectors are noncoplanar if and only if the one linear combination of them which is the zero vector is the trivial one.

The representation of an arbitrary vector **R** in the form $a\mathbf{U} + b\mathbf{V} + c\mathbf{W}$ is unique when the vectors **U**, **V**, and **W** are not coplanar. For, if also $\mathbf{R} = a'\mathbf{U} + b'\mathbf{V} + c'\mathbf{W}$, subtraction yields

$$0 = \mathbf{R} - \mathbf{R} = (a - a')\mathbf{U} + (b - b')\mathbf{V} + (c - c')\mathbf{W},$$

and the coefficients in this linear combination must all be zero when **U**, **V**, and **W** are not coplanar; that is, $a = a'$, $b = b'$, $c = c'$.

The foregoing discussion is often given in terms of the notion of linear independence. Vectors $\mathbf{V}_1, \ldots, \mathbf{V}_m$ are said to be *linearly independent* if and only if the only linear combination of them which is the zero vector is the trivial one; that is, if and only if the relation

$$\Sigma c_i V_i = 0$$

implies

$$c_1 = \cdots = c_m = 0.$$

If a nontrivial linear combination of the **V**'s *does* give **0**, they are linearly *dependent*. The following are evident:

(1) Vectors **U** and **V** are linearly independent if and only if they are not parallel and neither is **0**.

(2) Vectors **U**, **V**, and **W** are linearly independent if and only if they are not coplanar (when they issue from a common point).

(3) A set of more than three vectors (in three-dimensional space) is automatically a linearly dependent set.

Problems

1.9.   Vectors **U** and **V** have lengths four and six, respectively, and point in the same direction. Express **V** in terms of **U**.

1.10.   Show by induction that $k\Sigma V_i = \Sigma k V_i$, for any finite set of vectors $V_1, \ldots, V_n$.

1.11.   Draw a triangle exhibiting the relation **U** + **V** = **W**, for arbitrarily selected vectors **U** and **V**, and then draw a triangle exhibiting the relation $-3\mathbf{U} - 3\mathbf{V} = -3\mathbf{W}$.

1.12.   Let **U** and **V** be given vectors, with **V** issuing from a specified reference point O. Sketch the vector $t\mathbf{U} + \mathbf{V}$ (let it also issue from O) for several values of t, and describe the locus of the tip of this vector as t varies over $(-\infty, \infty)$.

1.13.   Given vectors **U**, **V**, and **W**, let **W** and the linear combination $s\mathbf{U} + t\mathbf{V} + \mathbf{W}$ initiate from a fixed reference point O. Sketch $s\mathbf{U} + t\mathbf{V} + \mathbf{W}$ for various choices of (s, t) and describe the locus of the tip of this vector as s and t vary over $(-\infty, \infty)$.

1.14.   Show that the vectors $\mathbf{0}, V_1, \ldots, V_n$ are linearly dependent, for any vectors $V_1, \ldots, V_n$.

1.15.   In Fig. 1.16 it is clear that the vectors

$$\mathbf{V} - \mathbf{U}, \mathbf{W} - \mathbf{U} \quad \text{and} \quad \alpha\mathbf{U} + \beta\mathbf{V} + \gamma\mathbf{W} - \mathbf{U}$$

are coplanar. Determine a nontrivial linear combination of them equal to **0**. (Note: $\alpha + \beta + \gamma = 1$.)

1.16.   Show that if $V_1, \ldots, V_k$ are linearly dependent, so are the vectors $V_1, \ldots, V_k, V_{k+1}, \ldots, V_n$.

1.17. Show that the medians of a triangle intersect in a point, as follows. Consider vectors **U**, **V**, and **W** drawn from an arbitrary point to the three vertices (as in Fig. 1.16), and show that the tip of $\frac{1}{3}(\mathbf{U} + \mathbf{V} + \mathbf{W})$ lies on each of the medians, two thirds of the way from the vertex to the opposite side. (To do this, show that

$$\mathbf{U} + \tfrac{3}{2}[\tfrac{1}{3}(\mathbf{U} + \mathbf{V} + \mathbf{W}) - \mathbf{U}] = \tfrac{1}{2}(\mathbf{V} + \mathbf{W}),$$

and interpret this geometrically.)

1.18 Let (x, y, z) denote the point in space with rectangular coordinates x, y, and z relative to a given coordinate system.

(a) How do you know that the position vectors **i** of the point $(1, 0, 0)$, **j** of the point $(0, 1, 0)$, and **k** of the point $(0, 0, 1)$ are linearly independent?

(b) Referring to a sketch if necessary, express the position vector **r** of the point $(3, 2, -4)$ as a linear combination of **i**, **j**, and **k**.

1.4   *Vector products*

There are two important binary operations—combinations of two vectors—which behave in many respects like products of ordinary numbers. Each of them arises in applications of vector analysis, and both are called products. One of these operations results in a new vector, the other in a scalar. Although these operations resemble number multiplication, so that much of vector algebra is formally like number algebra, there will be instances in which the vector analogue of a valid manipulation of numbers is not correct.

The *vector product* (also called *cross product* or *outer product*) of the vectors **U** and **V** is symbolized by **U** × **V**. It is a *vector*, the vector whose magnitude is

$$|\mathbf{U} \times \mathbf{V}| = |\mathbf{U}||\mathbf{V}| \sin \theta,$$

and whose direction is normal to the plane of **U** and **V** (when **U** and **V** issue from a common point) in a sense determined by the "right-hand rule." This rule is carried out by having fingers of the right hand point from **U** to **V**, the thumb then indicating the sense of **U** × **V**. (See Fig. 1.17.) This definition is not symmetrical, and the vector **V** × **U** is different from **U** × **V**, but only in that its sense is opposite; that is, **V** × **U** = −**U** × **V**. This may well be the reader's first contact with an operation called by the name *multiplication* which is not commutative, that is, in which the *order* of the factors in the product makes a difference.

(In pointing from **U** to **V** the smaller angle should be used, and then sin θ will be non-negative automatically. But if the larger angle were used, sin θ would be negative and the net effect would be the same.)

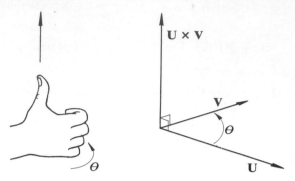

Figure 1.17.   Vector product.

To cite an instance in which the cross product arises in physics, consider a solid body fixed at a point O. If a force **F** is applied at the point P whose position vector relative to O is **r**, the body will acquire angular momentum about an axis which is perpendicular to **F** and also to **r**; this axis is then along the direction of **r** $\times$ **F**. The quantity **r** $\times$ **F** is called *torque*. A use of the cross product in geometry is indicated in the following example.

E X A M P L E 1.6   A line through a point P_0 parallel to a given vector **A** $\neq$ **0** can be described by a vector equation. Let $\mathbf{r}_0$ denote the position vector of P_0

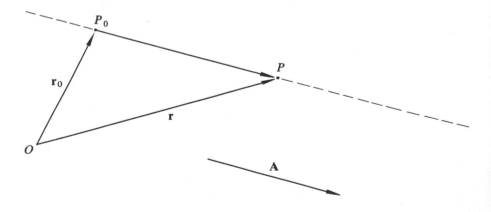

Figure 1.18.   (See Example 1.6.)

relative to some given origin and **r**, the position vector of an arbitrary point P, as in Fig. 1.18. This point P is on the desired line if and only if the vector $\overrightarrow{P_0P} =$ **r** − **r₀** is parallel to **A**. But the angle between parallel vectors is 0, and so their cross product must vanish. Thus, P is on the desired line if and only if

$$\mathbf{A} \times (\mathbf{r} - \mathbf{r_0}) = \mathbf{0}.$$

(If it is on the line, **A** is parallel to **r** − **r₀** and their cross product is zero; if the cross product is zero, either **A** is parallel to **r** − **r₀** or **r** − **r₀** = 0, and in either case the point P is on the line.) This equation then characterizes points P on the line and is a form of the equation of the line through a specified point having a specified direction.

The line can also be represented by a *parametric* equation. The vector **r** − **r₀** is parallel to **A** if and only if it is a scalar multiple of **A**:

$$\mathbf{r} = \mathbf{r_0} + t\mathbf{A}.$$

As t varies from $-\infty$ to ∞ the point P traces out the entire line; each t corresponds to exactly one point on the line.

The vector product has been seen to be not commutative, and now in Example 1.6 another unusual property is evident: a product can vanish even though neither factor is "zero" (in this case, the zero vector). For, if $\mathbf{U} \times \mathbf{V} = \mathbf{0}$, then either (a) $\mathbf{U} = \mathbf{0}$, (b) $\mathbf{V} = \mathbf{0}$, or (c) sin $\theta = 0$ (parallel vectors). This is in contrast to the case of ordinary multiplication of numbers, in which the vanishing of a product can occur only if at least one factor is zero.

What about *associativity?* Since $\mathbf{U} \times \mathbf{V}$ is a vector, one can form such a combination as $(\mathbf{U} \times \mathbf{V}) \times \mathbf{W}$. This triple product will be studied in more detail in Sect. 1.6. For the present it is simply observed that $(\mathbf{U} \times \mathbf{V}) \times \mathbf{W}$ is *not* always the same as $\mathbf{U} \times (\mathbf{V} \times \mathbf{W})$, even though the order of the factors be preserved. This is seen by considering the product $(\mathbf{U} \times \mathbf{V}) \times \mathbf{V}$, which is *not* necessarily zero, and the product $\mathbf{U} \times (\mathbf{V} \times \mathbf{V})$, which *is* necessarily zero, since $\mathbf{V} \times \mathbf{V} = \mathbf{0}$.

So far the vector combination called *product* seems to behave not at all like a product. Yet there is one important property which *does* hold. Vector multiplication is *distributive* over vector addition:

$$\mathbf{U} \times (\mathbf{V} + \mathbf{W}) = \mathbf{U} \times \mathbf{V} + \mathbf{U} \times \mathbf{W}.$$

The next few paragraphs will be devoted to deriving this relation. With it one can multiply polynomials together as in ordinary algebra provided he preserves the order in multiplications.

added proof $\bar{u} \times \bar{v} + \bar{u} \times \bar{w} = \bar{u}(\bar{v} + \bar{w})$

The magnitude of a product of two vectors has a convenient geometrical interpretation. When **U** and **V** issue from the same point, the length of the perpendicular from the tip of **V** to **U** is equal to $V \sin \theta$, θ being again the angle between **U** and **V**, acute or obtuse. The product of this perpendicular distance and the magnitude U is then the *area* of the parallelogram formed by **U** and **V**, as in Fig. 1.19. Observe also that the

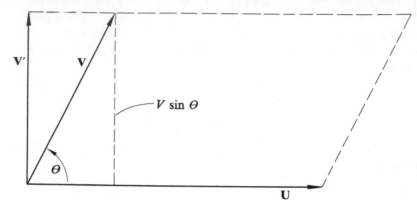

Figure 1.19

rectangle formed by **V**′ (in this figure) and **U** has the same area as the parallelogram formed by **V** and **U**, and that the magnitude of the cross product **U** × **V**′ is therefore the same as the magnitude of **U** × **V**. But the directions of these cross products are also the same, so that **U** × **V**′ = **U** × **V**. As a result, any cross product can be replaced by a cross product

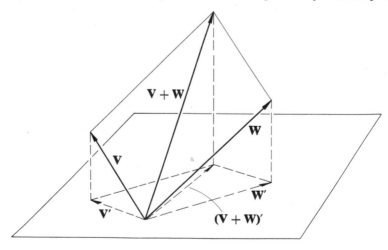

Figure 1.20

in which one factor has been replaced by a projection of that factor along the direction (in their common plane) perpendicular to the other factor.

Consider now the vectors $\mathbf{U}$, $\mathbf{V}$, and $\mathbf{W}$ and let $\mathbf{V}'$ and $\mathbf{W}'$, as shown in Fig. 1.20, be the projections of $\mathbf{V}$ and $\mathbf{W}$ in the plane perpendicular to $\mathbf{U}$. Then

$$\mathbf{U} \times \mathbf{V} = \mathbf{U} \times \mathbf{V}',$$
$$\mathbf{U} \times \mathbf{W} = \mathbf{U} \times \mathbf{W}',$$

and

$$\mathbf{U} \times (\mathbf{V} + \mathbf{W}) = \mathbf{U} \times (\mathbf{V} + \mathbf{W})'.$$

Examination of the geometry involved shows that also

$$(\mathbf{V} + \mathbf{W})' = \mathbf{V}' + \mathbf{W}';$$

that is, the projection of the sum is the sum of the projections. Hence

$$\mathbf{U} \times \mathbf{V} + \mathbf{U} \times \mathbf{W} = \mathbf{U} \times \mathbf{V}' + \mathbf{U} \times \mathbf{W}'$$

and

$$\mathbf{U} \times (\mathbf{V} + \mathbf{W}) = \mathbf{U} \times (\mathbf{V}' + \mathbf{W}').$$

So to establish the distributive property it suffices to show that

$$\mathbf{U} \times (\mathbf{V}' + \mathbf{W}') = \mathbf{U} \times \mathbf{V}' + \mathbf{U} \times \mathbf{W}'.$$

These vectors all lie in the plane containing $\mathbf{V}'$ and $\mathbf{W}'$, that is, in the

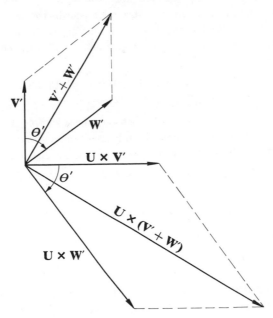

Figure 1.21

plane normal to **U**. Consider then Fig. 1.21 which shows these vectors in the plane normal to **U**, with **U** directed into the paper. Because **V′**, **W′**, and **V′** + **W′** are all perpendicular to **U**, the cross products with **U** have lengths obtained by multiplying their lengths by |**U**|; and since the cross products **U** × **V′**, **U** × **W′**, and **U** × (**V′** + **W′**) are 90 degrees from the positions of **V′**, **W′**, and (**V′** + **W′**), respectively, the two parallelograms in Fig. 1.21 are similar. Therefore the diagonal **U** × **V′** + **U** × **W′** must be the same as the vector **U** × (**V′** + **W′**).

EXAMPLE 1.7   The relation between **U** × **V** and **V** × **U** can be obtained as follows. Since the cross product of a vector with itself is **0**,

$$\mathbf{0} = (\mathbf{U} + \mathbf{V}) \times (\mathbf{U} + \mathbf{V}) = \mathbf{U} \times \mathbf{U} + \mathbf{U} \times \mathbf{V} + \mathbf{V} \times \mathbf{U} + \mathbf{V} \times \mathbf{V}$$
$$= \mathbf{0} + \mathbf{U} \times \mathbf{V} + \mathbf{V} \times \mathbf{U} + \mathbf{0},$$

and this implies that **U** × **V** = −**V** × **U**. The distributive law was applied twice in multiplying **U** + **V** by itself.

Problems

1.19.   Show that |**U** × **V**| ≤ |**U**||**V**|.

1.20.   Let **i**, **j**, and **k** denote the position vectors, respectively, of the points $(1, 0, 0)$, $(0, 1, 0)$, $(0, 0, 1)$ in a given rectangular coordinate system. Show that **i** × **j** = **k**, **k** × **i** = **j**; determine also the other four of the six possible products. (Assume a right-handed coordinate system, but observe also the effect of using a left-handed system.)

1.21.   Referring to the results and notation of Problem 1.20, compute **A** × (**B** × **C**), where **A** = **i** + **j**, **B** = **k**, **C** = 2**j** − **k**.

1.22.   Show that **U** × **V** = **U** × **W** does not always imply **V** = **W** (that is, "cancellation" is not generally permitted), by describing a situation in which the former holds but not the latter. (Hint: transpose and use the distributive law.)

1.23.   Obtain the vector equation of a line through the points P_0 and P_1. (Cf. Example 1.6.)

1.24.   Show that $(a\mathbf{U}) \times (b\mathbf{V}) = ab(\mathbf{U} \times \mathbf{V})$.

1.5   *Scalar products*

In many applications two vectors combine naturally to yield a scalar quantity, an operation called *scalar multiplication*. The *scalar product* (or *dot product* or *inner product*) of vectors **U** and **V**, denoted by **U·V**, is defined as follows:

$$\mathbf{U} \cdot \mathbf{V} = |\mathbf{U}||\mathbf{V}| \cos \theta,$$

where θ is the angle between **U** and **V**. This operation is somewhat unusual in that it combines elements of one kind (vectors) to produce an element of another kind (a number or scalar), whereas ordinary multiplication of numbers produces a number, and vector multiplication of vectors produces a vector.

Scalar products are *commutative*, since the definition does not involve the order of the factors: **U·V = V·U**. However, there cannot be an associative property, since the symbol **U·(V·W)** would have no meaning, the quantity in parentheses being a scalar. A kind of associativity involving multiplication by a scalar is given in the following property:

$$(a\mathbf{U}) \cdot (b\mathbf{V}) = ab(\mathbf{U} \cdot \mathbf{V}).$$

(Cf. Problem 1.25.)

Geometrically, a scalar product has to do with projections. The projection of one vector onto another is obtained by dropping perpendiculars from the initial and terminal points of the one down to the line of the other. The locations of the vectors are immaterial in this process—just the orientations and lengths count, as seen in Fig. 1.22, and so it can be considered that **U** and **V** issue from the same point and lie in the same plane. The quantity $|\mathbf{U}| \cos \theta$ can be thought of as the length of the projection of **U** along **V** together with a sign, plus if θ is acute, and minus if θ is obtuse. (See Fig. 1.23.) Then the scalar product **U·V** is the product of the magnitude of one factor times the length of the projection of the other along the direction of the first together with the appropriate sign.

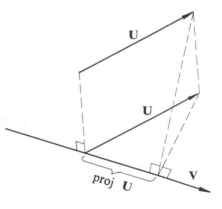

Figure 1.22

The distributive law for scalar multiplication over vector addition is now readily established:

$$\mathbf{U} \cdot (\mathbf{V} + \mathbf{W}) = \mathbf{U} \cdot \mathbf{V} + \mathbf{U} \cdot \mathbf{W}.$$

This is clearly true if the projection of the sum of two vectors is the sum

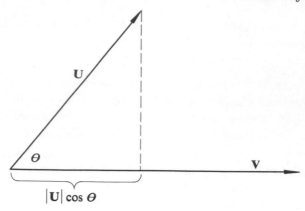

Figure 1.23

of their projections (including algebraic signs). But this in turn is indeed
so, as is at once clear from Fig. 1.24, drawn for the case of three summands. Again the distributive law implies that multinomials can be worked
out according to the usual algebraic process. For instance,

$$(\mathbf{A} + \mathbf{B}) \cdot (\mathbf{C} + \mathbf{D}) = (\mathbf{A} + \mathbf{B}) \cdot \mathbf{C} + (\mathbf{A} + \mathbf{B}) \cdot \mathbf{D}$$
$$= \mathbf{A} \cdot \mathbf{C} + \mathbf{B} \cdot \mathbf{C} + \mathbf{A} \cdot \mathbf{D} + \mathbf{B} \cdot \mathbf{D}.$$

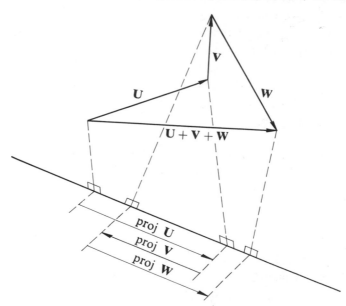

Figure 1.24.   Projection of a sum.

The length of a vector, the angle between two vectors, and the length of the projection of one vector along another can all be expressed in terms of the scalar product. Observe first that

$$\mathbf{U} \cdot \mathbf{U} = |\mathbf{U}||\mathbf{U}| \cdot 1 = |\mathbf{U}|^2,$$

so that the length of $\mathbf{U}$ is given by

$$|\mathbf{U}| = (\mathbf{U} \cdot \mathbf{U})^{1/2}.$$

Simply by dividing the definition of $\mathbf{U} \cdot \mathbf{V}$ by $|\mathbf{U}||\mathbf{V}|$ one obtains

$$\cos \theta = \frac{\mathbf{U} \cdot \mathbf{V}}{|\mathbf{U}||\mathbf{V}|},$$

where θ is the angle between $\mathbf{U}$ and $\mathbf{V}$. The projection of $\mathbf{U}$ along $\mathbf{V}$ is obtained by dividing the definition of $\mathbf{U} \cdot \mathbf{V}$ by $|\mathbf{V}|$:

$$\text{proj}_{\mathbf{V}} \mathbf{U} = |\mathbf{U}| \cos \theta = \mathbf{U} \cdot \frac{\mathbf{V}}{|\mathbf{V}|},$$

which is the scalar product of $\mathbf{U}$ by a *unit* vector along $\mathbf{V}$.

A scalar product $\mathbf{U} \cdot \mathbf{V}$ will vanish if either $\mathbf{U}$ or $\mathbf{V}$ is the zero vector; but it will also vanish if $\cos \theta = 0$, that is, if $\mathbf{U}$ and $\mathbf{V}$ are perpendicular. The statement $\mathbf{U} \cdot \mathbf{V} = 0$, therefore, does not necessarily mean that $\mathbf{U}$ or $\mathbf{V}$ must be the zero vector. As a result (as in the case of vector multiplication), cancellation is not automatic. For, if

$$\mathbf{U} \cdot \mathbf{V} = \mathbf{U} \cdot \mathbf{W}$$

or

$$\mathbf{U} \cdot (\mathbf{V} - \mathbf{W}) = 0,$$

this could happen because $\mathbf{U}$ is perpendicular to $\mathbf{V} - \mathbf{W}$; that is, $\mathbf{V}$ need not be equal to $\mathbf{W}$.

E X A M P L E 1.8   The set of points on a plane can be characterized in terms of vectors, that is, by the vector equation of the plane. Suppose that a plane is specified as passing through the point P_0 with position vector $\mathbf{r}_0$ relative to a given origin O, and as being perpendicular to the direction $\mathbf{A}$. Then a point P with position vector $\mathbf{r}$ lies on the plane if and only if the vector from P_0 to P, that is, the vector $\mathbf{r} - \mathbf{r}_0$ is perpendicular to $\mathbf{A}$ (see Fig. 1.25):

$$\mathbf{A} \cdot (\mathbf{r} - \mathbf{r}_0) = 0,$$

or if the point P is P_0, in which case the vector $\mathbf{r}$ equals $\mathbf{r}_0$ and again $\mathbf{A} \cdot (\mathbf{r} - \mathbf{r}_0) = 0$. This is the vector equation desired.

E X A M P L E 1.9   The familiar "law of cosines" is easily obtained using the

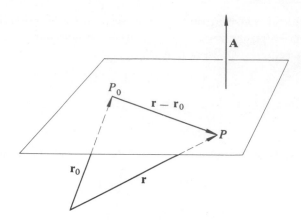

Figure 1.25.   (See Example 1.8.)

distributive property of scalar multiplication. Consider a triangle with sides **U**, **V**, and **U** − **V**, and the following computation:

$$|\mathbf{U} - \mathbf{V}|^2 = (\mathbf{U} - \mathbf{V}) \cdot (\mathbf{U} - \mathbf{V}) = U^2 + V^2 - 2|\mathbf{U}||\mathbf{V}|\cos\theta.$$

Perhaps the most prominent application of the scalar product in physics is to the computation of work. Work done by a constant force **F** acting on an object as it moves through a distance d in the direction of the force is defined as the product of the magnitude of the force and the distance: $W = Fd$. However, if the directions of the force and motion are different, the F in this formula is replaced by the component of the force in the direction of the motion; thus, work is defined generally as $Fd\cos\theta$, where θ is the angle between **F** and the displacement **d**, that is,

$$\text{work} = \mathbf{F} \cdot \mathbf{d}.$$

In particular, no work is done by a force which acts in a direction perpendicular to the motion, and the maximum work is done when the motion is in the same direction as the force.

1.6   *Triple products*

There are three ways in which one can "multiply" together three vectors. One way is $(\mathbf{U} \cdot \mathbf{V})\mathbf{W}$, which is just a scalar multiple of **W**. A second way combines scalar and vector multiplication to yield a scalar: $\mathbf{U} \cdot \mathbf{V} \times \mathbf{W}$. This is called a *scalar triple product*. No parentheses are needed,

(third way is $\mathbf{U} \times \mathbf{V} \times \mathbf{W}$ − vector triple product — see p. 29, top.)

since the vector multiplication $\mathbf{V} \times \mathbf{W}$ must be performed first; there would be no meaning to the expression $(\mathbf{U} \cdot \mathbf{V}) \times \mathbf{W}$, since $\mathbf{U} \cdot \mathbf{V}$ is a scalar.

Because reversing the factors in a scalar product has no effect, and in a vector product just changes the sign, there follows:

$$\mathbf{U} \cdot (\mathbf{V} \times \mathbf{W}) = (\mathbf{V} \times \mathbf{W}) \cdot \mathbf{U} = -(\mathbf{W} \times \mathbf{V}) \cdot \mathbf{U} = -\mathbf{U} \cdot (\mathbf{W} \times \mathbf{V}).$$

A fact not quite so obvious is that the dot and cross can be interchanged in a scalar triple product without changing the value:

$$\mathbf{U} \cdot \mathbf{V} \times \mathbf{W} = \mathbf{U} \times \mathbf{V} \cdot \mathbf{W}.$$

This will be demonstrated next.

Given vectors $\mathbf{U}$, $\mathbf{V}$, and $\mathbf{W}$, let $\mathbf{i}$ denote a unit vector along $\mathbf{V}$, let $\mathbf{j}$ be a unit vector in the plane of $\mathbf{V}$ and $\mathbf{W}$ perpendicular to $\mathbf{V}$ on the same side of $\mathbf{V}$ as $\mathbf{W}$, and let $\mathbf{k} = \mathbf{i} \times \mathbf{j}$ (which is then a unit vector normal to the plane of $\mathbf{V}$ and $\mathbf{W}$), as in Fig. 1.26. Then $\mathbf{V}$ is a multiple of $\mathbf{i}$, $\mathbf{W}$ is a

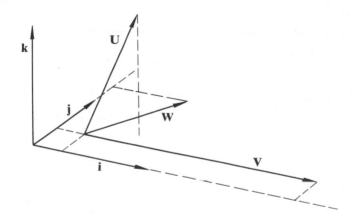

Figure 1.26

linear combination of $\mathbf{i}$ and $\mathbf{j}$, and $\mathbf{U}$ is a linear combination of $\mathbf{i}$, $\mathbf{j}$, and $\mathbf{k}$:

$$\mathbf{V} = V\mathbf{i},$$
$$\mathbf{W} = a\mathbf{i} + b\mathbf{j},$$
$$\mathbf{U} = c\mathbf{i} + d\mathbf{j} + e\mathbf{k},$$

where a, b, c, d, and e are uniquely defined scalar multipliers. Cross products can be computed as follows:

$$\mathbf{V} \times \mathbf{W} = (V\mathbf{i}) \times (a\mathbf{i} + b\mathbf{j}) = Vb\mathbf{k},$$
$$\mathbf{U} \times \mathbf{V} = (c\mathbf{i} + d\mathbf{j} + e\mathbf{k}) \times (V\mathbf{i}) = -dV\mathbf{k} + eV\mathbf{j},$$

from which there is obtained

$$\mathbf{U} \cdot \mathbf{V} \times \mathbf{W} = (c\mathbf{i} + d\mathbf{j} + e\mathbf{k}) \cdot (Vb\mathbf{k}) = Vbe$$

and

$$\mathbf{U} \times \mathbf{V} \cdot \mathbf{W} = (-dV\mathbf{k} + eV\mathbf{j}) \cdot (a\mathbf{i} + b\mathbf{j}) = Vbe = \mathbf{U} \cdot \mathbf{V} \times \mathbf{W}.$$

This shows that the interchange of dot and cross is permitted. The validity of the interchange is also evident from a geometrical interpretation of the scalar triple product.

Geometrically, a scalar triple product $\mathbf{U} \cdot \mathbf{V} \times \mathbf{W}$ gives the volume of the parallelepiped having $\mathbf{U}$, $\mathbf{V}$, and $\mathbf{W}$ as adjacent edges, provided $\mathbf{U}$ is on the same side of the plane of $\mathbf{V}$ and $\mathbf{W}$ as is $\mathbf{V} \times \mathbf{W}$. For, the magnitude of $\mathbf{V} \times \mathbf{W}$ is the area of the base of the parallelepiped, and the product of U with the cosine of the angle between $\mathbf{U}$ and $\mathbf{V} \times \mathbf{W}$ is the length of

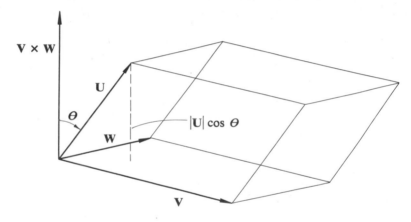

Figure 1.27

the altitude of the parallelepiped. (If $\mathbf{U}$ and $\mathbf{V} \times \mathbf{W}$ are on opposite sides of the plane of $\mathbf{V}$ and $\mathbf{W}$, the product $\mathbf{U} \cdot \mathbf{V} \times \mathbf{W}$ is the negative of the volume.) With this interpretation of the scalar triple product as volume, then, the equivalence of $\mathbf{V} \cdot (\mathbf{W} \times \mathbf{U})$, $\mathbf{W} \cdot (\mathbf{U} \times \mathbf{V})$, and $\mathbf{U} \cdot (\mathbf{W} \times \mathbf{V})$ is apparent when it is realized that the "base" in the foregoing discussion can be taken to be the parallelogram defined by $\mathbf{V}$ and $\mathbf{W}$, that defined by $\mathbf{W}$ and $\mathbf{U}$, or that defined by $\mathbf{U}$ and $\mathbf{V}$. In summary, there are twelve possible scalar triple products of three vectors (six choices of order and two choices of location of dot and cross), all equal numerically, six of one sign and six of the other. The six equal to each other involve cyclic permutations of the factors and interchange of dot and cross.

A third way of multiplying three vectors is in a *vector triple product*:
$U \times (V \times W)$. This vector is normal to U and to $V \times W$; and since $V \times W$ is normal to the plane of V and W, the triple cross product must lie in the plane of V and W. But any vector in that plane is representable uniquely as a linear combination of V and W (unless V is parallel to W, in which case $V \times W = 0$ and the triple product is also 0):

$$U \times (V \times W) = rV + sW.$$

To see that $r = U \cdot W$ and $s = -U \cdot V$, again let $V = Vi$, $W = ai + bj$, and $U = ci + dj + ek$, as above. Then

$$U \times (V \times W) = (ci + dj + ek) \times (Vbk) = -Vbcj + Vbdi,$$
$$(U \cdot W)V = (ac + bd)(Vi) = Vaci + Vbdi,$$
$$(U \cdot V)W = (Vc)(ai + bj) = Vaci + Vbcj,$$

and therefore

$$U \times (V \times W) = (U \cdot W)V - (U \cdot V)W.$$

Problems

1.25. Show that $(aU) \cdot (bV) = ab(U \cdot V)$.

1.26. Vectors U and V are adjacent sides of an equilateral triangle whose sides have length a. Compute $U \cdot V$.

1.27. Show that the diagonals of a rectangle are perpendicular if and only if it is a square. (Express the diagonal vectors in terms of the sides and compute the dot product.)

1.28. Show that $|U \cdot V| \leq |U||V|$, and state what condition would imply equality.

1.29. Obtain the vector equation of the plane through P_1, P_2, and P_3 in terms of their position vectors, respectively, r_1, r_2, and r_3.

1.30. State a necessary and sufficient condition for linear independence of U, V, and W in terms of the scalar triple product.

1.31. Establish the triangle inequality using a manipulation similar to that of Example 1.9.

1.32. Use vector methods to show that the line drawn from the midpoint of the base of an isosceles triangle to the opposite vertex is perpendicular to the base.

1.33. Obtain (in terms of dot products) a formula for the distance from the point P to a line through Q having direction A.

1.34. Obtain a formula for the distance from the point P to the plane through the point Q normal to $\mathbf{A}$.

1.35. By using an interchange of dot and cross and the formula for the vector triple product obtain an expression involving only scalar products for $(\mathbf{U} \times \mathbf{V}) \cdot (\mathbf{W} \times \mathbf{Z})$.

1.36. Using the formula for vector triple products express the product $(\mathbf{U} \times \mathbf{V}) \times (\mathbf{W} \times \mathbf{Z})$ as a linear combination of $\mathbf{W}$ and $\mathbf{Z}$, and also as a linear combination of $\mathbf{U}$ and $\mathbf{V}$. What is the significance of the fact that it can be expressed in either way?

1.37. Denoting by $\mathbf{i}$, $\mathbf{j}$, and $\mathbf{k}$ the position vectors out to the points $(1, 0, 0)$, $(0, 1, 0)$, and $(0, 0, 1)$, respectively, in a rectangular coordinate system, compute the various possible dot products (e.g., $\mathbf{i} \cdot \mathbf{j}$, $\mathbf{i} \cdot \mathbf{i}$, etc.), and also $\mathbf{i} \cdot \mathbf{j} \times \mathbf{k}$ and $\mathbf{i} \times (\mathbf{j} \times \mathbf{k})$. (Assume a right-handed system.)

1.7 *Representations in terms of components*

It has been seen that an arbitrary vector can be uniquely represented as a linear combination of three nonzero, noncoplanar vectors. When these three are mutually perpendicular unit vectors, such representations are particularly convenient for computations. Let $\mathbf{i}_1$ and $\mathbf{i}_2$ denote given perpendicular unit vectors, and let $\mathbf{i}_3 = \mathbf{i}_1 \times \mathbf{i}_2$, so that $\mathbf{i}_3$ is a unit vector perpendicular to both $\mathbf{i}_1$ and $\mathbf{i}_2$. Any vector $\mathbf{V}$ can then be expressed in the form

$$\mathbf{V} = V_1 \mathbf{i}_1 + V_2 \mathbf{i}_2 + V_3 \mathbf{i}_3,$$

where V_1, V_2, and V_3 are uniquely defined scalar multipliers. These coefficients can be given in terms of scalar products; for, taking the scalar product on both sides of the above representation with, respectively, $\mathbf{i}_1$, $\mathbf{i}_2$, and $\mathbf{i}_3$, one finds

$$\mathbf{V} \cdot \mathbf{i}_1 = V_1,$$
$$\mathbf{V} \cdot \mathbf{i}_2 = V_2,$$

and

$$\mathbf{V} \cdot \mathbf{i}_3 = V_3.$$

(This, incidentally, again demonstrates the uniqueness of the representation.) The numbers V_1, V_2, and V_3 are referred to as *scalar components* of $\mathbf{V}$ relative to the *basis* $(\mathbf{i}_1, \mathbf{i}_2, \mathbf{i}_3)$.

The simplicity of the above formulas for the magnitudes of the components of a vector along $\mathbf{i}_1$, $\mathbf{i}_2$, and $\mathbf{i}_3$ is a result of a fact that $(\mathbf{i}_1, \mathbf{i}_2, \mathbf{i}_3)$ is an *orthonormal* basis (consisting of mutually orthogonal vectors normalized to have unit lengths).

If $\mathbf{U} = \mathbf{V}$, then $\mathbf{U} \cdot \mathbf{i}_1 = \mathbf{V} \cdot \mathbf{i}_1$, and so the components along $\mathbf{i}_1$ of the two vectors must agree. In like fashion the components along $\mathbf{i}_2$ must agree and the components along $\mathbf{i}_3$ must agree. That is, two vectors are equal if and only if they agree component by component:

$$U_1 = V_1,$$
$$U_2 = V_2,$$

and

$$U_3 = V_3.$$

Thus, an equation expressing equality of two vectors is equivalent to three scalar equations.

Sums are readily computed in terms of components. Given the vectors $\mathbf{V} = V_1 \mathbf{i}_1 + V_2 \mathbf{i}_2 + V_3 \mathbf{i}_3$ and $\mathbf{U} = U_1 \mathbf{i}_1 + U_2 \mathbf{i}_2 + U_3 \mathbf{i}_3$ their sum can be written

$$\mathbf{U} + \mathbf{V} = (U_1 \mathbf{i}_1 + U_2 \mathbf{i}_2 + U_3 \mathbf{i}_3) + (V_1 \mathbf{i}_1 + V_2 \mathbf{i}_2 + V_3 \mathbf{i}_3)$$
$$= (U_1 + V_1) \mathbf{i}_1 + (U_2 + V_2) \mathbf{i}_2 + (U_3 + V_3) \mathbf{i}_3,$$

by virtue of the associative and commutative properties of vector addition and the distributivity of multiplication by a scalar over vector addition. In words, the components of a sum of two vectors relative to a given orthonormal set are the sums of the corresponding components of the two vectors. The result is of course immediately extendable by induction to any finite sum of vectors.

Scalar products are easily computed in terms of rectangular components. With $\mathbf{U}$ and $\mathbf{V}$ as above, multiplying out a scalar product using the distributive law and the properties of $(\mathbf{i}_1, \mathbf{i}_2, \mathbf{i}_3)$ yields the desired result:

$$\mathbf{U} \cdot \mathbf{V} = (U_1 \mathbf{i}_1 + U_2 \mathbf{i}_2 + U_3 \mathbf{i}_3) \cdot (V_1 \mathbf{i}_1 + V_2 \mathbf{i}_2 + V_3 \mathbf{i}_3)$$
$$= U_1 V_1 + U_2 V_2 + U_3 V_3.$$

A similar manipulation results in an expression for the vector product:

$$\mathbf{U} \times \mathbf{V} = (U_1 \mathbf{i}_1 + U_2 \mathbf{i}_2 + U_3 \mathbf{i}_3) \times (V_1 \mathbf{i}_1 + V_2 \mathbf{i}_2 + V_3 \mathbf{i}_3)$$
$$= (U_2 V_3 - U_3 V_2) \mathbf{i}_1 + (U_3 V_1 - U_1 V_3) \mathbf{i}_2 + (U_1 V_2 - U_2 V_1) \mathbf{i}_3.$$

A handy mnemonic device is to list the components of $\mathbf{U}$ and $\mathbf{V}$ as the second and third row elements of a determinant, putting then $\mathbf{i}_1$, $\mathbf{i}_2$, and $\mathbf{i}_3$ in the first row. Formal expansion of the determinant, as though $\mathbf{i}_1$, $\mathbf{i}_2$, and

over

i_3 were numbers, produces the above expression for the vector product:

$$\mathbf{U} \times \mathbf{V} = \begin{vmatrix} \mathbf{i}_1 & \mathbf{i}_2 & \mathbf{i}_3 \\ U_1 & U_2 & U_3 \\ V_1 & V_2 & V_3 \end{vmatrix}.$$

The equal sign here is really valid only after the determinant is formally expanded.

The length of a vector $\mathbf{V}$ is expressible in terms of the scalar product:

$$|\mathbf{V}| = (\mathbf{V} \cdot \mathbf{V})^{1/2} = (V_1{}^2 + V_2{}^2 + V_3{}^2)^{1/2},$$

which, in view of Fig. 1.28, is equivalent to the Pythagorean theorem.

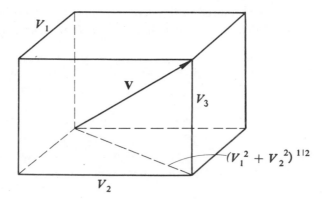

Figure 1.28

In attacking the scalar triple product, it is observed first that a scalar product of $\mathbf{U}$ and $\mathbf{V}$ can be thought of as obtained by replacing the $\mathbf{i}_1$, $\mathbf{i}_2$, and $\mathbf{i}_3$ in the expression for $\mathbf{U}$ by the corresponding components of $\mathbf{V}$ (or vice versa). In computing $\mathbf{U} \cdot \mathbf{V} \times \mathbf{W}$, then, one can replace the $\mathbf{i}_1$, $\mathbf{i}_2$, and $\mathbf{i}_3$ in the expression for $\mathbf{V} \times \mathbf{W}$ by the components of $\mathbf{U}$, to obtain

$$\mathbf{U} \cdot \mathbf{V} \times \mathbf{W} = \begin{vmatrix} U_1 & U_2 & U_3 \\ V_1 & V_2 & V_3 \\ W_1 & W_2 & W_3 \end{vmatrix}.$$

This expression for the scalar triple product shows again that the various possible scalar triple products of $\mathbf{U}$, $\mathbf{V}$, and $\mathbf{W}$ are equal in magnitude, with some differing only in algebraic sign. For, interchanging two rows of a determinant (which changes a cyclic to a noncyclic order) changes the sign of the determinant, whereas a cyclic permutation of rows in a third order determinant leaves it unchanged in value. It is also clear that the vanishing of the scalar triple product implies linear dependence of the vectors, since the vanishing of a determinant implies that one row is a linear combination of the other two rows. Conversely, of course, *nonvanishing* of the determinant implies that no row can be expressed as a linear combination of the others.

E X A M P L E 1.10   Given the vectors $\mathbf{U} = \mathbf{i}_1 - 2\mathbf{i}_2 + \mathbf{i}_3$, $\mathbf{V} = 2\mathbf{i}_1 + \mathbf{i}_2 + \mathbf{i}_3$, and $\mathbf{W} = 3\mathbf{i}_1 - \mathbf{i}_2 + 2\mathbf{i}_3$. Then

$$\mathbf{U} + \mathbf{V} = 3\mathbf{i}_1 - \mathbf{i}_2 + 2\mathbf{i}_3,$$
$$\mathbf{U} \cdot \mathbf{V} = 1 \cdot 2 - 2 \cdot 1 + 1 \cdot 1 = 1,$$

and

$$\mathbf{U} \times \mathbf{V} = \begin{vmatrix} \mathbf{i}_1 & \mathbf{i}_2 & \mathbf{i}_3 \\ 1 & -2 & 1 \\ 2 & 1 & 1 \end{vmatrix} = -3\mathbf{i}_1 + \mathbf{i}_2 + 5\mathbf{i}_3.$$

The lengths are

$$|\mathbf{U}| = (1^2 + 2^2 + 1^2)^{1/2} = \sqrt{6},$$
$$|\mathbf{V}| = (2^2 + 1^2 + 1^2)^{1/2} = \sqrt{6},$$
$$|\mathbf{W}| = (3^2 + 1^2 + 2^2)^{1/2} = \sqrt{14},$$

and the cosine of the angle between $\mathbf{U}$ and $\mathbf{V}$ is

$$\cos(\mathbf{U}, \mathbf{V}) = \frac{\mathbf{U} \cdot \mathbf{V}}{|\mathbf{U}||\mathbf{V}|} = \frac{1}{\sqrt{6}\sqrt{6}} = \frac{1}{6}.$$

The scalar triple product of $\mathbf{U}$, $\mathbf{V}$, and $\mathbf{W}$ is

$$= 1\left(2+1\right) + \left(-2\right)\left(3-1\right) + 1\left(-2-3\right)$$
$$= 3 + 2 - 5 - 0$$

$$\mathbf{U} \cdot \mathbf{V} \times \mathbf{W} = \begin{vmatrix} 1 & -2 & 1 \\ 2 & 1 & 1 \\ 3 & -1 & 2 \end{vmatrix} = 0.$$

The volume of the parallelepiped defined by these three vectors is zero, indicating that they are coplanar—linearly dependent. One is a linear combination of the other two. It is easily seen that $\mathbf{U} + \mathbf{V} = \mathbf{W}$. If this relation is not noticed upon inspection, it can be found by writing out the vector equation $a\mathbf{U} + b\mathbf{V} = \mathbf{W}$ in terms of components:

$$\begin{cases} aU_1 + bV_1 = W_1, \\ aU_2 + bV_2 = W_2, \\ aU_3 + bV_3 = W_3, \end{cases} \quad \text{or} \quad \begin{cases} a + 2b = 3, \\ -2a + b = -1, \\ a + b = 2. \end{cases}$$

Solving, say, the first two equations one obtains $a = 1$, $b = 1$. (Only two of the three equations are needed to define a and b; the other is automatically satisfied.)

The relation between solving linear equations and linear independence of vectors should perhaps be made a bit more explicit. Consider the system of linear equations:

$$\begin{cases} a_1 x_1 + b_1 x_2 + c_1 x_3 = 0, \\ a_2 x_1 + b_2 x_2 + c_2 x_3 = 0, \\ a_3 x_1 + b_3 x_2 + c_3 x_3 = 0. \end{cases}$$

This homogeneous system has the solution $(0, 0, 0)$ for (x_1, x_2, x_3), no matter what the coefficients, and this is called the *trivial solution*. If the determinant of the coefficients is not zero, this trivial solution is unique, and conversely. Therefore, there is a *non*trivial solution if and only if the determinant of the coefficients *is* zero:

$$\begin{vmatrix} a_1 & b_1 & c_1 \\ a_2 & b_2 & c_2 \\ a_3 & b_3 & c_3 \end{vmatrix} = \begin{vmatrix} a_1 & a_2 & a_3 \\ b_1 & b_2 & b_3 \\ c_1 & c_2 & c_3 \end{vmatrix} = 0.$$

Now, writing

$$\mathbf{A} = a_1\mathbf{i}_1 + a_2\mathbf{i}_2 + a_3\mathbf{i}_3,$$
$$\mathbf{B} = b_1\mathbf{i}_1 + b_2\mathbf{i}_2 + b_3\mathbf{i}_3,$$

and

$$\mathbf{C} = c_1\mathbf{i}_1 + c_2\mathbf{i}_2 + c_3\mathbf{i}_3,$$

the above homogeneous system of linear equations is equivalent to the vector equation

$$x_1\mathbf{A} + x_2\mathbf{B} + x_3\mathbf{C} = \mathbf{0}.$$

(The vectors $\mathbf{i}_1$, $\mathbf{i}_2$ and $\mathbf{i}_3$ are as before an orthonormal set). This vector equation has a nontrivial solution (x_1, x_2, x_3) if and only if the vectors $\mathbf{A}$, $\mathbf{B}$, and $\mathbf{C}$ are linearly dependent—this is the definition of linear dependence. And the vectors **A**, **B**, and **C** are linearly dependent if and only if their scalar triple product is zero, which is precisely the condition above that the determinant of the coefficients of the linear system be zero.

Problems

1.38. Given i_1 perpendicular to i_2, $|i_1| = |i_2| = 1$, and $i_3 = i_1 \times i_2$, show that $i_2 = i_3 \times i_1$ and $i_3 = i_1 \times i_2$.

1.39. Show that:
(a) $k\mathbf{V} = kV_1 i_1 + kV_2 i_2 + kV_3 i_3$,
(b) $\mathbf{U} - \mathbf{V} = (U_1 - V_1)i_1 + (U_2 - V_2)i_2 + (U_3 - V_3)i_3$,
the various symbols here being defined as in the above section.

1.40. Let (i_1, i_2, i_3) be an orthonormal set of vectors, and $\mathbf{A} = i_1 - 2i_2 + i_3$, $\mathbf{B} = 2i_1 - i_2 + 3i_3$, $\mathbf{C} = i_1 + 2i_2 + 3i_3$, and $\mathbf{D} = i_1 + i_2 + 2i_3$. Compute the following:

(a) $\mathbf{A} + \mathbf{B}$,
(b) $\mathbf{A} - \mathbf{B}$,
(c) $\mathbf{A} \cdot \mathbf{B}$,
(d) $\mathbf{A} \times \mathbf{B}$,
(e) $\mathbf{A} \cdot \mathbf{B} \times \mathbf{C}$,
(f) $\mathbf{A} \times (\mathbf{B} \times \mathbf{C})$, (two ways),
(g) $(\mathbf{A} \times \mathbf{B}) \times (\mathbf{C} \times \mathbf{D})$, (two ways),
(h) $|\mathbf{A}|$,
(i) $\cos(\mathbf{A}, \mathbf{B})$,
(j) projection of **B** along **D**,
(k) unit vector along **D**,
(l) $3\mathbf{A} - 2\mathbf{B} + \mathbf{C}$.

1.41. Given **A**, **B**, **C**, and **D** as in Problem 1.40.
(a) Show that **A** is perpendicular to **C**.
(b) Show that **A**, **B**, and **D** are linearly dependent.
(c) Show that **A**, **B**, and **C** are linearly independent.
(d) Express **D** in terms of **A** and **B**.
(e) Express **D** as a linear combination of **A**, **B**, and **C**.

1.42. Show that vectors **U** and **V** are parallel if and only if their components relative to an orthonormal set are proportional:

$$U_1 : U_2 : U_3 = V_1 : V_2 : V_3.$$

1.8 *Vectors in analytic geometry*

Consider a rectangular coordinate system in three-dimensional space: points are identified according to their locations relative to three mutually perpendicular *coordinate planes*. Pairs of these planes intersect in the mutually perpendicular *coordinate axes*, and their common point is the *origin*. For each coordinate axis there is chosen a direction (one way or the other along the axis) called *positive*, pointing into what is called the positive side of the coordinate plane to which it is perpendicular. A given point is then assigned the coordinates (x, y, z), where x denotes the distance from the point along one axis (called the x-axis) to a coordinate plane (called the yz-plane) together with a plus $(+)$ or a minus $(-)$ sign according as the point is on the positive side of the yz-plane or not; and where y and z denote similar distances with signs, along the directions of the other two axes.

The following orthonormal set of vectors is especially convenient: $\mathbf{i}$, the position vector of $(1, 0, 0)$; $\mathbf{j}$, the position vector of $(0, 1, 0)$; and $\mathbf{k}$, the position vector of $(0, 0, 1)$; that is, $\mathbf{i}$, $\mathbf{j}$, and $\mathbf{k}$ are mutually perpendicular unit vectors along the x-, y-, and z-directions, respectively. If $\mathbf{i} \times \mathbf{j} = \mathbf{k}$, the coordinate system is called right-handed; if $\mathbf{i} \times \mathbf{j} = -\mathbf{k}$, the system is left-handed. Unless otherwise specified, a right-handed system will be assumed throughout.

Consider now the arbitrary point (x, y, z) with the position vector $\mathbf{r}$. Since any vector can be exhibited as a linear combination of the linearly independent set $\mathbf{i}$, $\mathbf{j}$, and $\mathbf{k}$, the vector $\mathbf{r}$ can be so represented. The coefficient of $\mathbf{i}$ is the inner product of $\mathbf{r}$ with $\mathbf{i}$, which is just the scalar projection of $\mathbf{r}$ along the x-axis; namely, x. Similarly, the coefficients of $\mathbf{j}$ and $\mathbf{k}$ are y and z, respectively:

$$\mathbf{r} = x\mathbf{i} + y\mathbf{j} + z\mathbf{k}.$$

This representation is indicated in Fig. 1.29. The notation $\mathbf{r}$ will be re-

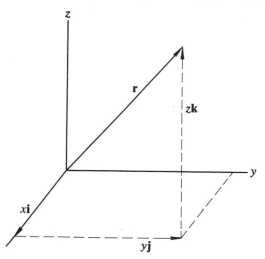

Figure 1.29.   Resolution of a position vector.

served for the position vector of (x, y, z), and its length will be consistently denoted by r:

$$r = (\mathbf{r} \cdot \mathbf{r})^{1/2} = (x^2 + y^2 + z^2)^{1/2}.$$

(The only apparent exception will be in working in the xy-plane, where $\mathbf{r}$ may denote the position vector $x\mathbf{i} + y\mathbf{j}$, with $r^2 = x^2 + y^2$.)

Consider now two points, P_1: (x_1, y_1, z_1), and P_2: (x_2, y_2, z_2). Their position vectors are, respectively,

$$\mathbf{r}_1 = x_1\mathbf{i} + y_1\mathbf{j} + z_1\mathbf{k},$$

and

$$\mathbf{r}_2 = x_2\mathbf{i} + y_2\mathbf{j} + z_2\mathbf{k}.$$

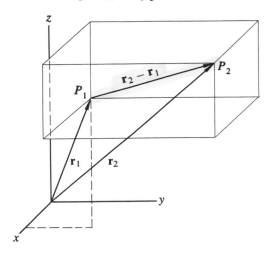

Figure 1.30.   **Difference of position vectors.**

The difference $\mathbf{r}_2 - \mathbf{r}_1$ is the vector $\overrightarrow{P_1P_2}$ (see Fig. 1.30):

$$\mathbf{r}_2 - \mathbf{r}_1 = (x_2 - x_1)\mathbf{i} + (y_2 - y_1)\mathbf{j} + (z_2 - z_1)\mathbf{k}.$$

The length of this vector is the distance $|\overrightarrow{P_1P_2}|$:

$$|\overrightarrow{P_1P_2}| = |\mathbf{r}_2 - \mathbf{r}_1| = [(x_2 - x_1)^2 + (y_2 - y_1)^2 + (z_2 - z_1)^2]^{1/2}.$$

The numbers $(x_2 - x_1)$, $(y_2 - y_1)$, and $(z_2 - z_1)$ are a set of *direction numbers* of the line through P_1 and P_2.

More generally, the direction numbers of a line are any set of three numbers which are components of some vector along the direction of the line (one way or the other); that is, they are defined only up to a multiplicative constant, and are often written in the form $l : m : n$. The direction cosines of a directed line are the cosines of the angles between the positive direction of the line and the vectors $\mathbf{i}$, $\mathbf{j}$, and $\mathbf{k}$. For the line through P_1 and P_2 directed from P_1 to P_2, as in Fig. 1.30, the quantities $x_2 - x_1$, $y_2 - y_1$, and $z_2 - z_1$ are direction numbers. The direction cosines are clearly

$$\frac{(x_2 - x_1)}{|\mathbf{r}_2 - \mathbf{r}_1|}, \quad \frac{(y_2 - y_1)}{|\mathbf{r}_2 - \mathbf{r}_1|}, \quad \text{and} \quad \frac{(z_2 - z_1)}{|\mathbf{r}_2 - \mathbf{r}_1|};$$

these are obtained by dividing the direction numbers $(x_2-x_1):(y_2-y_1):(x_2-z_1)$ by the square root of the sum of their squares. Similarly, the vector $l\mathbf{i} + m\mathbf{j} + n\mathbf{k}$ has direction cosines obtained by dividing the direction numbers $l : m : n$ by $(l^2 + m^2 + n^2)^{1/2}$. Observe, then, that the direction cosines of a *unit* vector are its components!

EXAMPLE 1.11 The vector equation of a sphere with center at P_0 and radius a is simply the condition

$$|\mathbf{r} - \mathbf{r}_0| = a,$$

satisfied by those points P (and only those points) which lie on the sphere; that is, whose distance $|\mathbf{r} - \mathbf{r}_0|$ from P_0 is a, where $\mathbf{r}$ and $\mathbf{r}_0$ are position vectors, respectively, of P and P_0. Since

$$\mathbf{r} - \mathbf{r}_0 = (x - x_0)\mathbf{i} + (y - y_0)\mathbf{j} + (z - z_0)\mathbf{k},$$

the above equation can be written, upon squaring both sides, in the form

$$(x - x_0)^2 + (y - y_0)^2 + (z - z_0)^2 = a^2.$$

This is the usual equation of a sphere in rectangular coordinates.

EXAMPLE 1.12 The equation of a line through P_0 parallel to $\mathbf{V}$ was found in Example 1.6 to be

$$\mathbf{V} \times (\mathbf{r} - \mathbf{r}_0) = 0.$$

If $\mathbf{V} = a\mathbf{i} + b\mathbf{j} + c\mathbf{k}$, this can be written

$$\begin{vmatrix} \mathbf{i} & \mathbf{j} & \mathbf{k} \\ a & b & c \\ x - x_0 & y - y_0 & z - z_0 \end{vmatrix} = \mathbf{0},$$

or, equating components along $\mathbf{i}$, $\mathbf{j}$, and $\mathbf{k}$,

$$b(z - z_0) - c(y - y_0) = 0,$$
$$c(x - x_0) - a(z - z_0) = 0,$$
$$a(y - y_0) - b(x - x_0) = 0.$$

When a, b, and c are not zero, these relations can be written in the form

$$\frac{x - x_0}{a} = \frac{y - y_0}{b} = \frac{z - z_0}{c}.$$

If, say, $a = 0$, one has

$$\frac{y - y_0}{b} = \frac{z - z_0}{c} \quad \text{and} \quad x = x_0.$$

If $a = b = 0$, so that $\mathbf{V}$ is in the z-direction, the equations become

$$x = x_0 \quad \text{and} \quad y = y_0,$$

with no condition on z, since the point (x_0, y_0, z) will lie on the given vertical line no matter what the value of z.

EXAMPLE 1.13   The equation of a plane through P_0 perpendicular to the direction $\mathbf{V} = a\mathbf{i} + b\mathbf{j} + c\mathbf{k}$ was found in Example 1.8 to be

$$\mathbf{V} \cdot (\mathbf{r} - \mathbf{r}_0) = 0.$$

This is now seen to be equivalent to

$$a(x - x_0) + b(y - y_0) + c(z - z_0) = 0.$$

$\sim \quad ax + by + cz + d = 0$

Conversely, any linear equation in x, y, and z represents a plane. For instance, the equation

$$2x - 3y + 4z = 6$$

can be written in the form

$$2(x - 0) - 3(y + 2) + 4(z - 0) = 0,$$

which can be interpreted as stating that the point (x, y, z) must be such that $(x\mathbf{i} + y\mathbf{j} + z\mathbf{k}) - (0\mathbf{i} - 2\mathbf{j} + 0\mathbf{k})$ is perpendicular to the direction $2\mathbf{i} - 3\mathbf{j} + 4\mathbf{k}$. That is, the equation represents a plane through the point $(0, -2, 0)$ perpendicular to $2\mathbf{i} - 3\mathbf{j} + 4\mathbf{k}$.

EXAMPLE 1.14   A plane is defined by giving a point and two vectors in it. Suppose that a plane contains the point $(1, -2, 0)$ and the two vectors $\mathbf{i} - \mathbf{j} - 2\mathbf{k}$ and $2\mathbf{i} + \mathbf{k}$. The vector from $(1, -2, 0)$ to an arbitrary point (x, y, z) is a linear combination of the two given vectors if and only if the point (x, y, z) lies in the plane:

$$(x - 1)\mathbf{i} + (y + 2)\mathbf{j} + z\mathbf{k} = a(\mathbf{i} - \mathbf{j} - 2\mathbf{k}) + b(2\mathbf{i} + \mathbf{k}).$$

This is equivalent to the equations

$$\begin{cases} x = 1 + a + 2b, \\ y = -2 - a, \\ z = -2a + b, \end{cases}$$

$-y - 2 = a$
$x = 1 - y - 2 + 2b; \quad b = \frac{x + y + 1}{2}$

$z = -2(-y - 2) + \frac{1}{2}(x + y + 1)$
$2z = 4y + 8 + x + y + 1$
$x + 5y - 2z = -9$

which are parametric equations of the plane. Each choice of a and b yields a point in the plane. Elimination of a and b yields the usual linear equation for the plane:

$$x + 5y - 2z = -9.$$

EXAMPLE 1.15   The distance from the point P_1: $(1, 3, -2)$ to the plane $4x - 3y + 12z = 10$ is computed as follows. Choose any point P_0 on the plane, for example, $(1, 2, 1)$. The desired distance is then the length of the projection of the

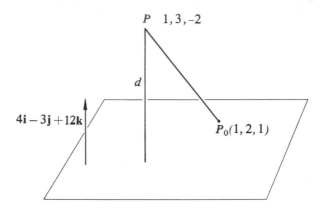

Figure 1.31.   (See Example 1.15.)

vector $\overrightarrow{P_0P_1} = \mathbf{j} - 3\mathbf{k}$ along the normal to the plane, $4\mathbf{i} - 3\mathbf{j} + 12\mathbf{k}$:

$$\text{distance} = \left| (\mathbf{j} - 3\mathbf{k}) \cdot \frac{(4\mathbf{i} - 3\mathbf{j} + 12\mathbf{k})}{(16 + 9 + 144)^{1/2}} \right| = \left| \frac{-39}{13} \right| = 3.$$

(See Fig. 1.31.)

EXAMPLE 1.16   The computation of the distance between two skew lines is similar to the computation of the preceding example. Consider, for instance, the two lines

$$\frac{x - 1}{4} = \frac{y + 2}{-3} = \frac{z - 3}{1}$$

and

$$\frac{x + 1}{1} = \frac{y - 2}{0} = \frac{z - 1}{-3}.$$

Notice that the second equation has been written in the form used for the case in which no direction number is zero; it is understood that the outside terms are equal (one equation) and that $y = 2$ (another equation), and these two equations define the line. Now choose points P_1 on the first line and P_2 on the second, say P_1: $(1, -2, 3)$ and P_2: $(-1, 2, 1)$. The desired distance (see Fig. 1.32) is the length of the projection of the vector $\overrightarrow{P_1P_2}$ along the direction normal to each of

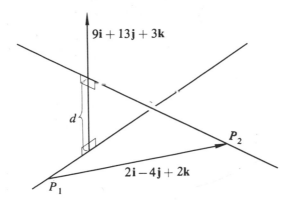

Figure 1.32.   (See Example 1.16.)

the lines. The direction perpendicular to each of the vectors $4\mathbf{i} - 3\mathbf{j} + \mathbf{k}$ and $\mathbf{i} - 3\mathbf{k}$ is their cross product:

$$\begin{vmatrix} \mathbf{i} & \mathbf{j} & \mathbf{k} \\ 4 & -3 & 1 \\ 1 & 0 & -3 \end{vmatrix} = 9\mathbf{i} + 13\mathbf{j} + 3\mathbf{k}.$$

The vector $\overrightarrow{P_1P_2}$ is

$$\overrightarrow{P_1P_2} = \mathbf{r}_2 - \mathbf{r}_1 = [1 - (-1)]\mathbf{i} + (-2 - 2)\mathbf{j} + (3 - 1)\mathbf{k} = 2\mathbf{i} - 4\mathbf{j} + 2\mathbf{k},$$

and the desired distance is the magnitude of the dot product of this with a unit vector along $9\mathbf{i} + 13\mathbf{j} + 3\mathbf{k}$:

$$\text{distance} = \left| (2\mathbf{i} - 4\mathbf{j} + 2\mathbf{k}) \cdot \frac{9\mathbf{i} + 13\mathbf{j} + 3\mathbf{k}}{(81 + 169 + 9)^{1/2}} \right| = \frac{28}{\sqrt{259}}.$$

Problems

1.43.   Write the vector from $(1, 2, -1)$ to $(4, 2, 3)$ in terms of $\mathbf{i}$, $\mathbf{j}$, and $\mathbf{k}$. Determine the distance between these two points.

1.44.   Write equations of the line normal to $x - 2y + z = 4$ at $(2, 0, 2)$.

1.45.   Write the equation of the plane through $(1, 0, -3)$ perpendicular to the direction $2\mathbf{i} - \mathbf{j} + \mathbf{k}$.

1.46.   Write equations of the line through the points $(1, 2, -1)$ and $(4, 2, 3)$.

1.47.   Write the equation of the plane through the three points $(1, 2, -1)$, $(1, 0, 3)$, and $(0, 2, 1)$.

1.48.   Determine a vector along the line of intersection of the planes $x - y + 2z = 3$ and $2x + y - 4z = 1$.

1.49.   Determine a set of direction cosines of the line in Problem 1.48.

1.50.   Write the equations of the line perpendicular to $2\mathbf{i} - \mathbf{j} + \mathbf{k}$, parallel to the plane $2x + y - 4z = 1$, and passing through the point $(1, 0, -3)$.

1.51.   Determine the distance from the line through the origin parallel to $\mathbf{i} + \mathbf{j} + \mathbf{k}$, to the line through $(1, 2, -2)$ parallel to $2\mathbf{i} - \mathbf{j} + 2\mathbf{k}$.

1.52.   Determine the distance from $(2, 3, 1)$ to $x - 2y + z = 4$. Is the point above or below the plane (in the sense of $+z$ as "above")?

1.53.   Determine the equation of the plane tangent to the sphere $r = 13$ at the point $(3, -4, 12)$.

1.54.   Show that vectors drawn from the points $(a, 0, 0)$ and $(-a, 0, 0)$ to any point on the sphere $r = a$ are perpendicular. Observe then that the equation of the sphere can be written $(\mathbf{r} - \mathbf{a}) \cdot (\mathbf{r} + \mathbf{a}) = 0$, where $\mathbf{a}$ is the position vector of $(a, 0, 0)$. Finally, obtain the vector equation of the sphere when the origin is translated to the point $(a, 0, 0)$ (replace the old position vector $\mathbf{r}$ by $\mathbf{r}' + \mathbf{a}$, where $\mathbf{r}'$ is the new position vector), and then obtain the corresponding equation in rectangular coordinates centered at this new origin.

1.9   *Reciprocal sets*†

The sets of vectors $(\mathbf{A}_1, \mathbf{A}_2, \mathbf{A}_3)$ and $(\mathbf{B}_1, \mathbf{B}_2, \mathbf{B}_3)$ are called reciprocal sets if each is a linearly independent set and

$$\mathbf{A}_m \cdot \mathbf{B}_n = \delta_{mn} \equiv \begin{cases} 1, & \text{if } m = n, \\ 0, & \text{if } m \neq n. \end{cases}$$

There is at most one set reciprocal to $(\mathbf{A}_1, \mathbf{A}_2, \mathbf{A}_3)$; for, if there were another, say $(\mathbf{C}_1, \mathbf{C}_2, \mathbf{C}_3)$, with $\mathbf{A}_m \cdot \mathbf{C}_n = \delta_{mn}$, then for $m = 1, 2, 3$ and $n = 1, 2, 3$:

$$\mathbf{A}_m \cdot \mathbf{B}_n - \mathbf{A}_m \cdot \mathbf{C}_n = \mathbf{A}_m \cdot (\mathbf{B}_n - \mathbf{C}_n) = 0,$$

and so it must be that $\mathbf{B}_n \equiv \mathbf{C}_n$.

On the other hand, if $(\mathbf{A}_1, \mathbf{A}_2, \mathbf{A}_3)$ are linearly independent:

$$d \equiv \mathbf{A}_1 \cdot \mathbf{A}_2 \times \mathbf{A}_3 \neq 0,$$

†The material of this section will not be required until Chapter 6.

then the vectors

$$\mathbf{B}_1 = \frac{1}{d}\,\mathbf{A}_2 \times \mathbf{A}_3, \quad \mathbf{B}_2 = \frac{1}{d}\,\mathbf{A}_3 \times \mathbf{A}_1, \quad \mathbf{B}_3 = \frac{1}{d}\,\mathbf{A}_1 \times \mathbf{A}_2$$

form a set reciprocal to the **A**'s, as is readily verified. For instance,

$$\mathbf{B}_1 \cdot \mathbf{A}_2 = \frac{1}{d}\,\mathbf{A}_2 \times \mathbf{A}_3 \cdot \mathbf{A}_2 = 0,$$

and

$$\mathbf{B}_1 \cdot \mathbf{A}_1 = \frac{1}{d}\,\mathbf{A}_2 \times \mathbf{A}_3 \cdot \mathbf{A}_1 = \frac{d}{d} = 1.$$

Thus, there *is* one, but only one, set reciprocal to the **A**'s.

E X A M P L E 1.17   Consider the vectors $\mathbf{A}_1 = 2\mathbf{i}$, $\mathbf{A}_2 = \mathbf{i} + \mathbf{j}$, and $\mathbf{A}_3 = \mathbf{i} + \mathbf{j} + \mathbf{k}$. These are not coplanar:

$$\mathbf{A}_1 \cdot \mathbf{A}_2 \times \mathbf{A}_3 = \begin{vmatrix} 2 & 0 & 0 \\ 1 & 1 & 0 \\ 1 & 1 & 1 \end{vmatrix} = 2.$$

The reciprocal set is given as follows:

$$\mathbf{B}_1 = \frac{1}{2}\,(\mathbf{A}_2 \times \mathbf{A}_3) = \frac{1}{2}\begin{vmatrix} \mathbf{i} & \mathbf{j} & \mathbf{k} \\ 1 & 1 & 0 \\ 1 & 1 & 1 \end{vmatrix} = \frac{\mathbf{i} - \mathbf{j}}{2},$$

$$\mathbf{B}_2 = \frac{1}{2}\,(\mathbf{A}_3 \times \mathbf{A}_1) = \mathbf{j} - \mathbf{k},$$

$$\mathbf{B}_3 = \frac{1}{2}\,(\mathbf{A}_1 \times \mathbf{A}_2) = \mathbf{k}.$$

(Those with a background in matrices will recognize that the computation is just that of inverting a matrix, and should verify that the matrix of components of the **A**'s and the transposed matrix of the components of the **B**'s are inverse matrices.)

If a vector **V** is represented as a linear combination of the noncoplanar vectors $\mathbf{A}_1$, $\mathbf{A}_2$, $\mathbf{A}_3$,

$$\mathbf{V} = a_1\mathbf{A}_1 + a_2\mathbf{A}_2 + a_3\mathbf{A}_3,$$

the coefficients can be determined by using the reciprocal set. For,

$$\mathbf{V} \cdot \mathbf{B}_1 = a_1(\mathbf{A}_1 \cdot \mathbf{B}_1) + a_2(\mathbf{A}_2 \cdot \mathbf{B}_1) + a_3(\mathbf{A}_3 \cdot \mathbf{B}_1) = a_1,$$

and similarly,

$$a_2 = \mathbf{V} \cdot \mathbf{B}_2,$$

and

$$a_3 = \mathbf{V} \cdot \mathbf{B}_3.$$

E X A M P L E 1.18   Suppose that it is desired to locate the two points, P on the line through P_0: $(1, 0, 2)$ parallel to $\mathbf{u} = \mathbf{i} - \mathbf{j}$, and Q on the line through P_1: $(-1, 1, 0)$ parallel to $\mathbf{v} = \mathbf{i} + \mathbf{k}$, such that the distance $\overline{PQ}$ is the shortest distance between these lines. Referring to Fig. 1.33 it is evident that (for certain constants a, b, and c)

$$\mathbf{r}_1 + b\mathbf{v} = \mathbf{r}_0 + a\mathbf{u} + \overrightarrow{PQ},$$

where

$$\overrightarrow{PQ} = c(\mathbf{u} \times \mathbf{v}).$$

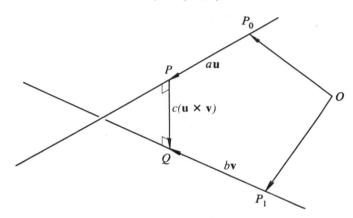

Figure 1.33

That is,

$$a(\mathbf{i} - \mathbf{j}) - b(\mathbf{i} + \mathbf{k}) + c(-\mathbf{i} - \mathbf{j} + \mathbf{k}) = \mathbf{r}_1 - \mathbf{r}_0$$
$$= -2\mathbf{i} + \mathbf{j} - 2\mathbf{k}.$$

The vectors reciprocal to $\mathbf{u}$, $\mathbf{v}$, and $\mathbf{u} \times \mathbf{v}$ are

$$\mathbf{B}_1 = \frac{\mathbf{v} \times (\mathbf{u} \times \mathbf{v})}{\mathbf{u} \cdot \mathbf{v} \times (\mathbf{u} \times \mathbf{v})} = \frac{\mathbf{i} - 2\mathbf{j} - \mathbf{k}}{3},$$

$$\mathbf{B}_2 = \frac{(\mathbf{u} \times \mathbf{v}) \times \mathbf{u}}{\mathbf{u} \cdot \mathbf{v} \times (\mathbf{u} \times \mathbf{v})} = \frac{\mathbf{i} + \mathbf{j} + 2\mathbf{k}}{3},$$

and

$$\mathbf{B}_3 = \frac{\mathbf{u} \times \mathbf{v}}{\mathbf{u} \cdot \mathbf{v} \times (\mathbf{u} \times \mathbf{v})} = \frac{-\mathbf{i} - \mathbf{j} + \mathbf{k}}{3}.$$

The coefficients a, b, and c are then computed as follows:

$$a = (-2\mathbf{i} + \mathbf{j} - 2\mathbf{k}) \cdot \mathbf{B}_1 = -\tfrac{2}{3},$$
$$-b = (-2\mathbf{i} + \mathbf{j} - 2\mathbf{k}) \cdot \mathbf{B}_2 = -\tfrac{5}{3} \cdot$$
$$c = (-2\mathbf{i} + \mathbf{j} - 2\mathbf{k}) \cdot \mathbf{B}_3 = -\tfrac{1}{3},$$

and finally

$$\mathbf{r}_Q = \mathbf{r}_1 + b\mathbf{v} = -\mathbf{i} + \mathbf{j} + \tfrac{5}{3}(\mathbf{i} + \mathbf{k}) = \tfrac{1}{3}(2\mathbf{i} + 3\mathbf{j} + 5\mathbf{k}),$$
$$\mathbf{r}_P = \mathbf{r}_0 + a\mathbf{u} = \mathbf{i} + 2\mathbf{k} - \tfrac{2}{3}(\mathbf{i} - \mathbf{j}) = \tfrac{1}{3}(\mathbf{i} + 2\mathbf{j} + 6\mathbf{k}).$$

The distance $\overline{PQ}$ can of course be computed now as $|\mathbf{r}_P - \mathbf{r}_Q| = 1/\sqrt{3}$.

Problems

1.55.   Determine the set reciprocal to $\mathbf{A}_1 = \mathbf{i} + \mathbf{j}$, $\mathbf{A}_2 = \mathbf{i} - \mathbf{k}$, $\mathbf{A}_3 = \mathbf{i} + \mathbf{j} + \mathbf{k}$.

1.56.   Show that if $(\mathbf{A}_1, \mathbf{A}_2, \mathbf{A}_3)$ is a set of mutually orthogonal vectors, the reciprocal set consists of vectors parallel to these.

1.57.   Is there a reciprocal set if $\mathbf{A}_1$, $\mathbf{A}_2$, and $\mathbf{A}_3$ are coplanar?

1.58.   Determine points P and Q such that $\overrightarrow{PQ}$ is perpendicular to each of the lines in Example 1.16.

2 FUNCTIONS OF A SINGLE VARIABLE

ALTHOUGH the purpose of this chapter is the study of vector functions of a single variable, material is included on the calculus of scalar functions which for many will be a review. This review seems desirable not only for purposes of refreshment but also because the definitions for vector functions are so nearly like those for scalar functions.

2.1 *Scalar functions of one variable*

The *limit* of the scalar function (or real-valued function) $f(x)$ at $x = a$ is said to be the finite number L provided that to each $\epsilon > 0$ there corresponds a $\delta > 0$ such that

$$|f(x) - L| < \epsilon \qquad \text{whenever} \qquad 0 < |x - a| < \delta.$$

From this definition can be proved the various pertinent properties: the limit of a sum is the sum of the limits; the limit of a product is the product of the limits; the limit of a quotient of two functions is the quotient of the limits provided the denominator does not have the limit 0. It can also be shown that the limit of a constant function is its constant value (any choice of δ will do), and that the limit of the function $f(x) = x$ at $x = a$ is just a (choose $\delta = \epsilon$). (These and other theorems to be given in this section without proof can be found, with proofs, in any good calculus book.)

46

A function is said to be *continuous at* $x = a$ if it has a limit there and if that limit is the value of the function at $x = a$:

$$\lim_{x \to a} f(x) = f(a).$$

It is called continuous in a region of x-values if it is continuous at each point of the region. The theorems on limits just given are readily exploited to show that the sum, product, or quotient of continuous functions is continuous (if the denominator in the quotient stays away from the value 0), and that a constant and the function $f(x) = x$ are continuous. It follows that any polynomial function is continuous everywhere, as is any rational fraction (quotient of two polynomials) except at points where the denominator vanishes. Further, the exponential, logarithmic, and trigonometric functions are continuous wherever they are defined.

Intuitively, the significance of the statement that $f(x)$ is continuous is that a small change in x can produce at most a small change in $f(x)$, and the change in $f(x)$ can be kept as small as desired by suitably restricting the amount of the change in x. The graphical significance is that the curve representing $y = f(x)$ in the xy-plane can be drawn without lifting the pencil from the paper.

If the notion of continuity signifies that small changes in x produce small changes in $f(x)$, the notion of derivative is designed to relate the amounts of these small changes. Consider the point x_0, a small change in x to the new value $x_0 + x$, and the corresponding change in the value of y:

$$\Delta y = f(x_0 + \Delta x) - f(x_0).$$

The ratio $\Delta y / \Delta x$ is an average change in y per unit change in x; it depends on x_0 and on Δx as well as on the function $f(x)$. If, for fixed x_0, this ratio has a limit at $\Delta x = 0$, this limit is called the *derivative* of $f(x)$ with respect to x at the point x_0,

$$f'(x_0) = \lim_{\Delta x \to 0} \frac{f(x_0 + \Delta x) - f(x_0)}{\Delta x}.$$

The notation dy/dx will also be used for this derivative, with a vertical bar and subscript to denote the point at which it is computed, if this is needed for clarity:

$$\left. \frac{dy}{dx} \right|_{x=x_0} = \lim_{\Delta x \to 0} \frac{\Delta y}{\Delta x}.$$

An equivalent way of writing this relation is useful:

$$\frac{\Delta y}{\Delta x} = \frac{dy}{dx} + \epsilon,$$

where ϵ is a number depending on Δx which has the limit zero at $\Delta x = 0$. Upon multiplication by Δx this becomes

$$\Delta y = \frac{dy}{dx} \Delta x + \epsilon \, \Delta x$$

(a relation which holds, incidentally, even for $\Delta x = 0$). It is quite clear from this that, if dy/dx exists as a finite number, Δy tends to zero as Δx tends to zero, so that $f(x)$ must be continuous at $x = x_0$. However, this implication cannot be reversed; there are functions which are continuous but not differentiable.

In the expression for the change in $f(x)$, called Δy, as just given, the first term predominates, the ratio of the second term to the first term having the limit zero. This dominating part is called the *differential* of $f(x)$ corresponding to the change in x from x_0 to $x_0 + \Delta x$ and is written dy or $df(x)$:

$$dy = \frac{dy}{dx} \Delta x.$$

The quantity dy/dx is sometimes called the *differential coefficient*. Geometrically, the differential is the approximation to Δy obtained using the tangent line as an approximation to the function, as indicated in Fig. 2.1.

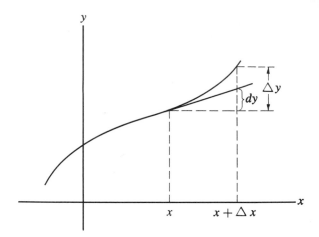

Figure 2.1

The increment quotient $\Delta y / \Delta x$ is an *average* rate of change of $y = f(x)$ over the interval from x_0 to $x_0 + \Delta x$, approximately equal to the *instantaneous* rate $f'(x_0)$ when Δx is small. The *mean value theorem* states that whether Δx is small or not, the average rate over the interval is exactly equal to the instantaneous rate $f'(x^*)$ at some point x^* between x_0 and $x_0 + \Delta x$:

$$\frac{f(x_0 + \Delta x) - f(x_0)}{\Delta x} = f'(x^*),$$

provided that $f(x)$ is differentiable over the interval in question. If x is a measure of time and $f(x)$ is distance traveled after x time units, $\Delta y/\Delta x$ is the average speed over a trip taking Δx time units. According to the mean value theorem, the instantaneous speed must at some time during the trip equal the average speed. (The mean value theorem is proved in almost every calculus book; for the most complete and correct proofs, books on advanced calculus should be consulted.)

When $y = f(x)$ and $z = g(y)$, each value of x determines a value of y which in turn determines a value of z, namely, $g(f(x))$. Thus, z is a function of x, and this dependence on x has properties which depend on those of the two functions $f(x)$ and $g(y)$. If both $f(x)$ and $g(y)$ are continuous functions (of x and y, respectively), then a small change in x produces only a small change in $y = f(x)$, which in turn produces only a small change in $z = g(y)$. From this it is clear (and can be made quite rigorous in terms of ϵ and δ) that z is continuous in its dependence on x; that is, a continuous function of a continuous function is continuous.

The derivative with respect to x of the composite function $g(f(x))$ can be expressed in terms of $f'(x)$ and $g'(y)$ by what is sometimes called the *chain rule:*

$$\left.\frac{dz}{dx}\right|_{x=x_0} = g'(f(x_0))f'(x_0),$$

more easily remembered in the form

$$\frac{dz}{dx} = \frac{dz}{dy}\frac{dy}{dx}.$$

This is derived as follows. Let $y_0 = f(x_0)$, and consider a change in x from x_0 to $x_0 + \Delta x$, which then produces a change in y from y_0 to $y_0 + \Delta y$. This increment Δy results in an increment Δz related to it and to the derivative:

$$\Delta z = \frac{dz}{dy}\Delta y + \epsilon\,\Delta y.$$

Division by Δx then yields

$$\frac{\Delta z}{\Delta x} = \frac{dz}{dy}\cdot\frac{\Delta y}{\Delta x} + \epsilon\frac{\Delta y}{\Delta x},$$

and passing to the limit as $\Delta x \to 0$ yields the desired result, provided that the derivatives involved are defined and finite. Notice that, as obtained upon multiplication of both sides of the chain rule by Δx, the following formula for a differential holds even though the y is not thought of as the independent variable:

$$dz = \frac{dz}{dy}\, dy.$$

2.2 *Vector functions of a single variable*

The definitions of limit, continuity, and differentiation in the case of vector functions are completely analagous to those in the case of scalar functions; indeed, the definitions *look* identical.

The vector function $\mathbf{V}(u)$ is said to have the vector $\mathbf{L}$ as a *limit* at $u = a$ if and only if given any $\epsilon > 0$, there is a corresponding $\delta > 0$ such that

$$|\mathbf{V}(u) - \mathbf{L}| < \epsilon \qquad \text{whenever} \qquad 0 < |u - a| < \delta.$$

In the first inequality the minus sign denotes *vector* subtraction, and the absolute value indicates the *length* of the vector $\mathbf{V}(u) - \mathbf{L}$. The absolute value of the difference vector is thus the distance between the tip of $\mathbf{V}$ and the tip of $\mathbf{L}$ (when $\mathbf{V}$ and $\mathbf{L}$ issue from the same point); it is a measure of closeness of $\mathbf{V}(u)$ to the vector $\mathbf{L}$. In words, then, $\mathbf{V}(u)$ has the limit $\mathbf{L}$ provided it can be made arbitrarily close to $\mathbf{L}$ by taking u sufficiently close to a.

A vector function $\mathbf{V}(u)$ is called continuous at $u = a$ if and only if

$$\lim_{u \to a} \mathbf{V}(u) = \mathbf{V}(a).$$

It is continuous over a set of u-values if it is continuous at each value in the set.

E x a m p l e 2.1   Consider the vector function

$$\mathbf{V}(u) = u\mathbf{A} + (1 - u)\mathbf{B},$$

where $\mathbf{A}$ and $\mathbf{B}$ are given fixed vectors. At $u = a$ the limit of $\mathbf{V}(u)$ is $\mathbf{V}(a) = a\mathbf{A} + (1 - a)\mathbf{B}$. For

$$\left| u\mathbf{A} + (1 - u)\mathbf{B} - [a\mathbf{A} + (1 - a)\mathbf{B}] \right| = |u - a|\,|\mathbf{A} - \mathbf{B}|,$$

and the absolute difference on the left-hand side can be made less than ϵ by taking $|u - a| < \epsilon/|\mathbf{A} - \mathbf{B}|$ (that is, choose $\delta = \epsilon/|\mathbf{A} - \mathbf{B}|$). Then, since the limit of $\mathbf{V}(u)$ is $\mathbf{V}(a)$, $\mathbf{V}(u)$ is continuous at $u = a$.

Because the length of a vector obeys many of the same rules as the absolute value of a number, theorems on limits of vector functions are similar to theorems on limits of scalar functions. In particular, if $\mathbf{V}(u) \to \mathbf{L}$, $\mathbf{W}(u) \to \mathbf{M}$, and $f(u) \to k$ as $u \to a$, then

(a) $\qquad\qquad |\mathbf{V}(u)| \to |\mathbf{L}|$,

(b) $\qquad\quad f(u)\,\mathbf{V}(u) \to k\mathbf{L}$,

(c) $\quad \mathbf{V}(u) + \mathbf{W}(u) \to \mathbf{L} + \mathbf{M}$,

(d) $\qquad \mathbf{V}(u) \cdot \mathbf{W}(u) \to \mathbf{L} \cdot \mathbf{M}$,

(e) $\quad \mathbf{V}(u) \times \mathbf{W}(u) \to \mathbf{L} \times \mathbf{M}$.

Proofs of the preceding properties are very similar to the proofs for purely scalar cases. Consider (d), for instance:

$$
\begin{aligned}
|\mathbf{V}(u)\cdot\mathbf{W}(u) - \mathbf{L}\cdot\mathbf{M}| &= |\mathbf{V}(u)\cdot\mathbf{W}(u) - \mathbf{L}\cdot\mathbf{W}(u) + \mathbf{L}\cdot\mathbf{W}(u) - \mathbf{L}\cdot\mathbf{M}| \\
&\leq |\mathbf{V}(u)\cdot\mathbf{W}(u) - \mathbf{L}\cdot\mathbf{W}(u)| + |\mathbf{L}\cdot\mathbf{W}(u) - \mathbf{L}\cdot\mathbf{M}| \\
&= |\mathbf{W}(u)\cdot[\mathbf{V}(u) - \mathbf{L}]| + |\mathbf{L}\cdot[\mathbf{W}(u) - \mathbf{M}]| \\
&\leq |\mathbf{W}(u)|\,|\mathbf{V}(u) - \mathbf{L}| + |\mathbf{L}|\,|\mathbf{W}(u) - \mathbf{M}|.
\end{aligned}
$$

(Use is made here of the triangle inequality, the distributive property of the scalar product, and the fact that $|\mathbf{A}\cdot\mathbf{B}| \leq |\mathbf{A}|\,|\mathbf{B}|$.) Now, by taking u sufficiently close to a one can make $|\mathbf{W}(u)| < 2M$, $|\mathbf{V}(u) - \mathbf{L}| < \epsilon/4M$, and $|\mathbf{W}(u) - \mathbf{M}| < \epsilon/2L$, so that the absolute difference $|\mathbf{V}\cdot\mathbf{W} - \mathbf{L}\cdot\mathbf{M}|$ is smaller than ϵ. This establishes (d).

That sums and products (inner and outer) of continuous vector functions are again continuous functions follows from (c), (d), and (e). Property (a) implies that $|\mathbf{V}(u)|$ is a continuous function of u if $\mathbf{V}(u)$ is continuous.

E x a m p l e 2.2   Suppose that as $u \to a$, the scalar functions $\xi(u)$, $\zeta(u)$, and $\eta(u)$ have limits, respectively, m, n, and p. The vector

$$\mathbf{V}(u) = \xi(u)\mathbf{i} + \zeta(u)\mathbf{j} + \eta(u)\mathbf{k}$$

then has the limit $m\mathbf{i} + n\mathbf{j} + p\mathbf{k}$, which is the sum of the limits of the individual terms in $\mathbf{V}(u)$. If, in addition, $\xi(u)$, $\zeta(u)$, and $\eta(u)$ are continuous functions of u at $u = a$, with limits $\xi(a)$, $\zeta(a)$, and $\eta(a)$, respectively, it follows that $\mathbf{V}(u)$ has the limit $\mathbf{V}(a)$ and so is continuous at $u = a$.

The derivative of the vector function $\mathbf{V}(u)$ at the point $u = a$ is defined to be the following limit (when it exists):

$$\mathbf{V}'(u) = \lim_{h \to 0} \frac{\mathbf{V}(a + h) - \mathbf{V}(a)}{h}.$$

Again the appearance of this expression is exactly that of the derivative of a scalar function. However, the subtraction in the numerator is vector subtraction, and dividing by h means altering the length of the numerator vector by a factor $1/h$. The notation $d\mathbf{V}/du$ will also be used for the derivative.

As in the scalar case, the increment in the function $\mathbf{V}(u)$ corresponding to the increment Δu in u can be expressed as follows:

$$\mathbf{V}(u + \Delta u) - \mathbf{V}(u) = \Delta\mathbf{V}(u) = \frac{d\mathbf{V}}{du}\Delta u + \boldsymbol{\epsilon}\Delta u,$$

where $\boldsymbol{\epsilon}$ is a vector whose limit is $\mathbf{0}$ as $\Delta u \to 0$. And once more it is evident that differentiability of $\mathbf{V}(u)$ implies its continuity, since in that case $\Delta\mathbf{V} \to \mathbf{0}$ (and then $|\Delta\mathbf{V}| \to 0$) as $\Delta u \to 0$. The principal part of the increment $\Delta\mathbf{V}$ is again called the differential:

$$d\mathbf{V}(u) = \frac{d\mathbf{V}}{du}\Delta u.$$

If $u = g(x)$, with $du = g'(x)\,dx$, it is clear that

$$d\mathbf{V}(u) = \frac{d\mathbf{V}}{du}du.$$

Because the derivative of a vector function is defined formally as is the derivative of a scalar function, and because the laws of vector algebra are so like the laws of the algebra of scalar quantities, differentiation rules for vector functions turn out to be much like those for scalar functions. Expressed in terms of differentials, some of the differentiation rules are as follows:

(1) $d[\mathbf{V}(u) + \mathbf{W}(u)] = d\mathbf{V}(u) + d\mathbf{W}(u),$
(2) $d[f(u)\mathbf{V}(u)] = f(u)\,d\mathbf{V}(u) + df(u)\mathbf{V}(u),$
(3) $d[\mathbf{V}(u)\cdot\mathbf{W}(u)] = \mathbf{V}(u)\cdot d\mathbf{W}(u) + \mathbf{W}(u)\cdot d\mathbf{V}(u),$
(4) $d[\mathbf{V}(u) \times \mathbf{W}(u)] = \mathbf{V}(u) \times d\mathbf{W}(u) + d\mathbf{V}(u) \times \mathbf{W}(u).$

Rule (4) is derived as follows:

$$\frac{d}{du}[\mathbf{V}(u) \times \mathbf{W}(u)] = \lim_{\Delta u \to 0}\frac{[\mathbf{V}(u) + \Delta\mathbf{V}] \times [\mathbf{W}(u) + \Delta\mathbf{W}] - \mathbf{V} \times \mathbf{W}}{\Delta u}$$

$$= \lim_{\Delta u \to 0}\left[\frac{\Delta\mathbf{V}}{\Delta u} \times \mathbf{W} + \mathbf{V} \times \frac{\Delta\mathbf{W}}{\Delta u} + \frac{\Delta\mathbf{V}}{\Delta u} \times \Delta\mathbf{W}\right]$$

$$= \frac{d\mathbf{V}}{du} \times \mathbf{W} + \mathbf{V} \times \frac{d\mathbf{W}}{du}.$$

(The manipulations here involve use of the distributive laws for vector multiplication and multiplication by a scalar, the fact that the limit of a vector product is the vector product of the limits, and the continuity of **W** implied in the assumption of its differentiability.)

An important application of rules (1) and (2) shows that when a vector function is expressed in terms of an orthonormal set of vectors:

$$\mathbf{V}(u) = \xi(u)\mathbf{i} + \zeta(u)\mathbf{j} + \eta(u)\mathbf{k},$$

where $\xi(u)$, $\zeta(u)$, and $\eta(u)$ are differentiable, then $d\mathbf{V}/du$ exists and is

$$\mathbf{V}'(u) = \xi'(u)\mathbf{i} + \zeta'(u)\mathbf{j} + \eta'(u)\mathbf{k}.$$

For, the derivative of **V** is the sum of the derivatives of its components, and the derivative of, say, $\xi(u)\mathbf{i}$ is the derivative of $\xi(u)$ times the constant vector **i**.

E x a m p l e 2.3   Consider the vector $\mathbf{V} = 2u\mathbf{i} + u^2\mathbf{j} - \mathbf{k}$. Term by term differentiation yields

$$\frac{d\mathbf{V}}{du} = 2\mathbf{i} + 2u\mathbf{j}.$$

If $u = g(t)$, then **V** becomes a function of t, with derivative

$$\frac{d\mathbf{V}}{dt} = \frac{d\mathbf{V}}{du} \cdot \frac{du}{dt} = [2\mathbf{i} + 2g(t)\mathbf{j}]\, g'(t).$$

E x a m p l e 2.4   Let **U** denote a variable vector of constant unit length, with orientation depending on the scalar variable u. Since $|\mathbf{U}|^2 = \mathbf{U} \cdot \mathbf{U} = 1$, the derivative of $\mathbf{U} \cdot \mathbf{U}$ must be zero:

$$0 = \frac{d}{du}(\mathbf{U} \cdot \mathbf{U}) = \mathbf{U} \cdot \frac{d\mathbf{U}}{du} + \mathbf{U} \cdot \frac{d\mathbf{U}}{du} = 2\mathbf{U} \cdot \frac{d\mathbf{U}}{du}.$$

The vanishing of this dot product implies that either the derivative $d\mathbf{U}/du$ is the zero vector or it is a vector perpendicular to **U**.

Problems

2.1.   Differentiate with respect to x:
(a) $(x^3 - 2x)^4$.
(b) $\sin(3x + 2)$.
(c) e^{-t^2}.
(d) $\log \dfrac{x}{x^2 - 4}$.

2.2.   Let $\mathbf{V}(t) = t\mathbf{i} + t^2\mathbf{j} + t^3\mathbf{k}$.

(a) Determine $\mathbf{V}'(t)$.

(b) Why is $\mathbf{V}(t)$ continuous at all t?

(c) Determine $\lim\limits_{t \to 2} \mathbf{V}(t)$.

2.3.   Show that $\dfrac{d}{dt}\left[\mathbf{U} \times \dfrac{d\mathbf{U}}{dt} \right] = \mathbf{U} \times \dfrac{d^2\mathbf{U}}{dt^2}$.

2.4.   Given that $\lim \mathbf{V}(t) = \mathbf{L}$ and $\lim \mathbf{W}(t) = \mathbf{M}$ as $t \to a$, show that $\lim[\mathbf{V}(t) + \mathbf{W}(t)] = \mathbf{L} + \mathbf{M}$ and $\lim[\mathbf{V}(t) \times \mathbf{W}(t)] = \mathbf{L} \times \mathbf{M}$.

2.5.   Let $\mathbf{V}(t) = t^2\mathbf{i} + t^3\mathbf{j}$.

(a) Show that there is *no* t on the interval $0 < t < 1$ such that

$$\frac{\mathbf{V}(1) - \mathbf{V}(0)}{1 - 2} = \mathbf{V}'(t).$$

(b) Determine a value of u on the interval $0 < u < 1$ for which

$$\frac{|\mathbf{V}(1) - \mathbf{V}(0)|}{1 - 0} = |\mathbf{V}'(u)|.$$

2.6.   Let $\mathbf{W}(\theta) = (\cos\theta)\mathbf{i} + (\sin\theta)\mathbf{j}$.

(a) Show that $\dfrac{d^2\mathbf{W}}{d\theta^2} + \mathbf{W} = 0$.

(b) Given that θ is a function of t, determine $\dfrac{d^2\mathbf{W}}{dt^2}$ in terms of θ, $\dot{\theta}$, and $\ddot{\theta}$. (Each dot over a variable indicates a differentiation with respect to t.)

(c) Show that there is no value of θ on the range $0 < \theta < \pi/2$ such that

$$\frac{|\mathbf{W}(\pi/2) - \mathbf{W}(0)|}{\pi/2 - 0} = |\mathbf{W}'(\theta)|.$$

2.7.   Given differentiable functions $f(u)$ and $\mathbf{V}(u)$, show that

$$d[f(u)\mathbf{V}(u)] = f(u)\,d\mathbf{V}(u) + \mathbf{V}(u)\,df(u).$$

2.8.   Show that $|\mathbf{V}(u)|$ is a continuous function of u if $\mathbf{V}(u)$ is continuous.

2.9.   Derive the rules for differentiating the following:

(a) a dot product of vector functions:

(b) the product of a scalar function and a vector function.

2.3   *Arc length*

A *curve* (or *arc*) can be thought of as an ordered set of points in three-dimensional space defined by the locus of the equation

$$\mathbf{r} = \mathbf{f}(u),$$

where the parameter u ranges over some set of real numbers, and $\mathbf{r}$ is again the position vector of the generic point P on the locus. An order among points on the locus is induced by the order among the values of u. As u increases, say, from $u = a$ to $u = b$, the point P moves in space along the curve from $\mathbf{f}(a)$ to $\mathbf{f}(b)$. The representation of a curve as the locus of an equation of the form $\mathbf{r} = \mathbf{f}(u)$ is called a *parametrization* of the curve. Such a representation is not unique, as the following example illustrates.

EXAMPLE 2.5   Given fixed vectors $\mathbf{A}$ and $\mathbf{B}$, the equation

$$\mathbf{r} = u\mathbf{A} + (1 - u)\mathbf{B}$$

defines a curve. For u on the range $0 \le u \le 1$ the vector $\mathbf{r}$ is a linear combination of the vectors $\mathbf{A}$ and $\mathbf{B}$, whose tip P is on the line segment joining the tips of $\mathbf{A}$ and $\mathbf{B}$. For other values of u the vector $\mathbf{r}$ will have its tip on the extension of that line segment (see Fig. 2.2). The same curve can be parametrized in other ways.

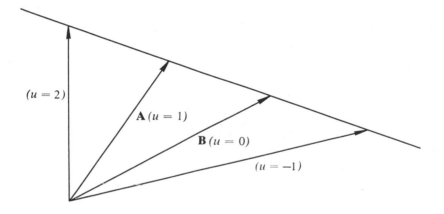

($u = 2$)

$\mathbf{A}\,(u = 1)$

$\mathbf{B}\,(u = 0)$

($u = -1$)

Figure 2.2.   (See Example 2.5.)

For instance, the equation

$$\mathbf{r} = (\cos^2 \theta)\mathbf{A} + (\sin^2 \theta)\mathbf{B}$$

also defines the line segment joining the tips of $\mathbf{A}$ and $\mathbf{B}$, as θ varies over $0 \le \theta \le \pi/2$. However, as θ varies outside this range, the point P moves periodically back and forth between the tips of $\mathbf{A}$ and $\mathbf{B}$ but never goes outside that segment. On the other hand, the equation

$$\mathbf{r} = u^3\mathbf{A} + (1 - u^3)\mathbf{B}$$

generates the same straight line as does $u\mathbf{A} + (1 - u)\mathbf{B}$, for $-\infty < u < \infty$.

Without some restriction on the function $\mathbf{f}(u)$ which defines a curve, the curve can be quite wild, whereas useful curves usually permit a parametrization in terms of a smooth function. A curve is called *continuous* if it admits a parametrization in terms of a continuous function $\mathbf{f}(u)$. Curves to be considered here will be at least continuous, but the assumption of continuity is not strong enough even to guarantee that the notion of length is defined. Indeed, there have been constructed continuous curves which fill up (pass through each point of) a two-dimensional set such as the set of points in a square. It is not overly restrictive, from the point of view of applications, to consider only curves that are "rectifiable" and even "continuously differentiable" in pieces—to use words which are about to be defined.

Consider a curve with the parametrization $\mathbf{r} = \mathbf{f}(u)$, where $a \leq u \leq b$. This curve (or portion of a curve, if $\mathbf{f}(u)$ is also defined outside $[a, b]$) lies between the tips of $\mathbf{r}_A = \mathbf{f}(a)$ and $\mathbf{r}_B = \mathbf{f}(b)$ in the sense of the ordering induced by the ordering of the u-values; that is, P lies between the *end points* A and B if $\mathbf{r}_P = \mathbf{f}(u^*)$ for some u^* on the u-interval from a to b. Let $u_0, u_1, \ldots, u_n$ denote the points of a partition of the interval $[a, b]$, with

$$a = u_0 < u_1 < \cdots < u_n = b.$$

This u-partition induces a partition of the curve by means of the points $P_0, P_1, \ldots, P_n$ with position vectors $\mathbf{r}_0 = \mathbf{f}(u_0), \ldots, \mathbf{r}_n = \mathbf{f}(u_n)$, respectively. (See Fig. 2.3.) Joining the partition points P_i with straight line

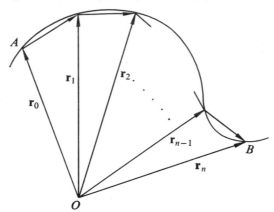

Figure 2.3. Partitioning an arc.

segments yields a polygonal line, which has assigned as its *length* the sum of the lengths of the straight line segments of which it is composed:

$$\text{length of polygonal line} = \sum_{i=1}^{n} |\mathbf{r}_i - \mathbf{r}_{i-1}|.$$

Each partition results in a polygonal line and corresponding length, and if these lengths are bounded (considering all partitions), the curve is said to be *rectifiable*. The least upper bound (l.u.b.) of such polygonal lengths (that is, the upper bound which is not greater than any other upper bound) is defined to be the *length* of the curve segment from A to B:

$$\widehat{AB} = \text{l.u.b.} \sum_{i=1}^{n} |\mathbf{r}_i - \mathbf{r}_{i-1}|.$$

It is useful to know that the length of a rectifiable curve can also be obtained as the limit of polygonal lengths taken over any sequence of partitions such that the maximum diameter of the arcs $\widehat{P_{i-1}P_i}$ tends to zero—a situation guaranteed, for a continuous curve, by having the maximum subinterval length in the u-partition tend to zero. [See Philip Franklin, *A Treatise on Advanced Calculus* (New York, Wiley, 1940), p. 278 ff.]

E X A M P L E   2.6   The equation $\mathbf{r} = (\cos \theta)\mathbf{i} + (\sin \theta)\mathbf{j}$, $0 \leq \theta \leq 2\pi$, defines a continuous curve in the xy-plane, called a circle, having the property that $r = 1$; that is, P is always one unit from the origin. Consider a subinterval (θ', θ''); the length of the line segment joining the points on the circle corresponding to θ' and θ'' is

$$|(\cos \theta'' - \cos \theta')\mathbf{i} + (\sin \theta'' - \sin \theta')\mathbf{j}| = 2 \sin \frac{|\theta'' - \theta'|}{2}.$$

This is bounded by $|\theta'' - \theta'|$, and therefore the sum of the lengths of the segments in an inscribed polygon is bounded by the length of the θ-interval, 2π. The curve is therefore rectifiable, and being rectifiable its length can be computed as the limit of polygonal approximations corresponding to a sequence of partitions. Taking partitions with equal subintervals $\theta = 2\pi/n$, we find

$$\text{length} = \lim_{n \to \infty} \sum_{i=1}^{n} 2 \sin \frac{\pi}{n} = \lim_{n \to \infty} 2\pi \frac{\sin(\pi/n)}{\pi/n} = 2\pi.$$

(To avoid circular reasoning in this example—defining π geometrically in terms of the length of a circle and then concluding that a circle has finite length—it would be necessary to consider the trigonometric functions and π as defined in terms of infinite series or in terms of definite integrals. Alternatively, the boundedness of the lengths of polygons inscribed in a circle can be demonstrated geometrically, thereby establishing the rectifiability of the circle and providing a basis for defining π and the trigonometric functions.)

It should be understood that the length of arc as defined refers to the total length traced out by the tip of $\mathbf{r}$ as the parameter u varies from a to b. If the curve retraces itself, this computed length would exceed what is ordinarily thought of as the length of the curve. Using only a range of u-values which results in a single tracing of the curve would reconcile these quantities. In some cases it is the geometrical arc length which is desired, but in others it is the *path* length which is really wanted—the distance covered by a particle moving along the arc and possibly traversing some parts of the arc more than once.

If the arc from A to B is rectifiable, so also are the arcs from A to P and from P to B, where P is any point between A and B. For, the sum of the polygonal lengths corresponding to a partition of $\widehat{AP}$ and a partition of $\widehat{PB}$ would be the length of the polygonal line defined by a partition of $\widehat{AB}$ and would therefore be bounded. Hence, $\widehat{AP}$ and $\widehat{PB}$ are rectifiable. Furthermore, passing to the limit over a sequence of partitions of $\widehat{AB}$ each of which has P as a partition point yields the additivity property:

$$\widehat{AP} + \widehat{PB} = \widehat{AB}.$$

(The symbol $\widehat{PQ}$ has been used either to denote the arc from P to Q or its length.)

The curves used in subsequent chapters will be not only continuous and rectifiable but also *continuously differentiable*, or made up of a finite number of such pieces. A curve is called *differentiable* if it admits a representation $\mathbf{r} = \mathbf{f}(u)$ such that $\mathbf{f}(u)$ is a differentiable function of the parameter u, and *continuously differentiable* if $\mathbf{f}'(u)$ is continuous. It will be shown below that the length of a continuously differentiable curve is expressible as a definite integral:

$$\widehat{AB} = \int_a^b |\mathbf{f}'(u)|\,du,$$

where A and B are the terminal points, respectively, of $\mathbf{f}(a)$ and $\mathbf{f}(b)$. The assumption of continuity of $\mathbf{f}'(u)$ implies continuity of $|\mathbf{f}'(u)|$, and so ensures existence of the definite integral.

The length of arc along the continuously differentiable curve $\mathbf{r} = \mathbf{f}(u)$ from an arbitrarily selected fixed point A, with $\mathbf{r}_A = \mathbf{f}(a)$, to the variable point P, with $\mathbf{r}_p = \mathbf{f}(u)$, will be denoted by $l(u)$:

$$l(u) = \int_a^u |\mathbf{f}'(v)|\,dv.$$

The distance along the curve from B to C, with $\mathbf{r}_B = \mathbf{f}(b)$ and $\mathbf{r}_C = \mathbf{f}(c)$, is then

$$\widehat{BC} = l(c) - l(b) = \int_b^c |\mathbf{f}'(v)|\,dv,$$

because of the additivity of lengths of adjacent intervals. Equivalent to the integral definition of $l(u)$ is the differential relation

$$dl(u) = |\mathbf{f}'(v)|\,dv, \qquad |f'(u)|\,du$$

or

$$l'(u) = |\mathbf{f}'(u)|.$$

It is this last relation that will be derived below, following Example 2.8.

The length of $\widehat{AB}$ was defined in terms of a particular parametrization. It is easily seen now, at least for continuously differentiable arcs (whose lengths are expressed as integrals), that the same length is obtained using any other equivalent parametrization. This follows from the change of variable rule for definite integrals. For, if the variable w is used as the parameter, where

$$\phi(c) = a \qquad \phi(d) = b$$

$$u = \phi(w), \qquad \text{with} \qquad \phi'(w) > 0, \qquad \text{and} \qquad \phi(a) = c, \qquad \phi(b) = d,$$

$$du = \phi'(w)\,dw$$

then

$$\mathbf{f}(u) = \mathbf{f}(\phi(w)) \equiv \mathbf{g}(w),$$

which is a continuously differentiable function of w if $\phi'(w)$ is continuous; and

$$|\mathbf{g}'(w)|\,dw = |\mathbf{f}'(u)|\,\phi'(w)\,dw = |\mathbf{f}'(u)|\,du = dl(u).$$

Hence

$$l(b) - l(a) = \int_a^b |\mathbf{f}'(u)|\,du = \int_c^d |\mathbf{g}'(w)|\,dw.$$

If $\phi'(w) < 0$, then $|\phi'(w)| = -\phi'(w)$, and

$$l(b) - l(a) = \int_d^c |\mathbf{g}'(w)|\,dw.$$

Now, if in particular one introduces the variable $s = l(u)$, and if $l'(u) = |\mathbf{f}'(u)| \neq 0$ on $a \le u \le b$, there is an inverse function $u = l^{-1}(s)$, and the parameter s can be used to represent the curve:

$$\mathbf{r} = \mathbf{f}(u) = \mathbf{f}(l^{-1}(s)) \equiv \mathbf{h}(s).$$

This is a continuously differentiable representation, with

$$\left|\frac{d\mathbf{r}}{ds}\right| = |\mathbf{h}'(s)| = |\mathbf{f}'(u)|\left|\frac{du}{ds}\right| = |\mathbf{f}'(u)|\frac{1}{|\mathbf{f}'(u)|} = 1.$$

$\frac{d\mathbf{r}}{ds} = \mathbf{t} = \text{unit tangent vector}$

E X A M P L E 2.7   Consider the curve (which happens to be a straight line)

$$\mathbf{r} = u\mathbf{A} + (1 - u)\mathbf{B},$$

where **A** and **B** are given, fixed vectors. Then

$$\frac{d\mathbf{r}}{du} = \mathbf{A} - \mathbf{B},$$

or

$$ds = |\mathbf{A} - \mathbf{B}|\, du,$$

and for $u_0 \leq u_1$,

$$l(u_1) - l(u_0) = |\mathbf{A} - \mathbf{B}| \int_{u_0}^{u_1} du = |\mathbf{A} - \mathbf{B}|\,(u_1 - u_0).$$

In particular, the length of arc from the tip of **A** to the tip of **B** is

$$l(1) - l(0) = |\mathbf{A} - \mathbf{B}|,$$

which should not be too surprising if one recalls that the definition of arc length is based on the lengths of straight line segments.

E X A M P L E   2.8   Suppose that $\mathbf{r} = \mathbf{f}(u)$ is expressed in terms of an orthonormal set $(\mathbf{i}, \mathbf{j}, \mathbf{k})$:

$$\mathbf{r} = \xi(u)\mathbf{i} + \zeta(u)\mathbf{j} + \eta(u)\mathbf{k}.$$

The functions ξ, ζ, and η are continuously differentiable if and only if $\mathbf{f}(u)$ is continuously differentiable, and

$$|\mathbf{f}'(u)| = \{[\xi'(u)]^2 + [\zeta'(u)]^2 + [\eta'(u)]^2\}^{1/2}.$$

Hence

$$l(u) = \int_{a}^{u} \{[\xi'(v)]^2 + [\zeta'(v)]^2 + [\eta'(v)]^2\}^{1/2} dv.$$

It follows from this that if $s = l(u)$, $x = \xi(u)$, $y = \zeta(u)$, and $z = \eta(u)$,

$$ds^2 = dx^2 + dy^2 + dz^2.$$

If, to consider a particular case, $\mathbf{r} = (5 \cos \theta)\mathbf{i} + (3 \sin \theta)\mathbf{j}$, then

$$ds^2 = [25 \sin^2 \theta + 9 \cos^2 \theta]\, d\theta.$$

The scheme to be followed in showing, for each u_0,

$$l'(u_0) = |\mathbf{f}'(u_0)|$$

will be to consider an arbitrary increment h and obtain the inequality

$$\left| \frac{\mathbf{f}(u_0 + h) - \mathbf{f}(u_0)}{h} \right| \leq \frac{l(u_0 + h) - l(u_0)}{h} \leq |\mathbf{f}'(u^*)|,$$

where u^* is a value of u between u_0 and $u_0 + h$. Passing to the limit as h tends to zero, establishes the existence of $l'(u_0)$ as well as giving its value to be $|\mathbf{f}'(u_0)|$. The left-hand inequality follows at once from the fact that (for $h > 0$) the quantity $l(u_0 + h) - l(u_0)$ is the length of arc from u_0 to $u_0 + h$ and that this length is an upper bound for all polygonal approximations—exceeding in particular the length of the chord from u_0 to $u_0 + h$, $|\mathbf{f}(u_0 + h) - \mathbf{f}(u_0)|$. (For $h < 0$ both numerator and denominator of the middle fraction are negative, and the inequality is still correct.)

The right-hand inequality requires a bit more work. Consider the partition of the interval from u_0 to $u_0 + h$ obtained by dividing it into n equal parts, using the partition points $u_k = u_0 + kh/n$. Then according to the triangle inequality,

$$\left| \frac{\mathbf{f}(u_k) - \mathbf{f}(u_{k-1})}{u_k - u_{k-1}} \right| \leq |\mathbf{f}'(u_k)| + |\epsilon_k|,$$

where ϵ_k is the difference between the derivative and the increment quotient. Letting u^* denote a u-value at which $|\mathbf{f}'(u)|$ assumes its maximum on the interval $u_0 \leq u \leq u_0 + h$, which exists by virtue of the continuity of $\mathbf{f}'(u)$, and letting $\epsilon(n)$ denote the largest of the n quantities $|\epsilon_k|$ for $k = 1, \ldots, n$, we obtain

$$\sum_{k=1}^{n} |\mathbf{f}(u_k) - \mathbf{f}(u_{k-1})| \leq \sum_{k=1}^{n} \{|\mathbf{f}'(u_k)| + |\epsilon_k|\}(u_k - u_{k-1})$$

$$\leq \{|\mathbf{f}'(u^*)| + \epsilon(n)\}h.$$

Since the left-most member approaches the arc length $l(u_0 + h) - l(u_0)$, the desired inequality follows as soon as it is seen that $\epsilon(n)$ tends to zero as n becomes infinite.

To show that $\epsilon(n) \to 0$ it seems necessary to consider the components of $\mathbf{f}$ in some orthonormal system:

$$\mathbf{f}(u) = \xi(u)\mathbf{i}_1 + \zeta(u)\mathbf{i}_2 + \eta(u)\mathbf{i}_3.$$

Using the symbol Δ to denote an increment corresponding to the u-increment from u_{k-1} to u_k, we have

$$\frac{\Delta \mathbf{f}}{\Delta u} = \frac{\Delta \xi}{\Delta u}\mathbf{i}_1 + \frac{\Delta \zeta}{\Delta u}\mathbf{i}_2 + \frac{\Delta \eta}{\Delta u}\mathbf{i}_3.$$

It follows from the mean value theorem that there is a $\bar{u}_k$ (on the kth subinterval) such that

$$\frac{\Delta \xi}{\Delta u} = \xi'(u_k) + \epsilon_{1k} = \xi'(\bar{u}_k),$$

where then

$$|\xi'(u_k) - \xi'(\bar{u}_k)| = |\epsilon_{1k}|.$$

Because of the continuity (and therefore uniform continuity) of $\xi'(u)$ over the interval $u_0 \leq u \leq u_0 + h$ (written for $h > 0$), these quantities $|\epsilon_{1k}|$ can be made uniformly smaller than any given ϵ by taking n sufficiently large. Similar reasoning for the remaining components then results in the fact that

$$\epsilon(n) = \max_k \, (|\epsilon_{1k}|^2 + |\epsilon_{2k}|^2 + |\epsilon_{3k}|^2)^{1/2}$$

has the limit zero, thereby completing the argument.

Problems

2.10.   Set up a vector equation for the line segment from the point $(1, 2, 0)$ to the point $(0, 1, -1)$, and use the integral formula to compute the length of this segment. What are the scalar parametric equations of the curve? (To obtain them, equate the components of $\mathbf{f}(u)$ and $\mathbf{r}$.)

2.11.   Show that the equation $\mathbf{r} = g(u)\mathbf{i} + [1 - g(u)]\mathbf{j}$ defines a line, and state conditions on $g(u)$ which would imply that the whole line is traced out as u varies over $(-\infty, \infty)$.

2.12.   Show that if $\mathbf{r} = (5 \cos \theta)\mathbf{i} + (3 \sin \theta)\mathbf{j}$, and $\mathbf{A} = 4\mathbf{i}$, then

$$|\mathbf{r} - \mathbf{A}| + |\mathbf{r} + \mathbf{A}| = 10.$$

Interpret this geometrically. Express the total arc length of this locus as an integral. (Can you evaluate it?)

2.13.   Show that $\mathbf{r} = u^2\mathbf{A} + u\mathbf{B}$ represents a parabola ($\mathbf{A}$ and $\mathbf{B}$ are fixed vectors). [Express $\mathbf{A}$ and $\mathbf{B}$ in terms of an orthonormal set and obtain a scalar equation for the curve, taking $\mathbf{A} = a\mathbf{i}$, without loss of generality.] Obtain the arc length from the point given by $u = 0$ to the point given by $u = \frac{1}{2}$ for the case $\mathbf{A} = \mathbf{i}$, $\mathbf{B} = \mathbf{j}$.

2.14.   Determine the geometrical nature of the curve

$$\mathbf{r} = (\cos \theta)\mathbf{A} + (\sin \theta)\mathbf{B} + \theta(\mathbf{A} \times \mathbf{B}).$$

In the particular case $\mathbf{A} = \mathbf{i}$ and $\mathbf{B} = \mathbf{j}$, determine the length of arc from $\theta = 0$ to $\theta = 2\pi$.

2.15.   Compute the length of arc along $\mathbf{r} = 3u\mathbf{i} + (3u^2 + 2)\mathbf{j} + 4u^{3/2}\mathbf{k}$ from $u = 0$ to $u = 1$.

2.16.   Consider the curve defined by $\mathbf{r} = u\mathbf{i} + (u + e^{-u})\mathbf{j} + e^{-u}\mathbf{k}$.
  (a) Show that a parametrization in terms of the arc length parameter s is possible. (Can you obtain this representation?)
  (b) Show that for any point on this curve the position vector $\mathbf{r}$ can be ex-

pressed as a linear combination of two vectors. What conclusion can then be drawn concerning this curve?

2.17.   Determine the length of arc from the origin to the point corresponding to an arbitrary θ along the curve defined by

$$\mathbf{r} = (\theta \cos \theta)\mathbf{i} + (\theta \sin \theta)\mathbf{j} + \theta\mathbf{k}.$$

2.4   *Space curve geometry*

A curve is defined as the locus of an equation $\mathbf{r} = \mathbf{f}(u)$, and it was pointed out in the preceding section that if $\mathbf{f}'(u)$ is continuous and does not vanish, the variable s measuring the length of arc from a fixed point can be used as the curve parameter. Further, the vector $d\mathbf{r}/ds$ is defined, and has length one. It is a unit vector, and its direction is readily seen to be that of the tangent to the curve. For, the increment quotient $\Delta\mathbf{r}/\Delta u$ is in the direction of a secant line, which moves into the position of the tangent as $\Delta u \to 0$. [The direction of the tangent line would be defined as the limiting position of the secant lines as $|\Delta\mathbf{r}|$ tends to zero; but this is guaranteed by having Δu approach zero, when $\mathbf{f}(u)$ is continuous.] The symbol $\mathbf{t}$ will be used for the unit tangent vector:

$$\mathbf{t} = \frac{d\mathbf{r}}{ds}.$$

In Example 2.4 it was seen that the derivative of a vector having constant length is either zero or is normal to the vector. Hence, the vector

$$\frac{d\mathbf{t}}{ds} = \frac{d^2\mathbf{r}}{ds^2}$$

is either zero or normal to $\mathbf{t}$. A unit vector in this direction (when $d\mathbf{t}/ds \neq \mathbf{0}$) is denoted by $\mathbf{n}$, and the direction is called the *principal normal* direction. Then

$$\frac{d\mathbf{t}}{ds} = \kappa\mathbf{n},$$

where κ, the magnitude of $d\mathbf{t}/ds$, is called the *curvature* of the curve at the point at which it is computed:

$$\kappa = \left|\frac{d\mathbf{t}}{ds}\right|.$$

The unit *binormal* is defined to be

$$\mathbf{b} = \mathbf{t} \times \mathbf{n},$$

so that $(\mathbf{t}, \mathbf{n}, \mathbf{b})$ make up an orthonormal triad of vectors attached to each point along the curve where $d\mathbf{t}/ds$ is not zero. Observe that

$$\mathbf{b} = \mathbf{t} \times \mathbf{n}$$

$$\mathbf{t} = \mathbf{n} \times \mathbf{b},$$

and

$$\mathbf{n} = \mathbf{b} \times \mathbf{t}.$$

(See Problem 2.15.)

The rates of change of $\mathbf{b}$ and $\mathbf{n}$ are readily computed. Thus

$$\frac{d\mathbf{b}}{ds} = \frac{d}{ds}(\mathbf{t} \times \mathbf{n}) = \frac{d\mathbf{t}}{ds} \times \mathbf{n} + \mathbf{t} \times \frac{d\mathbf{n}}{ds}$$

$$= \kappa \, (\mathbf{n} \times \mathbf{n}) + \mathbf{t} \times \frac{d\mathbf{n}}{ds} = \mathbf{t} \times \frac{d\mathbf{n}}{ds}.$$

But then

$$\mathbf{n} \times \frac{d\mathbf{b}}{ds} = \mathbf{t}\left(\mathbf{n}\cdot\frac{d\mathbf{n}}{ds}\right) - \frac{d\mathbf{n}}{ds}(\mathbf{n}\cdot\mathbf{t}) = 0,$$

since the inner product of $\mathbf{n}$ with its derivative is zero ($\mathbf{n}$ is a unit vector). Therefore $\mathbf{n}$ is along the direction of $d\mathbf{b}/ds$:

$$\frac{d\mathbf{b}}{ds} = -\tau\mathbf{n}.$$

The quantity τ is called the *torsion* and its reciprocal $1/\tau$, the *radius of torsion*. Further,

$$\frac{d\mathbf{n}}{ds} = \mathbf{b} \times \frac{d\mathbf{t}}{ds} + \frac{d\mathbf{b}}{ds} \times \mathbf{t} = \kappa\mathbf{b} \times \mathbf{n} - \tau\mathbf{n} \times \mathbf{t}$$

$$= -\kappa\mathbf{t} + \tau\mathbf{b}.$$

These various expressions for $d\mathbf{t}/ds$, $d\mathbf{n}/ds$, and $d\mathbf{b}/ds$ are called the "Frenet formulas":

$$\frac{d\mathbf{t}}{ds} = \kappa\mathbf{n},$$

$$\frac{d\mathbf{b}}{ds} = -\tau\mathbf{n},$$

$$\frac{d\mathbf{n}}{ds} = -\kappa\mathbf{t} + \tau\mathbf{b}.$$

put on
card

The torsion of a plane curve is zero. For, if a curve is represented by

$$\mathbf{r} = \mathbf{f}(u) = g(u)\mathbf{i}_1 + h(u)\mathbf{i}_2,$$

the derivatives $g'(u)\mathbf{i}_1 + h'(u)\mathbf{i}_2$ and $g''(u)\mathbf{i}_1 + h''(u)\mathbf{i}_2$ are both in the plane of the curve; that is, $\mathbf{t}$ and $\mathbf{n}$ are in that plane, so that $\mathbf{b} = \mathbf{t} \times \mathbf{n}$ is *normal*

$$K^2 = r'' \cdot r''$$

$$K = +(r'' \cdot r'')^{\frac{1}{2}}$$

to the plane. The vector **b** is therefore constant, and $d\mathbf{b}/ds = \mathbf{0}$. This implies that the torsion is zero.

An alternative computation of **n** and κ, which may occasionally be useful, is as follows. Differentiating the relation

$$\frac{d\mathbf{r}}{du} = \frac{ds}{du}\mathbf{t} \quad = \dot{\mathbf{t}} \; \dot{s}$$

we obtain

$$\ddot{r} = \frac{d^2\mathbf{r}}{du^2} = \left(\frac{ds}{du}\right)^2 \frac{d\mathbf{t}}{ds} + \frac{d^2s}{du^2}\mathbf{t},$$

so that

$$\kappa\left(\frac{ds}{du}\right)^2 \mathbf{n} = \frac{d^2\mathbf{r}}{du^2} - \frac{d^2s}{du^2}\mathbf{t}. \quad =\ddot{r} - \bar{t}\,\frac{d^2s}{du^2}$$

The vector **n** is then a unit vector in this direction, and the magnitude equality yields

$$\kappa\left(\frac{ds}{du}\right)^2 = \left|\frac{d^2\mathbf{r}}{du^2} - \frac{d^2s}{du^2}\mathbf{t}\right|, \quad =\left|\ddot{r} - \bar{t}\,\frac{d^2s}{du^2}\right|$$

which can be solved for κ.

Still another formula is obtained by forming cross products with $\mathbf{r}'$ on each side of the above expression for $\mathbf{r}''$ (where primes denote differentiation with respect to u):

$$\mathbf{r}'' \times \mathbf{r}' = \left(\frac{ds}{du}\right)^2 \frac{d\mathbf{t}}{ds} \times \mathbf{r}' + \frac{d^2s}{du^2}\mathbf{t} \times \mathbf{r}'$$

$$= \left(\frac{ds}{du}\right)^3 \kappa\mathbf{n} \times \mathbf{t} + \mathbf{0}$$

$$= -\kappa\mathbf{b}\left(\frac{ds}{du}\right)^3.$$

(handwritten:) $\dfrac{\left(\frac{dr}{du}\right)}{\left|\frac{dr}{du}\right|} = t$

$r' = \dfrac{dr}{du} = \dfrac{dr}{ds}\dfrac{ds}{du} = t\,\dfrac{ds}{du}$

Thus, *(handwritten: put on card)*

$$\boxed{\;|\kappa| = \frac{|\mathbf{r}'' \times \mathbf{r}'|}{|\mathbf{r}'|^3}.\;}$$

(handwritten:) τ — a measure of the twist of a curve along its path.

E X A M P L E 2.9   Consider the curve represented by the equation

$$\mathbf{r} = (\sqrt{2}\cos 3\theta)\mathbf{i} + (\sqrt{2}\cos 3\theta)\mathbf{j} + (2\sin 3\theta)\mathbf{k}.$$

Differentiation with respect to θ yields

$$\frac{d\mathbf{r}}{d\theta} = (-3\sqrt{2}\sin 3\theta)\mathbf{i} - (3\sqrt{2}\sin 3\theta)\mathbf{j} + (6\cos 3\theta)\mathbf{k},$$

whence

$$\frac{ds}{d\theta} = \left|\frac{d\mathbf{r}}{d\theta}\right| = (18\sin^2 3\theta + 18\sin^2 3\theta + 36\cos^2 3\theta)^{1/2} = 6,$$

(handwritten:) $\tau = \dfrac{\dot{r}\cdot\ddot{r}\times\dddot{r}}{|\dot{r}\times\ddot{r}|^2}$ where $\dot{r} = \dfrac{dr}{du}$

so that

$$\mathbf{t} = \frac{d\mathbf{r}}{ds} = \frac{d\mathbf{r}}{d\theta}\frac{d\theta}{ds} = \frac{1}{6}\frac{d\mathbf{r}}{d\theta}.$$

Then

$$\frac{d\mathbf{t}}{ds} = \frac{1}{6}\frac{d}{ds}\left(\frac{d\mathbf{r}}{d\theta}\right) = \frac{1}{36}\frac{d^2\mathbf{r}}{d\theta^2}$$

$$= \frac{1}{36}\{-(9\sqrt{2}\cos 3\theta)\mathbf{i} - (9\sqrt{2}\cos 3\theta)\mathbf{j} - (18\sin 3\theta)\mathbf{k}\},$$

from which

$$\kappa = \left|\frac{d\mathbf{t}}{ds}\right| = \frac{\sqrt{324}}{36} = \frac{1}{2}.$$

The unit normal is

$$\mathbf{n} = \frac{1}{\kappa}\frac{d\mathbf{t}}{ds} = \left(-\frac{1}{\sqrt{2}}\cos 3\theta\right)\mathbf{i} - \left(\frac{1}{\sqrt{2}}\cos 3\theta\right)\mathbf{j} - \left(\sin 3\theta\right)\mathbf{k}.$$

The unit binormal is the cross product

$$\mathbf{b} = \mathbf{t} \times \mathbf{n} = \frac{1}{\sqrt{2}}(\mathbf{i} - \mathbf{j}).$$

Since this unit binormal is independent of θ, its derivative vanishes; the torsion is therefore zero. That this is a plane curve is, of course, clear from the original equation, in which $x = y$. Only points whose coordinates satisfy this relation are on the curve, and so the curve is contained entirely in the plane $x = y$. Further, the curvature was seen to be one half, independent of θ. The curve is therefore a circle of radius two.

EXAMPLE 2.10   Consider the curve of intersection of the loci defined by the equations $x^2 - y^2 = z$ and $x^2 + y^2 = 1$ (hyperbolic paraboloid and circular cylinder, respectively). The curve is the set of points whose coordinates satisfy these two relations simultaneously. If the portion of the curve on which $x > 0$ and $y > 0$ is considered, the variable z may be used as a curve parameter, in terms of which the equation is

$$\mathbf{r} = [\tfrac{1}{2}(z + 1)]^{1/2}\mathbf{i} + [\tfrac{1}{2}(1 - z)]^{1/2}\mathbf{j} + z\mathbf{k},$$

from $z = -1$ to $z = 1$. With $z = 2u^2 - 1$, the curve can be represented in terms of the parameter u:

$$\mathbf{r} = u\mathbf{i} + (1 - u^2)^{1/2}\mathbf{j} + (2u^2 - 1)\mathbf{k},$$

from $u = 0$ to $u = 1$. Differentiation yields

$$\frac{d\mathbf{r}}{du} = \mathbf{i} - u(1 - u^2)^{-1/2}\mathbf{j} + 4u\mathbf{k},$$

and

$$\frac{d^2\mathbf{r}}{du^2} = -(1 - u^2)^{-3/2}\mathbf{j} + 4\mathbf{k}.$$

Suppose the curvature is desired at the point where the curve cuts through the xy-plane; that is, at $u^2 = \frac{1}{2}$. At this point,

$$\mathbf{r} = (\mathbf{i} + \mathbf{j})/\sqrt{2}$$
$$\mathbf{r'} = \mathbf{i} - \mathbf{j} + 2\sqrt{2}\mathbf{k},$$
$$\mathbf{r''} = -2\sqrt{2}\mathbf{j} + 4\mathbf{k},$$

where the prime (′) denotes d/du. The curvature at this point is then

$$\kappa = \frac{|\mathbf{r''} \times \mathbf{r'}|}{|\mathbf{r'}|^3} = \frac{|4\mathbf{i} - 4\mathbf{j} - 2\sqrt{2}\mathbf{k}|}{10^{3/2}} = \frac{1}{5}.$$

Problems

2.18.   Show that $d\mathbf{t}/ds$ is normal to $d\mathbf{n}/ds$.

2.19.   Let $\mathbf{r} = (\theta \cos \theta)\mathbf{i} + (\theta \sin \theta)\mathbf{j} + \theta\mathbf{k}$, and determine the curvature as a function of θ. Compute also the vector $\mathbf{b}$ at $\theta = 0$.

2.20.   Compute the torsion (at a general point) of the curve defined by $\mathbf{r} = (\cos \theta)\mathbf{i} + (\sin \theta)\mathbf{j} + a\theta\mathbf{k}$, where a is a positive constant.

2.21.   Compute $\mathbf{t}$, $\mathbf{n}$, and κ (as functions of the parameter) for the curve $\mathbf{r} = 3u\mathbf{i} + (3u^2 + 2)\mathbf{j} + 4u^{3/2}\mathbf{k}$.

2.22.   The *osculating plane* is the particular plane among those tangent to a curve at a certain point which contains the principal normal; that is, it contains $\mathbf{t}$ and $\mathbf{n}$. Determine the osculating plane at $u = 1$ for the curve

$$\mathbf{r} = 6u\mathbf{i} + 5u^2\mathbf{j} + 8u\mathbf{k}.$$

2.23.   The *center of curvature* is the point a distance $1/\kappa$ from the curve along the principal normal direction. Locate the center of curvature at $u = 1$ for the curve of Problem 2.22.

2.5   *Curvilinear motion*

The position of a particle moving in space can be specified by giving its position vector at each time t: $\mathbf{r} = \mathbf{f}(t)$. This equation represents, in terms of the time t as parameter, the path of motion of the particle. The vectors

$$\mathbf{v} = \frac{d\mathbf{r}}{dt}$$

and

$$\mathbf{a} = \frac{d^2\mathbf{r}}{dt^2}$$

are called, respectively, the *velocity* and *acceleration* of the particle. It was seen in the preceding section, using notation introduced there, that

$$\frac{d\mathbf{r}}{dt} = \frac{ds}{dt}\,\mathbf{t},$$

and

$$\frac{ds}{dt} = \left|\frac{d\mathbf{r}}{dt}\right|,$$

where $\mathbf{t}$ is the unit tangent vector (in the direction corresponding to increasing t), and s denotes arc length. The rate of change of s with respect to t is the time rate at which the particle traces out the path, called the *speed* of the particle.

A resolution of the acceleration vector in terms of $(\mathbf{t}, \mathbf{n}, \mathbf{b})$ can be obtained by differentiating the expression for $\mathbf{v}$:

$$\mathbf{a} = \frac{d}{dt}\left(\frac{ds}{dt}\,\mathbf{t}\right) = \frac{d^2s}{dt^2}\,\mathbf{t} + \kappa\left(\frac{ds}{dt}\right)^2\mathbf{n}.$$

Observe that the acceleration of a particle moving at constant speed would be directed along $\mathbf{n}$, with no tangential component.

Representations of the displacement, velocity, and acceleration vectors are often required in coordinate systems not linked to the path of motion as are $\mathbf{t}$, $\mathbf{n}$, and $\mathbf{b}$. In rectangular coordinates, for instance, let

$$\mathbf{r} = x(t)\mathbf{i} + y(t)\mathbf{j} + z(t)\mathbf{k}.$$

Using a dot over a variable to denote differentiation with respect to t, we have

$$\mathbf{v} = \dot{\mathbf{r}} = \dot{x}\mathbf{i} + \dot{y}\mathbf{j} + \dot{z}\mathbf{k},$$

and

$$\mathbf{a} = \dot{\mathbf{v}} = \ddot{\mathbf{r}} = \ddot{x}\mathbf{i} + \ddot{y}\mathbf{j} + \ddot{z}\mathbf{k},$$

two dots, of course, denoting two time derivatives.

EXAMPLE 2.11   Suppose a particle is subject to a constant force field, so that the acceleration is constant, say, $\mathbf{a} = g\mathbf{k}$. The velocity is found by integrating:

$$\mathbf{v} = gt\mathbf{k} + \mathbf{v}_0,$$

where $\mathbf{v}_0$ is the initial velocity (velocity at time $t = 0$). Another integration yields the displacement vector:

$$\mathbf{r} - \mathbf{r}_0 = \tfrac{1}{2}gt^2\mathbf{k} + \mathbf{v}_0 t,$$

where $\mathbf{r}_0$ is the position vector of the particle at $t = 0$. The motion is clearly in the plane defined by $\mathbf{k}$ and $\mathbf{v}_0$.

Needed for Chapter 6

Spherical coordinates are often convenient, and the corresponding ortho-normal set of vectors is as follows:

$$\mathbf{u}_r = (\sin \theta \cos \phi)\mathbf{i} + (\sin \theta \sin \phi)\mathbf{j} + (\cos \theta)\mathbf{k},$$
$$\mathbf{u}_\theta = (\cos \theta \cos \phi)\mathbf{i} + (\cos \theta \sin \phi)\mathbf{j} - (\sin \theta)\mathbf{k},$$
$$\mathbf{u}_\phi = -(\sin \phi)\mathbf{i} + (\cos \phi)\mathbf{j}.$$

Unit Vectors

These unit vectors and the coordinates r, θ, and ϕ are indicated in Fig. 2.4.

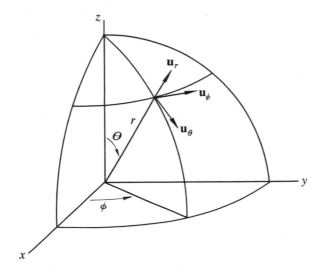

Figure 2.4.   Spherical coordinates.

The position vector $\mathbf{r}$ is of course given by

$$\mathbf{r} = r\mathbf{u}_r,$$

and equating components yields the usual transformation equations from spherical to rectangular coordinates:

$$x = r \sin \theta \cos \phi$$
$$y = r \sin \theta \sin \phi$$
$$z = r \cos \theta$$

The derivatives of the unit vectors are easily computed, and can be expressed as follows:

$$\dot{\mathbf{u}}_r = \dot{\theta}\mathbf{u}_\theta + (\sin \theta)\dot{\phi}\mathbf{u}_\phi,$$
$$\dot{\mathbf{u}}_\theta = -\dot{\theta}\mathbf{u}_r + (\cos \theta)\dot{\phi}\mathbf{u}_\phi,$$
$$\dot{\mathbf{u}}_\phi = -(\sin \theta)\dot{\phi}\mathbf{u}_r - (\cos \theta)\dot{\phi}\mathbf{u}_\theta.$$

With these derivatives the velocity and acceleration can be computed:

$$\mathbf{v} = \dot{r}\mathbf{u}_r + r\dot{\mathbf{u}}_r = \dot{r}\mathbf{u}_r + r\dot{\theta}\mathbf{u}_\theta + r(\sin\theta)\dot{\phi}\mathbf{u}_\phi,$$
$$\mathbf{a} = [\ddot{r} - r\dot{\theta}^2 - (r\sin^2\theta)\dot{\phi}^2]\mathbf{u}_r$$
$$+ [2\dot{r}\dot{\theta} + r\ddot{\theta} - (r\sin\theta\cos\theta)\dot{\phi}^2]\mathbf{u}_\theta$$
$$+ [2\dot{r}\dot{\phi}\sin\theta + 2r\dot{\theta}\dot{\phi}\cos\theta + r\ddot{\phi}\sin\theta]\mathbf{u}_\phi.$$

If the motion is restricted to the xy-plane, these reduce (with $\theta = \pi/2$) to

$$\mathbf{v} = \dot{r}\mathbf{u}_r + r\dot{\phi}\mathbf{u}_\phi,$$
$$\mathbf{a} = (\ddot{r} - r\dot{\phi}^2)\mathbf{u}_r + (2\dot{r}\dot{\phi} + \ddot{\phi}r)\mathbf{u}_\phi.$$

EXAMPLE 2.12   A particle subject to a force acting always along $\mathbf{u}_r$ will experience an acceleration proportional to that force, and hence along $\mathbf{u}_r$. An important instance of this is that in which the force is inversely proportional to r^2. Equating this magnitude to the product of the mass and the radial component of acceleration and setting the other components equal to zero, we obtain the differential equations of motion:

$$\ddot{r} - r\dot{\theta}^2 - r\dot{\phi}^2\sin^2\theta = (\text{const.})/r^2,$$
$$2\dot{r}\dot{\theta} + r\ddot{\theta} - r\dot{\phi}^2\sin\theta\cos\theta = 0,$$
$$2\dot{r}\dot{\phi}\sin\theta + 2r\dot{\theta}\dot{\phi}\cos\theta + r\ddot{\phi}\sin\theta = 0.$$

In the case of plane motion, one has (setting $\phi = 0$):

$$\ddot{r} - r\dot{\theta}^2 = (\text{const.})/r^2,$$
$$2\dot{r}\dot{\theta} + r\ddot{\theta} = 0.$$

The second equation can be written in the form

$$\frac{1}{r}\frac{d}{dt}(r^2\dot{\theta}) = 0,$$

which implies that $r^2\dot{\theta}$ is constant. This can then be substituted in the first equation to obtain a differential equation in r alone.

Problems

2.24.   Consider motion of a particle in a plane circle:

$$\mathbf{r} = (\cos u)\mathbf{i} + (\sin u)\mathbf{j},$$

where $u = g(t)$. Discuss the resolution of $\mathbf{v}$ and $\mathbf{a}$ in terms of $(\mathbf{t}, \mathbf{n}, \mathbf{b})$ and in terms of $(\mathbf{u}_r, \mathbf{u}_\theta, \mathbf{u}_\phi)$. Compute the speed and the curvature of the path.

2.25. A particle moves according to the relation

$$\mathbf{r} = (t \cos t)\mathbf{i} + (t \sin t)\mathbf{j} + t\mathbf{k}.$$

Resolve **a** into its tangential and normal components, and into components along $\mathbf{u}_r$, $\mathbf{u}_\theta$, and $\mathbf{u}_\phi$.

2.26. Determine the length of the path covered by the particle in Problem 2.25 between $t = 0$ and $t = \sqrt{2}$.

3 ANGULAR VELOCITY

A *rigid body* is essentially a set of points or point particles whose distances relative to one another do not change; but rather than be concerned about rigidity of the body, we prefer to define a *rigid motion* of a body as motion over some time interval during which the distances between the particles of the body do not change. The need for new concepts for such motion, over what was used in discussing the motion of a point, arises because a body can undergo (even in rigid motion) not only translational motion, in which every point undergoes the same vector displacement, but more general motion, in which different points in the body are displaced differently.

The term *motion* refers to a change in position with time, relative to some specified reference frame. It is always relative motion, although it is common practice to use the "fixed stars" as a rather absolute physical frame of reference (sometimes called "inertial space"). Mathematically it is always necessary to specify the frame relative to which motion occurs, and this frame is usually given as an origin and a set of coordinate axes which are fixed (by definition) for purposes of the study of the relative motion, but which may themselves be in motion relative to some other frame. (Indeed, the "fixed" frame is automatically moving as seen from the moving frame.) It will be assumed throughout that motions are continuous and smooth enough so that the derivatives to be used will exist.

If a coordinate system such as would be defined by an orthonormal set of vectors and a reference origin is fixed in the body at some point, motion of the body can be described by giving the motion of the coordinate system or of the orthonormal set and origin, and conversely; that is, rigid motion

72

of a body is mathematically equivalent to the motion of one coordinate system relative to another.

The position of a body at any particular time is described by giving the location or position vector of each of its points relative to the reference frame. A motion or change in the position of the body from one time instant to another is then a *transformation T* on position vectors in the reference frame. The image *T*r under this transformation of a given position vector **r** is the new location or position defined by the particle initially at **r**. (If no particle of the body happens to occupy the position **r**, this is immaterial, since motion of the body is equivalent to motion of an attached reference frame, and **r** does define some point in that coordinate system.)

3.1   *Angular velocity of a rigid body*

A rigid motion from a position at time t to a position at time t' can be achieved by a superposition of two motions (carried out in succession or simultaneously), one a translation, and the other a motion in which at least one point is fixed. Consider any point of the body and let its position at time t be P_0; this point will occupy some new position P_0' at time t'. A translational motion is thus defined by giving every point of the body the displacement $\overrightarrow{P_0P_0'}$, and a second motion with P_0' fixed is then necessary to bring the remaining points of the body into their positions at time t'. This second motion takes place relative to a system with axes parallel to the original axes and origin fixed at the particle which is at P_0 at time t, so the motion can be carried out while that axis system is being translated along with P_0.

A rigid motion with a point P_0 held fixed is a very special type of transformation, which in Sect. 3.5 will be seen to be a rotation. The axis of rotation and the angle of rotation will be seen to be independent of the point chosen to define the translational part of the motion.

To define the angular velocity of a body undergoing a rigid motion, we consider the body's position at time t and at a nearby time $t + \Delta t$. This displacement can be accomplished by a translation together with a rotation through a unique angle (acute, if Δt is sufficiently small) about an axis having a unique orientation. Let $\boldsymbol{\Delta\theta}$ denote the vector whose magnitude θ is the angle of rotation and whose direction is that of the axis of rotation in a sense determined by the right-hand rule; that is, with the fingers of the right hand following the generation of the angle the thumb indicates the sense of $\Delta\boldsymbol{\theta}$. The *angular velocity* of the body at time t is defined to be the vector

$$\boldsymbol{\omega} = \lim_{\Delta t \to 0} \frac{\Delta\boldsymbol{\theta}}{\Delta t}.$$

This angular velocity is attributed to the body as a whole and is shared by any subset of points of the body, by any coordinate system or orthonormal vector triad fixed in the body, and by any other body or frame whose points do not move with respect to those of the given body.

If a body moves with a line of its points fixed, the axis about which angular motion occurs has the direction of this fixed line, and the angular velocity vector is along that line. Any point not on the fixed line moves about it in a circle, and points in any plane perpendicular to the fixed line would remain in that plane under the motion.

It might be questioned whether it is proper to represent a magnitude-direction pair as a vector when such pairs do not combine like vectors. Angular displacements such as $\Delta\boldsymbol{\theta}$ above do *not* combine like vectors—one angular displacement following another does not necessarily yield their vector sum as a resultant angular displacement. This is obvious when it is noticed that the resultant angular displacement depends on the order in which the component displacements are applied, except in special circumstances. (See Problem 3.1.) However, angular *velocities* do combine as vectors when composed in a certain way, as will be seen in Sect. 3.4. Further, a physical device ("rate gyro") can be constructed which measures the magnitude of the vector component of the angular velocity vector along the axis of the device, so that three such devices placed along coordinate

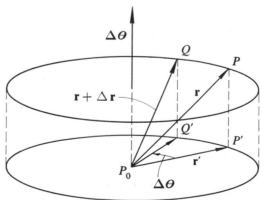

"Rigid Motion of Fixed Point"

Figure 3.1.

axes in a rigidly moving body will measure quantities which can be combined by vector addition to produce the angular velocity vector of the body.

The angular velocity of a body can be related to the (linear) velocity of points of the body. Consider a body moving with a point P_0 fixed, and let P denote an arbitrary point of the body whose position vector at time t with respect to P_0 is $\mathbf{r}$. Let $\Delta\theta$ denote the angular displacement from time t to time $t + \Delta t$, let Q denote the new position at $t + \Delta t$ of the particle that at time t was at P, and let P' and Q' (with position vectors $\mathbf{r}'$ and $\mathbf{r}' + \Delta\mathbf{r}'$) be the projections of P and Q in the plane through P_0 normal to $\Delta\theta$, as in Fig. 3.1. Since $\Delta\mathbf{r}' = \Delta\mathbf{r}$, it follows that $d\mathbf{r}/dt = d\mathbf{r}'/dt$. The vector $\Delta\theta \times \mathbf{r}'$ is equal to $\Delta\theta \times \mathbf{r}$, and is tangent at P' to the circle through P' and Q' shown in Fig. 3.1. The length $|\Delta\theta \times \mathbf{r}'|$ is the arc length $\overset{\frown}{P'Q'}$. If Δs denotes this arc length, then

$$\left|\frac{\Delta\mathbf{r}}{\Delta t}\right| = \left|\frac{\Delta\mathbf{r}'}{\Delta s}\frac{\Delta s}{\Delta t}\right| = \left|\frac{\Delta\mathbf{r}'}{\Delta s}\right|\left|\frac{\Delta\theta}{\Delta t} \times \mathbf{r}\right| \to |\boldsymbol{\omega} \times \mathbf{r}|$$

as $\Delta t \to 0$. Thus, $\boldsymbol{\omega} \times \mathbf{r}$ is a vector whose length is $\mathbf{v}$ (the velocity, $d\mathbf{r}/dt$) and whose direction is the direction of $\mathbf{v}$; that is,

$$\mathbf{v} = \frac{d\mathbf{r}}{dt} = \boldsymbol{\omega} \times \mathbf{r}.$$

3.2   Alternative development

It is possible to define the angular velocity of a body relative to a given reference frame without recourse to the decomposition (used in Sect. 3.1) of a general motion into a translation and a rotation. Let the reference frame be defined by the orthonormal set $(\mathbf{i}_1, \mathbf{j}_1, \mathbf{k}_1)$ and let the orientation of the body be defined by the orthonormal set $(\mathbf{i}_2, \mathbf{j}_2, \mathbf{k}_2)$. Whether the reference frame is conceived of as fixed is immaterial; the concern is with relative motion of frame 2 with respect to frame 1 (or vice versa). The time derivative of a quantity as seen in frame 1 will be denoted by d_1/dt, and as seen in frame 2 by d_2/dt. The vectors $d_1\mathbf{i}_2/dt$, $d_1\mathbf{j}_2/dt$, $d_1\mathbf{k}_2/dt$ can be represented, with coefficients c_{mn}, as linear combinations of the basis vectors of frame 2:

$$\frac{d_1\mathbf{i}_2}{dt} = c_{11}\mathbf{i}_2 + c_{12}\mathbf{j}_2 + c_{13}\mathbf{k}_2,$$

$$\frac{d_1\mathbf{j}_2}{dt} = c_{21}\mathbf{i}_2 + c_{22}\mathbf{j}_2 + c_{23}\mathbf{k}_2,$$

$$\frac{d_1\mathbf{k}_2}{dt} = c_{31}\mathbf{i}_2 + c_{32}\mathbf{j}_2 + c_{33}\mathbf{k}_2.$$

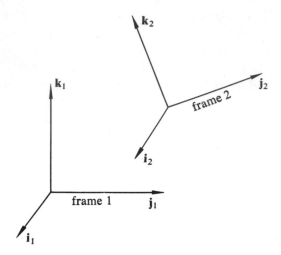

Figure 3.2.

Since $\mathbf{i}_2 \cdot \mathbf{i}_2 = 1$, it follows that

$$\mathbf{i}_2 \cdot \frac{d_1 \mathbf{i}_2}{dt} = c_{11} \mathbf{i}_2 \cdot \mathbf{i}_2 + c_{12} \mathbf{i}_2 \cdot \mathbf{j}_2 + c_{13} \mathbf{i}_2 \cdot \mathbf{k}_2 = 0,$$

from which it follows that $c_{11} = 0$. Similarly, $c_{22} = c_{33} = 0$. Since $\mathbf{i}_2 \cdot \mathbf{j}_2 = 0$, it follows that

$$\mathbf{i}_2 \cdot \frac{d_1 \mathbf{j}_2}{dt} + \mathbf{j}_2 \cdot \frac{d_1 \mathbf{i}_2}{dt} = 0,$$

which in turn implies that $c_{21} = -c_{12}$. It is similarly clear that $c_{31} = -c_{13}$, and $c_{32} = -c_{23}$. (In general, $c_{mn} = -c_{nm}$.) Thus,

$$\frac{d_1 \mathbf{i}_2}{dt} = c_{12} \mathbf{j}_2 + c_{13} \mathbf{k}_2,$$

$$\frac{d_1 \mathbf{j}_2}{dt} = -c_{12} \mathbf{i}_2 + c_{23} \mathbf{k}_2,$$

$$\frac{d_1 \mathbf{k}_2}{dt} = -c_{13} \mathbf{i}_2 - c_{23} \mathbf{j}_2.$$

The angular velocity of frame 2 relative to frame 1 is now defined to be

$$\omega_{12} = c_{23} \mathbf{i}_2 + c_{31} \mathbf{j}_2 + c_{12} \mathbf{k}_2.$$

This vector has the following readily verified properties:

$$\frac{d_1 \mathbf{i}_2}{dt} = \boldsymbol{\omega}_{12} \times \mathbf{i}_2,$$

$$\frac{d_1 \mathbf{j}_2}{dt} = \boldsymbol{\omega}_{12} \times \mathbf{j}_2,$$

$$\frac{d_1 \mathbf{k}_2}{dt} = \boldsymbol{\omega}_{12} \times \mathbf{k}_2,$$

and it is the *only* vector with these properties. For, if there were another such vector, $\boldsymbol{\omega}_{12}'$, then

$$(\boldsymbol{\omega}_{12} - \boldsymbol{\omega}_{12}') \times \mathbf{i}_2 = (\boldsymbol{\omega}_{12} - \boldsymbol{\omega}_{12}') \times \mathbf{j}_2 = (\boldsymbol{\omega}_{12} - \boldsymbol{\omega}_{12}') \times \mathbf{k}_2 = \mathbf{0},$$

so that $\boldsymbol{\omega}_{12} - \boldsymbol{\omega}_{12}' = \mathbf{0}$, or $\boldsymbol{\omega}_{12} = \boldsymbol{\omega}_{12}'$.

The quantity $\boldsymbol{\omega}$ defined in Sect. 3.1 *does* satisfy the conditions just seen to characterize $\boldsymbol{\omega}_{12}$, and so the definitions are equivalent: $\boldsymbol{\omega} = \boldsymbol{\omega}_{12}$. The definition given in Sect. 3.1 is more intuitive, and the one given here more satisfying mathematically.

The following example perhaps justifies the term *angular velocity* for $\boldsymbol{\omega}_{12}$ as defined above.

EXAMPLE 3.1   Suppose that frame 2 moves with respect to frame 1 so that $\mathbf{k}_2 = \mathbf{k}_1$ at all times. With θ as defined in Fig. 3.3, we have

$$\mathbf{i}_2 = (\cos \theta)\mathbf{i}_1 + (\sin \theta)\mathbf{j}_1,$$
$$\mathbf{j}_2 = (-\sin \theta)\mathbf{i}_1 + (\cos \theta)\mathbf{j}_1.$$

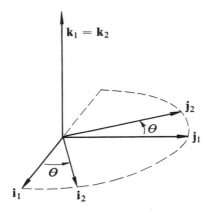

Figure 3.3.   **(See Example 3.1.)**

Then

$$\frac{d_1 \mathbf{i}_2}{dt} = \dot{\theta}[(-\sin\theta)\mathbf{i}_1 + (\cos\theta)\mathbf{j}_1] = \dot{\theta}(\mathbf{k}_2 \times \mathbf{i}_2),$$

$$\frac{d_1 \mathbf{j}_2}{dt} = \dot{\theta}[(-\cos\theta)\mathbf{i}_1 - (\sin\theta)\mathbf{j}_1] = \dot{\theta}(\mathbf{k}_2 \times \mathbf{j}_2),$$

and

$$\frac{d_1 \mathbf{k}_2}{dt} = \mathbf{0} = \dot{\theta}(\mathbf{k}_2 \times \mathbf{k}_2).$$

It follows that the angular velocity of frame 2 relative to frame 1 is $\boldsymbol{\omega}_{12} = \dot{\theta}\mathbf{k}_2$.

It has been assumed that the "body" in question is three-dimensional, but it is sometimes desirable to ascribe angular velocity to a moving *line* of points. This can be done as follows. Let $\mathbf{k}_2$ be a unit vector along the line, with prescribed motion, and let $\mathbf{i}_2$ and $\mathbf{j}_2$ be unit vectors which with $\mathbf{k}_2$ form an orthonormal triad. Then, no matter what motion $\mathbf{i}_2$ and $\mathbf{j}_2$ have about $\mathbf{k}_2$,

$$\frac{d\mathbf{k}_2}{dt} = \boldsymbol{\omega} \times \mathbf{k}_2,$$

where $\boldsymbol{\omega}$ is the angular velocity of the triad:

$$\boldsymbol{\omega} = \omega_x \mathbf{i}_2 + \omega_y \mathbf{j}_2 + \omega_z \mathbf{k}_2.$$

The angular velocity of $\mathbf{k}_2$ (or of any line in that direction) is then defined as

$$\boldsymbol{\omega}_{k_2} = \omega_x \mathbf{i}_2 + \omega_y \mathbf{j}_2,$$

which is the projection of $\boldsymbol{\omega}$ in the $\mathbf{i}_2\mathbf{j}_2$-plane—the plane normal to the moving vector $\mathbf{k}_2$. This angular velocity of $\mathbf{k}_2$ has the property

$$\frac{d\mathbf{k}_2}{dt} = \boldsymbol{\omega}_{k_2} \times \mathbf{k}_2 = (\omega_x \mathbf{i}_2 + \omega_y \mathbf{j}_2) \times \mathbf{k}_2.$$

Because (Fig. 3.4) there is only one vector in the $\mathbf{i}_2\mathbf{j}_2$-plane with this property, $\boldsymbol{\omega}_{k_2}$ is uniquely determined by $d\mathbf{k}_2/dt$, that is, by the specified motion of the line, independent of how $\mathbf{i}_2$ and $\mathbf{j}_2$ are defined. Notice that for any point on the line with position vector $\mathbf{r} = r\mathbf{k}_2$,

$$\frac{d\mathbf{r}}{dt} = \boldsymbol{\omega}_\mathbf{r} \times \mathbf{r},$$

where $\boldsymbol{\omega}_\mathbf{r} = \boldsymbol{\omega}_{k_2}$.

The angular velocity of a line can also be defined in the spirit of Sect. 3.1, and it turns out to be the same vector as that defined above.

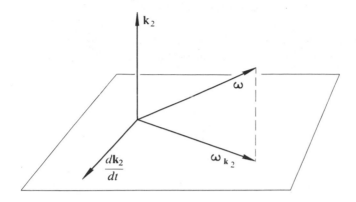

Figure 3.4

Problems

3.1. From some convenient initial position (say, on the desk in front of you) rotate a book 90 degrees about an axis along the binding of the book, and then from this position rotate it 90 degrees about an axis along the bottom edge of the front cover. Put the book again in its original position and carry out these rotations in the reverse order, noting the different resultant positions.

3.2. Express the angular velocity of a car wheel in terms of the speed S of the car and the outside radius a of the tire, giving explicitly the direction of the angular velocity vector.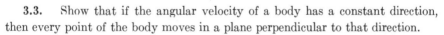

3.3. Show that if the angular velocity of a body has a constant direction, then every point of the body moves in a plane perpendicular to that direction.

3.4. Let $\boldsymbol{\omega} = p\mathbf{i} + q\mathbf{j} + r\mathbf{k}$ denote the angular velocity of an aircraft, expressed in terms of the unit vectors $\mathbf{i}$ along the aircraft axis (from tail to nose), $\mathbf{j}$ along the right wing, and $\mathbf{k} = \mathbf{i} \times \mathbf{j}$. What is the angular velocity of the aircraft axis? Of the direction $\mathbf{j}$? What is the velocity of a point on the wingtip (in terms of the wingspan A) relative to a coordinate system with axial directions fixed in space and coordinate origin at the point midway between the wingtips?

3.5. In radar tracking the motion of the "line of sight" of the antenna is used to give information about the target's motion. Given two "rate gyros," each of which measures the component of the angular velocity along its axis, how should these rate gyros be mounted to measure the angular velocity of the line of sight? If $\boldsymbol{\omega} = s\mathbf{i} + u\mathbf{j} + v\mathbf{k}$ is the angular velocity of the antenna "dish," where $\mathbf{i}$ is along the line of sight, and $\mathbf{j}$ and $\mathbf{k}$ are in the plane normal to the line of sight, what is the angular velocity of the line of sight?

3.3   *Derivative of a moving vector*

Consider the variable *unit* vector $\mathbf{u}(t)$ whose only variability is in its direction. With the initial point of $\mathbf{u}(t)$ at the origin, the derivative of $\mathbf{u}(t)$ with respect to time t is just the velocity vector of the point at its tip. But according to the preceding section this velocity can be expressed in terms of the angular velocity of $\mathbf{u}(t)$:

$$\frac{d\mathbf{u}}{dt} = \boldsymbol{\omega}_u \times \mathbf{u},$$

Same form as on p. 78 !!

where $\boldsymbol{\omega}_u$ denotes the angular velocity of $\mathbf{u}$. If the motion of the unit vector arises because of its being fixed to a body moving with angular velocity $\boldsymbol{\omega}$, then $\boldsymbol{\omega} \times \mathbf{u} = \boldsymbol{\omega}_u \times \mathbf{u}$, so that

$$\frac{d\mathbf{u}}{dt} = \boldsymbol{\omega} \times \mathbf{u}.$$

Consider next the variable vector $\mathbf{V}$, expressed in terms of the orthonormal triad $(\mathbf{u}_1, \mathbf{u}_2, \mathbf{u}_3)$:

$$\mathbf{V} = V_1\mathbf{u}_1 + V_2\mathbf{u}_2 + V_3\mathbf{u}_3.$$

If the triad $(\mathbf{u}_1, \mathbf{u}_2, \mathbf{u}_3)$ is undergoing rigid motion with angular velocity $\boldsymbol{\omega}$, then the derivative of $\mathbf{V}$ with respect to time is computed as follows:

$$\begin{aligned}
\frac{d\mathbf{V}}{dt} &= (V_1\dot{\mathbf{u}}_1 + \dot{V}_1\mathbf{u}_1) + (V_2\dot{\mathbf{u}}_2 + \dot{V}_2\mathbf{u}_2) + (V_3\dot{\mathbf{u}}_3 + \dot{V}_3\mathbf{u}_3) \\
&= (\dot{V}_1\mathbf{u}_1 + \dot{V}_2\mathbf{u}_2 + \dot{V}_3\mathbf{u}_3) + V_1\,\boldsymbol{\omega} \times \mathbf{u}_1 + V_2\,\boldsymbol{\omega} \times \mathbf{u}_2 + V_3\,\boldsymbol{\omega} \times \mathbf{u}_3 \\
&= (\dot{V}_1\mathbf{u}_1 + \dot{V}_2\mathbf{u}_2 + \dot{V}_3\mathbf{u}_3) + \boldsymbol{\omega} \times \mathbf{V}.
\end{aligned}$$

The first three terms give the derivative of $\mathbf{V}$ relative to the moving reference frame defined by $(\mathbf{u}_1, \mathbf{u}_2, \mathbf{u}_3)$; and if this frame has zero angular velocity, only those three terms remain. Referring to the moving frame as frame 2 and to the fixed frame as frame 1, the above relation can be written

$$\frac{d_1\mathbf{V}}{dt} = \frac{d_2\mathbf{V}}{dt} + \boldsymbol{\omega}_{12} \times \mathbf{V},$$

where again $\boldsymbol{\omega}_{12}$ is used to denote the angular velocity of frame 2 as seen in frame 1.

An expression for $d\mathbf{V}/dt$ in terms of the angular velocity of $\mathbf{V}$ is occasionally useful. Denote by $\mathbf{u}_\mathbf{V}$ a unit vector in the direction of $\mathbf{V}$, so that $\mathbf{V} = V\mathbf{u}_\mathbf{V}$. Then

$$\frac{d\mathbf{V}}{dt} = \dot{V}\mathbf{u}_\mathbf{V} + \boldsymbol{\omega}_\mathbf{V} \times \mathbf{V}.$$

In particular, if **r** denotes the position vector of a moving point P and $\mathbf{u_r}$ is a unit vector in the direction of **r**, then its velocity is

$$\mathbf{v} = \frac{d\mathbf{r}}{dt} = \dot{r}\mathbf{u_r} + \boldsymbol{\omega_r} \times \mathbf{r},$$

where $\boldsymbol{\omega_r}$ is the angular velocity of **r**. This angular velocity can be computed when **r** is given as a function of time; for, the cross products with **r** of each side of the above relation must agree:

$$\mathbf{r} \times \mathbf{v} = 0 + \mathbf{r} \times (\boldsymbol{\omega_r} \times \mathbf{r}) = (\mathbf{r} \cdot \mathbf{r})\boldsymbol{\omega_r} - (\mathbf{r} \cdot \boldsymbol{\omega_r})\mathbf{r},$$

and since $\boldsymbol{\omega_r}$ is perpendicular to **r**, it follows that

$$\boldsymbol{\omega_r} = \frac{1}{r^2} \mathbf{r} \times \mathbf{v}.$$

EXAMPLE 3.2   Consider a particle moving on the spiral

$$\mathbf{r} = (\cos \theta)\mathbf{i} + (\sin \theta)\mathbf{j} + \theta\mathbf{k},$$

where θ is some function of time. Then

$$\mathbf{r} \times \mathbf{v} = \dot{\theta} \begin{vmatrix} \mathbf{i} & \mathbf{j} & \mathbf{k} \\ \cos \theta & \sin \theta & \theta \\ -\sin \theta & \cos \theta & 1 \end{vmatrix},$$

and

$$r^2 = 1 + \theta^2,$$

so that

$$\boldsymbol{\omega_r} = \frac{\dot{\theta}}{1 + \theta^2}[(\sin \theta - \theta \cos \theta)\mathbf{i} - (\cos \theta + \theta \sin \theta)\mathbf{j} + \mathbf{k}].$$

Notice that as θ tends to infinity, the vector **r** tends to the direction of **k**, and the angular velocity of **r** tends to **0**, if $\dot{\theta}$ is bounded.

The above ideas can be exploited to relate the velocity and acceleration relative to a fixed reference frame to the velocity and acceleration relative to a moving frame. Let $\mathbf{i_0}$, $\mathbf{j_0}$, and $\mathbf{k_0}$ denote a fixed orthonormal set, O a fixed origin, P_0 the origin of a moving axis system, $(\mathbf{i}, \mathbf{j}, \mathbf{k})$ the orthonormal set defining the directions of the axes in the moving frame, and P a moving point. Let **r** denote the position vector of P in the moving frame: $\mathbf{r} = \overrightarrow{P_0P}$, let $\mathbf{r_0}$ denote its position vector in the fixed frame: $\mathbf{r_0} = \overrightarrow{OP}$, and let **R** denote the position vector of the moving origin in the fixed frame: $\mathbf{R} = \overrightarrow{OP_0}$, as shown in Fig. 3.5. It is then clear that

$$\mathbf{r_0} = \mathbf{r} + \mathbf{R}.$$

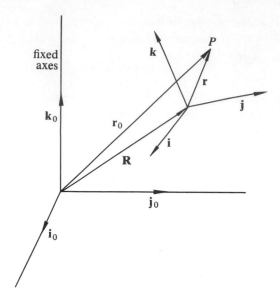

Figure 3.5

Since this holds at all instants of time, the derivatives are similarly related:

$$\mathbf{v}_0 \equiv \frac{d\mathbf{r}_0}{dt} = \frac{d\mathbf{r}}{dt} + \frac{d\mathbf{R}}{dt}$$

$$= \dot{\mathbf{R}} + \mathbf{v} + \boldsymbol{\omega} \times \mathbf{r},$$

where $\boldsymbol{\omega}$ is the angular velocity of the moving frame, and

$$\mathbf{v} = \dot{x}\mathbf{i} + \dot{y}\mathbf{j} + \dot{z}\mathbf{k},$$

the velocity of P relative to the moving frame—the apparent velocity. (As usual, dots indicate time differentiation, and $\mathbf{r} = x\mathbf{i} + y\mathbf{j} + z\mathbf{k}$.) In like manner, differentiation of $\mathbf{v}_0$ with respect to t yields the absolute acceleration of P:

$$\mathbf{a}_0 = \frac{d\mathbf{v}_0}{dt} = \ddot{\mathbf{R}} + \frac{d\mathbf{v}}{dt} + \boldsymbol{\omega} \times \frac{d\mathbf{r}}{dt} + \frac{d\boldsymbol{\omega}}{dt} \times \mathbf{r}.$$

The term $d\mathbf{v}/dt$ is computed as follows:

$$\frac{d\mathbf{v}}{dt} = \ddot{x}\mathbf{i} + \ddot{y}\mathbf{j} + \ddot{z}\mathbf{k} + \boldsymbol{\omega} \times \mathbf{v} = \mathbf{a} + \boldsymbol{\omega} \times \mathbf{v},$$

where $\mathbf{a}$ is the acceleration of P relative to the moving frame. The absolute acceleration $\mathbf{a}_0$ then becomes

$$\mathbf{a}_0 = \ddot{\mathbf{R}} + (\mathbf{a} + \boldsymbol{\omega} \times \mathbf{v}) + \boldsymbol{\omega} \times (\mathbf{v} + \boldsymbol{\omega} \times \mathbf{r}) + \frac{d\boldsymbol{\omega}}{dt} \times \mathbf{r}$$

$$= \ddot{\mathbf{R}} + \mathbf{a} + 2\boldsymbol{\omega} \times \mathbf{v} + \boldsymbol{\omega} \times (\boldsymbol{\omega} \times \mathbf{r}) + \frac{d\boldsymbol{\omega}}{dt} \times \mathbf{r}.$$

EXAMPLE 3.3   Relative to the "inertial frame" defined by the fixed stars, the earth rotates with angular velocity $\boldsymbol{\omega}_e$, a constant vector with magnitude approximately 7.3×10^{-5} radians per second. The acceleration of a particle relative to the earth, or relative to any axis system fixed with respect to the earth, is then

$$\mathbf{a} = \mathbf{a}_0 - 2\boldsymbol{\omega}_e \times \mathbf{v} - \boldsymbol{\omega}_e \times (\boldsymbol{\omega}_e \times \mathbf{r}) - \ddot{\mathbf{R}},$$

which would be used in determining motion relative to the earth. The absolute acceleration $\mathbf{a}_0$ is proportional to an applied force (if there is one). The term $2\boldsymbol{\omega}_e \times \mathbf{v}$ is called the Coriolis acceleration, and the term $\boldsymbol{\omega}_e \times (\boldsymbol{\omega}_e \times \mathbf{r})$ is called the centripetal acceleration.

Problems

3.6.   A particle moves in a circular path, with position vector

$$\mathbf{r} = (\cos \theta)\mathbf{i} + (\sin \theta)\mathbf{j},$$

where θ is some function of time. Determine the angular velocity of $\mathbf{r}$ in terms of θ and $\dot{\theta}$.

3.7.   The Coriolis component introduces a deflection (relative to the earth) of an air particle moving with the wind. Determine the directions of the deflections (that is, N, E, W, or S) when the wind is from, respectively, the north, east, west, and south:

(a) on the northern hemisphere;
(b) on the southern hemisphere;
(c) on the equator.

3.8.   An ant moves with constant speed v along a spoke of a wheel of radius a toward the center. The wheel is a wheel of a car moving with constant speed S and fixed direction relative to the ground. Determine the acceleration vector of the ant relative to the ground. Determine also the magnitude of its velocity relative to the ground at an instant when the spoke of the wheel is horizontal.

3.9.   Let $(\mathbf{i}, \mathbf{j}, \mathbf{k})$ denote unit vectors along the axes of an aircraft, as described in Problem 3.4. Consider only pitching motion: $\boldsymbol{\omega} = q\mathbf{j}$, and determine the acceleration of the nose relative to an axis system centered at the midpoint of the wingspan and fixed with respect to the earth. (Write the position of the nose as $A\mathbf{i}$, and differentiate twice, rather than try to specialize from a general formula.)

3.10. Use the relation

$$\frac{d_1\mathbf{V}}{dt} = \frac{d_2\mathbf{V}}{dt} + \boldsymbol{\omega}_{12} \times \mathbf{V}$$

to derive the fact that $\boldsymbol{\omega}_{12} = -\boldsymbol{\omega}_{21}$, where $\boldsymbol{\omega}_{21}$ is the angular velocity of frame 1 as seen from frame 2.

3.4 *Adding angular velocities*

Consider three frames, 1, 2, and 3, and let (as before)

$$\boldsymbol{\omega}_{ij} = \text{angular velocity of frame } j \text{ relative to frame } i.$$

Then according to the result of the preceding section, for any $\mathbf{V}$,

$$\frac{d_1\mathbf{V}}{dt} = \frac{d_2\mathbf{V}}{dt} + \boldsymbol{\omega}_{12} \times \mathbf{V},$$

$$\frac{d_2\mathbf{V}}{dt} = \frac{d_3\mathbf{V}}{dt} + \boldsymbol{\omega}_{23} \times \mathbf{V},$$

$$-\frac{d_1\mathbf{V}}{dt} = -\frac{d_3\mathbf{V}}{dt} - \boldsymbol{\omega}_{13} \times \mathbf{V}.$$

Addition of these results yields

$$\frac{d_2\mathbf{V}}{dt} = \frac{d_2\mathbf{V}}{dt} + (\boldsymbol{\omega}_{12} + \boldsymbol{\omega}_{23} - \boldsymbol{\omega}_{13}) \times \mathbf{V}.$$

Since $\mathbf{V}$ is arbitrary, we must have

$$\boldsymbol{\omega}_{12} + \boldsymbol{\omega}_{23} = \boldsymbol{\omega}_{13}.$$

In words, this states that the angular velocity of frame 3 relative to frame 1 is its angular velocity relative to frame 2 plus the angular velocity of frame 2 relative to frame 1.

E X A M P L E 3.4   Consider a directional antenna mounted on an aircraft so that the "dish" can tilt relative to its base which in turn can "swivel" relative to the aircraft (as shown in Fig. 3.6). Let $(\mathbf{i}, \mathbf{j}, \mathbf{k})$ denote an orthonormal set of vectors along aircraft axes (as in Problem 3.4); let $(\mathbf{i}', \mathbf{j}')$ denote orthonormal unit vectors fixed in the rotating base; and let $(\mathbf{i}'', \mathbf{j}'', \mathbf{k}'')$ be an orthonormal set fixed to the dish, with $\mathbf{i}''$ along the line of sight and $\mathbf{k}'' = \mathbf{i}'' \times \mathbf{j}'$. The position of the line of sight $\mathbf{i}''$ can be described by the angles θ and ϕ indicated in Fig. 3.6, which give the amount of tilt and swivel, respectively. The angular velocity of the dish relative to $(\mathbf{i}', \mathbf{j}', \mathbf{k})$ is clearly $\dot{\theta}\mathbf{j}'$, and the angular velocity of $(\mathbf{i}', \mathbf{j}', \mathbf{k})$ relative to $(\mathbf{i}, \mathbf{j}, \mathbf{k})$ is $\dot{\phi}\mathbf{k}$. The angular velocity of the radar dish relative to the aircraft is then the sum

$$\dot{\phi}\mathbf{k} + \dot{\theta}\mathbf{j}' = \dot{\phi}\mathbf{k} + \dot{\theta}(\cos\phi)\mathbf{i} - \dot{\theta}(\sin\phi)\mathbf{j}.$$

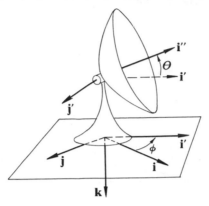

Figure 3.6.   (See Example 3.4.)

If, further, the aircraft is moving relative to the earth with angular velocity $p\mathbf{i} + q\mathbf{j} + r\mathbf{k}$, the angular velocity of the radar dish relative to the earth is the sum

$$(p\mathbf{i} + q\mathbf{j} + r\mathbf{k}) + \dot{\phi}\mathbf{k} + \dot{\theta}\mathbf{j}'.$$

The angular velocity of the line of sight of the antenna (i.e., of $\mathbf{i}''$) is then the projection in the plane normal to $\mathbf{i}''$ of the angular velocity of the dish.

E X A M P L E 3.5   The attitude of an aircraft can be described by means of "Euler angles." These are angular displacements which, when carried out in a specified order, would move the aircraft to its attitude from a reference orientation in which its axes coincide with earth axes. A heading change H followed by an elevation through an angle E, and that in turn followed by a bank through an angle B will bring an axis system from coincidence with earth axes to coincidence with aircraft axes. (See Fig. 3.7, in which the aircraft is represented schematically.) The angles H, E, and B are Euler angles, and if swept out in that order, are uniquely defined by the aircraft's attitude. Consider now orthonormal sets of vectors as follows:

$(\mathbf{i}_s, \mathbf{j}_s, \mathbf{k}_s)$ along earth axes, $\mathbf{i}_s$ pointing north,
$\qquad\qquad$ $\mathbf{j}_s$ pointing east, and $\mathbf{k}_s = \mathbf{i}_s \times \mathbf{j}_s$;

$(\mathbf{i}', \mathbf{j}', \mathbf{k}')$,   the result of rotating earth axes vectors
$\qquad\qquad$ through H about $\mathbf{k}_s$ $(= \mathbf{k}')$;

$(\mathbf{i}'', \mathbf{j}'', \mathbf{k}'')$,   the result of rotating $(\mathbf{i}', \mathbf{j}', \mathbf{k}')$ through
$\qquad\qquad$ E about $\mathbf{j}'$ $(= \mathbf{j}'')$;

$(\mathbf{i}, \mathbf{j}, \mathbf{k})$,   aircraft axes—the result of rotating $(\mathbf{i}'', \mathbf{j}'', \mathbf{k}'')$
through B about $\mathbf{i}''$ $(= \mathbf{i})$.

Then

$\dot{B}\mathbf{i}$ $=$ angular velocity of $(\mathbf{i}, \mathbf{j}, \mathbf{k})$ relative to $(\mathbf{i}'', \mathbf{j}'', \mathbf{k}'')$,
$\dot{E}\mathbf{j}'$ $=$ angular velocity of $(\mathbf{i}'', \mathbf{j}'', \mathbf{k}'')$ relative to $(\mathbf{i}', \mathbf{j}', \mathbf{k}')$,

and

$\dot{H}\mathbf{k}_s$ $=$ angular velocity of $(\mathbf{i}', \mathbf{j}', \mathbf{k}')$ relative to $(\mathbf{i}_s, \mathbf{j}_s, \mathbf{k}_s)$.

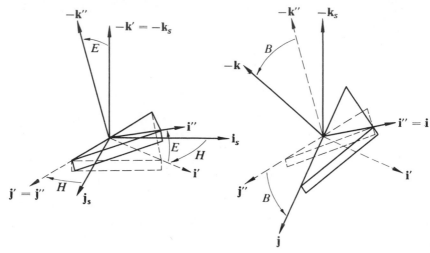

Figure 3.7

The angular velocity of the aircraft relative to the earth is then

$$\boldsymbol{\omega} = \dot{B}\mathbf{i} + \dot{E}\mathbf{j}' + \dot{H}\mathbf{k}_s.$$

Writing $\boldsymbol{\omega}$ in terms of aircraft axes as $p\mathbf{i} + q\mathbf{j} + r\mathbf{k}$ one can readily obtain relations
between p, q, and r and the rates of change of the Euler angles.

Problems

3.11.   A car wheel rotates with angular speed $\dot{\theta}$ about its axis. Express the
angular velocity of a spoke of the wheel in terms of axes fixed to the car, if the
car has angular velocity $\boldsymbol{\omega}$.

3.12.   Referring to Example 3.4, determine the angular velocity of the line
of sight in earth axes.

3.13.   Let the notation of Example 3.4 be carried over to a swivel chair. An
executive rocks gently up and down:

$$\theta = \delta \sin \omega t + \pi/6,$$

and simultaneously the chair swivels at a steady rate $\dot{\phi} = a$. What is the angular velocity of a cigar in his mouth (the cigar is parallel to the chair's $\mathbf{i}''$-axis)?

3.14.   By equating components in a convenient coordinate system, obtain expressions for $\dot{H}$, $\dot{B}$, and $\dot{E}$ in terms of p, q, and r for the aircraft of Example 3.5.

3.5   *Axis of rotation*

Consider a general rigid motion of a body from one position to another. As explained at the beginning of the chapter, the result of such a motion can be considered as a transformation T of position vectors: $\mathbf{r} \rightarrow T\mathbf{r}$. Further, the motion can be accomplished by a translation D followed by a motion R_Q in which a point Q is held fixed.

A translation of a rigid body—motion in which all points of the body are displaced by the same vector amount—can be characterized by its action on the coordinates of a point P in the body. If each point P undergoes a displacement $\mathbf{V}$, the new location of this point is $D\mathbf{r}$:

$$\mathbf{r}' = D\mathbf{r} = \mathbf{r} + \mathbf{V},$$

or equivalently, if $\mathbf{V} = a\mathbf{i} + b\mathbf{j} + c\mathbf{k}$,

$$x' = x + a,$$
$$y' = y + b,$$
$$z' = z + c.$$

(See Fig. 3.8, which is drawn as though the body and the motion were plane phenomena.)

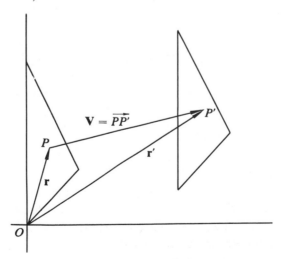

Figure 3.8.   Translation of a body.

A rigid motion with one point held fixed is a *linear* transformation on position vectors relative to that point; that is, if R_O is such a transformation, and $\mathbf{r}_1$ and $\mathbf{r}_2$ are position vectors relative to O, then

$$R_O(a_1\mathbf{r}_1 + a_2\mathbf{r}_2) = a_1 R_O \mathbf{r}_1 + a_2 R_O \mathbf{r}_2.$$

e.g. - defines linear transformation

This can be seen as follows. Consider first Fig. 3.9, in which points P' and Q' are the result of applying R_O to points P and Q, respectively, where $\mathbf{r} = \overrightarrow{OP}$ and $a\mathbf{r} = \overrightarrow{OQ}$. If the motion is rigid, it must be that $|\overrightarrow{OP}| = |\overrightarrow{OP'}|$, $|\overrightarrow{OQ}| = |\overrightarrow{OQ'}|$, and $|\overrightarrow{PQ}| = |\overrightarrow{P'Q'}|$, which in turn implies that $\overrightarrow{OQ'}$ is parallel

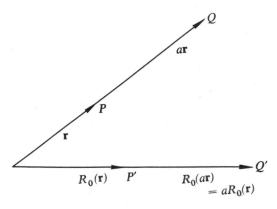

Figure 3.9

to $\overrightarrow{OP'}$ and that $\overrightarrow{OQ'} = a\,\overrightarrow{OP'}$, or $R_O(a\mathbf{r}) = a\,R_O(\mathbf{r})$. Thus, the transformation is *homogeneous*. Referring now to Fig. 3.10, it is clear that under a rigid motion with O fixed, points A, B, and C are carried into points A', B', and C' such that the various triangles formed with O after the transformation are congruent to the corresponding triangles before the transformation (because distances between all pairs of points remain fixed). Hence,

$$R_O(\mathbf{r}_1 + \mathbf{r}_2) = R_O\mathbf{r}_1 + R_O\mathbf{r}_2;$$

that is, the transformation is *additive*, and this together with the homogeneity shown first establish the asserted linearity.

Although R_O was assumed to apply to a position vector relative to O, it can be considered as a transformation on all vectors, since any vector has a representative which is such a position vector.

The linear transformation R_O with the point O held fixed can be expressed in terms of the change in coordinates (relative to O) of an arbitrary

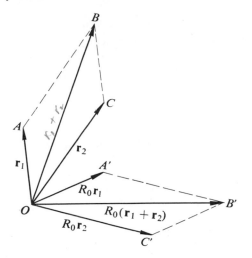

Figure 3.10

point P in the body. Consider an orthonormal triad $(\mathbf{i}, \mathbf{j}, \mathbf{k})$ fixed to the body, and let these be transformed under R_0 as follows:

$$R_0\mathbf{i} = \alpha_1\mathbf{i} + \beta_1\mathbf{j} + \gamma_1\mathbf{k},$$
$$R_0\mathbf{j} = \alpha_2\mathbf{i} + \beta_2\mathbf{j} + \gamma_2\mathbf{k},$$
$$R_0\mathbf{k} = \alpha_3\mathbf{i} + \beta_3\mathbf{j} + \gamma_3\mathbf{k}.$$

The image $\mathbf{r}'$ of $\mathbf{r} = x\mathbf{i} + y\mathbf{j} + z\mathbf{k}$, the position vector of P, is then computed in the following way (exploiting the linearity of R_0):

$$\begin{aligned} \mathbf{r}' = R_0\mathbf{r} &= R_0(x\mathbf{i} + y\mathbf{j} + z\mathbf{k}) \\ &= xR_0\mathbf{i} + yR_0\mathbf{j} + zR_0\mathbf{k} \\ &= (x\alpha_1 + y\alpha_2 + z\alpha_3)\mathbf{i} + (x\beta_1 + y\beta_2 + z\beta_3)\mathbf{j} + (x\gamma_1 + y\gamma_2 + z\gamma_3)\mathbf{k}, \end{aligned}$$

or

$$x' = \alpha_1 x + \alpha_2 y + \alpha_3 z,$$
$$y' = \beta_1 x + \beta_2 y + \beta_3 z,$$
$$z' = \gamma_1 x + \gamma_2 y + \gamma_3 z.$$

Thus, the components of $R_0\mathbf{r}$ are linear combinations of the components of $\mathbf{r}$, with coefficients determined by what happens to the basis vectors $(\mathbf{i}, \mathbf{j}, \mathbf{k})$ under the transformation.

The effect of a rigid motion with fixed point P different from O acting on position vectors relative to O can be determined as follows. Let $\mathbf{r}$

denote the position vector relative to O of a point Q. (See Fig. 3.11.) If $\mathbf{r}'$ denotes the position vector of Q', the new position of the point that was

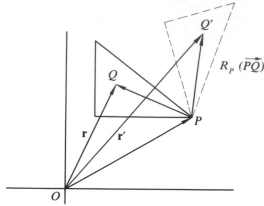

Figure 3.11

at Q, then

$$\mathbf{r}' = \overrightarrow{OP} + \overrightarrow{PQ'} = \mathbf{r}_P + R_P(\overrightarrow{PQ}),$$

where $\mathbf{r}_P$ is the position vector of P relative to O, and R_P is a transformation with P fixed (of the type just discussed).

Now consider a general motion, as suggested in Fig. 3.12 (which again,

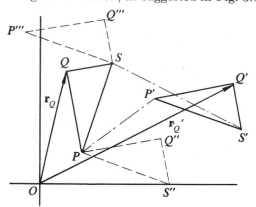

Figure 3.12

however, is shown as two-dimensional for simplicity), from position PQS to position $P'Q'S'$. Let a displacement D_P be defined by

$$D_P\mathbf{r} = \mathbf{r} + \overrightarrow{PP'},$$

and a displacement D_S by

$$D_S \mathbf{r} = \mathbf{r} + \overrightarrow{SS'}.$$

Let a transformation R_P be defined on the position vectors relative to P, with P fixed, as required to bring the body into position $PQ''S''$ from which the translation D_P brings it to the final position $P'Q'S'$; that is, for any point Q in the body with position vector $\mathbf{r}_Q = \overrightarrow{OQ}$,

$$D_P[R_P(\mathbf{r}_Q)] = \overrightarrow{OQ'}.$$

Let R_S be defined similarly with S fixed, so that

$$D_S[R_S(\mathbf{r}_Q)] = \overrightarrow{OQ'}.$$

Now

$$D_P[R_P(\mathbf{r}_Q)] = R_P(\mathbf{r}_Q) + \overrightarrow{PP'}$$

$$= \mathbf{r}_P + R_P(\overrightarrow{PQ}) + \overrightarrow{PP'} = \overrightarrow{OP'} + R_P(\overrightarrow{PQ}),$$

and similarly

$$D_S[R_S(\mathbf{r}_Q)] = \overrightarrow{OS'} + R_S(\overrightarrow{SQ}).$$

Since these are both equal to $\overrightarrow{OQ'}$, they are equal to each other:

$$\overrightarrow{OP'} + R_P(\overrightarrow{PQ}) = \overrightarrow{OS'} + R_S(\overrightarrow{SQ})$$

$$= \overrightarrow{OS'} + R_S(\overrightarrow{SP} + \overrightarrow{PQ})$$

$$= \overrightarrow{OS'} + R_S(\overrightarrow{SP}) + R_S(\overrightarrow{PQ}),$$

and then

$$(R_P - R_S)(\overrightarrow{PQ}) = \overrightarrow{OS'} - \overrightarrow{OP'} + R_S(\overrightarrow{SP})$$

$$= \overrightarrow{P'S'} - \overrightarrow{P'S'} = \mathbf{0}.$$

This is true for arbitrary Q, and hence the transformations R_S and R_P are the same transformation—they both treat each vector the same. This establishes what was asserted at the beginning of the chapter—that when a general rigid motion is "factored" into a translation followed by a motion about a fixed point, the latter is independent of the point chosen to determine the translation.

A rigid motion of a body with a point O held fixed is a *rotation*, in the sense that there is a line of points which are unmoved by the transformation and that the points in a plane perpendicular to that line remain in that plane. To show this it is necessary to determine that there are vectors $\mathbf{r}$

(position vectors relative to O) such that

$$R_O \mathbf{r} = \mathbf{r}$$

or, in terms of components (using notation introduced above),

$$\alpha_1 x + \alpha_2 y + \alpha_3 z = x,$$
$$\beta_1 x + \beta_2 y + \beta_3 z = y,$$
$$\gamma_1 x + \gamma_2 y + \gamma_3 z = z.$$

This system has always the solution, called *trivial:* $x = 0, y = 0, z = 0$. It has a *non*trivial solution $\mathbf{r}$ if and only if the determinant of the coefficients vanishes:

$$\begin{vmatrix} \alpha_1 - 1 & \alpha_2 & \alpha_3 \\ \beta_1 & \beta_2 - 1 & \beta_3 \\ \gamma_1 & \gamma_2 & \gamma_3 - 1 \end{vmatrix} = 0.$$

It can be shown† that for a rigid motion with a fixed point, this is always satisfied, and further, that two of the three equations for (x, y, z) can be solved for two unknowns in terms of the third, so that the set of solutions lie on a line—called the *axis* of rotation. This demonstration will not be presented here, but the example which follows indicates how to determine this axis and the angle of rotation about it.

EXAMPLE 3.6   Consider the rigid motion with O fixed, defined by giving the images of the unit vectors $\mathbf{i}$, $\mathbf{j}$, and $\mathbf{k}$, as follows:

$$R\mathbf{i} = (\mathbf{i} + 2\mathbf{j} - 2\mathbf{k})/3,$$
$$R\mathbf{j} = (2\mathbf{i} + \mathbf{j} + 2\mathbf{k})/3,$$
$$R\mathbf{k} = (2\mathbf{i} - 2\mathbf{j} - \mathbf{k})/3.$$

To locate the axis of rotation it is necessary to find (x, y, z) such that

$$(\tfrac{1}{3} - 1)x + \tfrac{2}{3}y + \tfrac{2}{3}z = 0,$$
$$\tfrac{2}{3}x + (\tfrac{1}{3} - 1)y - \tfrac{2}{3}z = 0,$$
$$-\tfrac{2}{3}x + \tfrac{2}{3}y + (-\tfrac{1}{3} - 1)z = 0.$$

One of these equations is a combination of the other two, and they are all satisfied by $x = k, y = k, z = 0$, for any k. (These solution values are found by transposing, say, the z term in two of the equations and solving for x and y in terms of z, which

†Cf. J. M. H. Olmsted, *Solid Analytic Geometry* (New York, Appleton-Century, 1947), p. 176.

can then be given any value.) Thus, the line defined by the family of vectors $k(\mathbf{i} + \mathbf{j})$ is the axis of rotation, and the plane $x + y = 0$ is normal to this axis. Any point on this plane is carried into another point on the same plane:

$$x' = \tfrac{1}{3}x + \tfrac{2}{3}(-x) + \tfrac{2}{3}z = -\tfrac{1}{3}x + \tfrac{2}{3}z,$$
$$y' = \tfrac{2}{3}x + \tfrac{1}{3}(-x) - \tfrac{2}{3}z = \tfrac{1}{3}x - \tfrac{2}{3}z,$$
$$z' = -\tfrac{2}{3}x + \tfrac{2}{3}(-x) - \tfrac{1}{3}z = -\tfrac{4}{3}x - \tfrac{1}{3}z.$$

(Notice that $x' + y' = 0$.) The angle θ of rotation can be found as follows. Take any point, say $(1, -1, 0)$, on the plane $x + y = 0$ normal to the axis of rotation through the fixed point. This is carried into $(-\tfrac{1}{3}, \tfrac{1}{3}, -\tfrac{4}{3})$, and the angle between the initial and final position vectors is θ, with

$$\cos \theta = \frac{-\mathbf{i} + \mathbf{j} - 4\mathbf{k}}{\sqrt{18}} \cdot \frac{\mathbf{i} - \mathbf{j}}{\sqrt{2}} = -\frac{1}{3}.$$

Problems

3.15.   Show that if $\mathbf{i}$, $\mathbf{j}$, and $\mathbf{k}$ are carried into $\mathbf{i}$, $\cos \theta \, \mathbf{j} - \sin \theta \, \mathbf{k}$, and $\sin \theta \, \mathbf{j} + \cos \theta \, \mathbf{k}$, respectively, by a rigid transformation with O fixed, then this is the rotation through an angle θ. Determine also the axis of rotation.

3.16.   Determine the axis of rotation and the angle of rotation when $\mathbf{i}$, $\mathbf{j}$, and $\mathbf{k}$ are carried, respectively, into $(2\mathbf{i} + 6\mathbf{j} - 3\mathbf{k})/7$, $(3\mathbf{i} + 2\mathbf{j} + 6\mathbf{k})/7$, and $(6\mathbf{i} - 3\mathbf{j} - 2\mathbf{k})/7$.

4 FUNCTIONS OF POSITION

THE assignment of a number w to each point P of a set of points in space defines a *scalar function* of position: $w = f(P)$, which can also be considered as a function of the position vector $\mathbf{r}$: $w = g(\mathbf{r})$. When the position or position vector is defined in terms of rectangular coordinates as $\mathbf{r} = x\mathbf{i} + y\mathbf{j} + z\mathbf{k}$, the variable w is a function of those coordinates—a function of three ordinary real variables:

$$w = g(x\mathbf{i} + y\mathbf{j} + z\mathbf{k}) \equiv \phi(x, y, z).$$

Examples of such functions are temperature, air pressure, humidity, gravity magnitude, and electric potential.

A *vector function* of position is defined by an assignment of a vector value to each point of a set: $\mathbf{V} = \mathbf{G}(\mathbf{r})$, or $\mathbf{V} = \mathbf{F}(x, y, z)$. Examples of vector functions are the velocity vector at each point of a steady-state fluid flow, and the force vector in an electric, gravitational, or magnetic field. These latter applications give rise to the term *vector field* for a vector function of position. (The term *scalar field* is then sometimes applied to a scalar function of position.)

Limits and continuity are defined almost word for word as in the case of a function of a single scalar variable. A function $g(\mathbf{r})$ is said to have the limit L as $\mathbf{r}$ tends to $\mathbf{r}_0$ if and only if given $\epsilon > 0$, there is a corresponding $\delta_\epsilon > 0$ such that

$$|g(\mathbf{r}) - L| < \epsilon \qquad \text{whenever} \qquad 0 < |\mathbf{r} - \mathbf{r}_0| < \delta_\epsilon.$$

Observe that the absolute value $|\mathbf{r} - \mathbf{r}_0|$ is the distance from P_0 to P:

$$|\mathbf{r} - \mathbf{r}_0| = [(x - x_0)^2 + (y - y_0)^2 + (z - z_0)^2]^{1/2}.$$

The function $g(\mathbf{r})$ is continuous at $\mathbf{r}_0$ if and only if it has a limit there equal to $g(\mathbf{r}_0)$.

The vector function $\mathbf{G}(\mathbf{r})$ has the vector limit $\mathbf{L}$ if and only if for any given $\epsilon > 0$ there is a $\delta_\epsilon > 0$ such that

$$|\mathbf{G}(\mathbf{r}) - \mathbf{L}| < \epsilon \qquad \text{whenever} \qquad 0 < |\mathbf{r} - \mathbf{r}_0| < \delta_\epsilon.$$

It is continuous if $\mathbf{G}(\mathbf{r}) \to \mathbf{G}(\mathbf{r}_0)$ as $\mathbf{r} \to \mathbf{r}_0$.

EXAMPLE 4.1   The function $g(\mathbf{r}) = 1/r$ is continuous at $\mathbf{r}_0 \neq 0$. For, if $|\mathbf{r} - \mathbf{r}_0| < r_0/2$, then $r > r_0/2$ and $1/r < 2/r_0$. Thus, when $\delta < r_0/2$ and $|\mathbf{r} - \mathbf{r}_0| < \delta$, it follows that

$$\left| \frac{1}{r} - \frac{1}{r_0} \right| = \frac{|r - r_0|}{rr_0} \leq \frac{|\mathbf{r} - \mathbf{r}_0|}{rr_0} < \frac{\delta}{rr_0} < \frac{2\delta}{r_0^2}.$$

Then given $\epsilon > 0$, the choice $\delta = \min(r_0/2, \epsilon r_0^2/2)$ is a δ with the desired property— showing that $1/r \to 1/r_0$ as $\mathbf{r} \to \mathbf{r}_0$, and therefore that $1/r$ is continuous at $\mathbf{r}_0$.

4.1   *Scalar functions of several variables*

Functions of several variables arise when position is defined in terms of coordinates (rectangular or otherwise). *Partial derivatives* of such functions are defined as ordinary derivatives of the functions of a single variable obtained when all but one of the independent variables are held fixed. For example, the partial derivative of ϕ with respect to x at the point (x_0, y_0, z_0) is defined to be

$$\phi_x(x_0, y_0, z_0) = \frac{d}{dx} \phi(x, y_0, z_0) \Big|_{x=x_0}$$

$$= \lim_{\Delta x \to 0} \frac{\phi(x_0 + \Delta x, y_0, z_0) - \phi(x_0, y_0, z_0)}{\Delta x}.$$

The notations $\partial \phi / \partial x$, $\partial w / \partial x$, and w_x [where $w = \phi(x, y, z)$] are also used for this derivative. The derivative is clearly dependent on the point (x_0, y_0, z_0) at which it is computed and so defines a function, usually written more simply as $\phi_x(x, y, z)$, without bothering to distinguish between the variable x with respect to which the differentiation is carried out and the coordinate x of the point at which it is computed.

When the above limit, which defines ϕ_x, exists, it must be that the quantity

$$\epsilon_1 = \frac{\phi(x + \Delta x, y, z) - \phi(x, y, z)}{\Delta x} - \phi_x(x, y, z)$$

tends to zero as $\Delta x \to 0$ (according to what is meant by saying that the limit exists). Thus, for a given Δx, the corresponding increment in ϕ can be written in the form

$$\phi(x + \Delta x, y, z) - \phi(x, y, z) = \phi_x \, \Delta x + \epsilon_1 \, \Delta x,$$

where ϵ_1 tends to zero with Δx. The second term on the right involves the product of two *infinitesimals* (quantities which are small when Δx is small), whereas the first term usually involves only one small factor. So for small Δx the first term predominates (if $\phi_x \neq 0$); it is called the *partial differential* of ϕ corresponding to Δx at the point (x, y, z):

$$\phi_x(x, y, z) \, \Delta x.$$

The *total differential* of ϕ is defined to be the sum of the three partial differentials corresponding to increments $\Delta x, \Delta y, \Delta z$:

$$d\phi = \phi_x(x, y, z) \, \Delta x + \phi_y(x, y, z) \, \Delta y + \phi_z(x, y, z) \, \Delta z.$$

Let $\Delta\phi$ denote the increment in ϕ produced by simultaneous increments $\Delta x, \Delta y,$ and Δz in $x, y,$ and z, respectively. The function ϕ is called differentiable at (x, y, z) if

$$\frac{\Delta\phi - d\phi}{|\Delta x| + |\Delta y| + |\Delta z|} \to 0$$

as $(\Delta x, \Delta y, \Delta z) \to (0, 0, 0)$. And this *will* be the case if the partial derivatives $\phi_x, \phi_y,$ and ϕ_z exist and if at least two of them are continuous. For, if ϕ_z and ϕ_y are continuous, $\Delta\phi$ can be written

$$
\begin{aligned}
\Delta\phi &= [\phi(x + \Delta x, y + \Delta y, z + \Delta z) - \phi(x + \Delta x, y + \Delta y, z)] \\
&\quad + [\phi(x + \Delta x, y + \Delta y, z) - \phi(x + \Delta x, y, z)] \\
&\quad + [\phi(x + \Delta x, y, z) - \phi(x, y, z)] \\
&= \phi_z(x + \Delta x, y + \Delta y, z) \, \Delta z + \phi_y(x + \Delta x, y, z) \, \Delta y \\
&\quad + \phi_x(x, y, z) \, \Delta x + \epsilon_1 \, \Delta x + \epsilon_2 \, \Delta y + \epsilon_3 \, \Delta z,
\end{aligned}
$$

where $(\epsilon_1, \epsilon_2, \epsilon_3)$ tends to $(0, 0, 0)$ with $(\Delta x, \Delta y, \Delta z)$. Then

$$
\begin{aligned}
\Delta\phi - d\phi &= \epsilon_1 \, \Delta x + \epsilon_2 \, \Delta y + \epsilon_3 \, \Delta z \\
&\quad + [\phi_y(x + \Delta x, y, z) - \phi_y(x, y, z)] \, \Delta y \\
&\quad + [\phi_z(x + \Delta x, y + \Delta y, z) - \phi_z(x, y, z)] \, \Delta z.
\end{aligned}
$$

When divided by $|\Delta x| + |\Delta y| + |\Delta z|$, these terms all tend to zero as $(\Delta x, \Delta y, \Delta z) \to (0, 0, 0)$, since $|\Delta x| / (|\Delta x| + |\Delta y| + |\Delta z|) \leq 1$, for instance, and all the multipliers of $\Delta x, \Delta y,$ and Δz tend to zero. The point is that $\Delta\phi$ can be expressed in the form

$$\Delta\phi = d\phi + \epsilon(|\Delta x| + |\Delta y| + |\Delta z|),$$

where ϵ is a number which tends to zero with Δx, Δy, and Δz. In this sense $d\phi$ is the dominant part of $\Delta\phi$ and can be used to approximate $\Delta\phi$ when the increments in x, y, and z are small.

E X A M P L E 4.2   The volume of a cylinder of radius r and altitude h is given by the formula $V = \pi r^2 h$. The volume of material in a closed cylindrical container of thickness δ is then approximately the differential of volume corresponding to the increments $\Delta r = \delta$ and $\Delta h = 2\delta$:

$$dV = \frac{\partial V}{\partial r}\Delta r + \frac{\partial V}{\partial h}\Delta h = \pi(2rh\,\Delta r + r^2\,\Delta h) = 2\pi\delta(rh + r^2).$$

It should be apparent that the notions of differential and differentiability are not restricted to functions of three variables but apply equally well to functions of any finite number of variables, and were applied in the example just given to a function of two variables.

The "chain rule" for obtaining derivatives of composite functions will now be derived. There are actually many rules, depending on the numbers of variables involved, but they are all in the same spirit; having seen how one rule is written out we can write out any other one by analogy. To be specific, suppose that

$$\begin{cases} r = h(u, v) \\ s = k(u, v) \end{cases} \quad \text{and} \quad \begin{cases} u = f(x, y, z), \\ v = g(x, y, z). \end{cases}$$

The variables r and s then depend ultimately on x, y, and z:

$$\begin{cases} r = h(f(x, y, z), g(x, y, z)), \\ s = k(f(x, y, z), g(x, y, z)), \end{cases}$$

and such direct substitution for u and v yields the functions of x, y, and z which can be differentiated. The chain rule, on the other hand, yields any desired derivative without an actual substitution. Suppose, for instance, that it is desired to compute $\partial r/\partial x$. An increment Δx in x produces increments in u and v, say Δu and Δv. These in turn produce an increment in r, which can be written

$$\Delta r = dh + \epsilon(|\Delta u| + |\Delta v|),$$

where $\epsilon \rightarrow 0$ with Δu and Δv, if $h(u, v)$ is differentiable. Division by Δx yields

$$\frac{\Delta r}{\Delta x} = h_u\frac{\Delta u}{\Delta x} + h_v\frac{\Delta v}{\Delta x} + \epsilon\left(\frac{|\Delta u|}{\Delta x} + \frac{|\Delta v|}{\Delta x}\right).$$

If the derivatives u_x and v_x exist, we obtain (on passing to the limit as $\Delta x \rightarrow 0$)

$$\frac{\partial r}{\partial x} = \frac{\partial r}{\partial u}\frac{\partial u}{\partial x} + \frac{\partial r}{\partial v}\frac{\partial v}{\partial x}.$$

The rule is then to differentiate the function $h(u, v)$ with respect to each of its arguments u and v, multiply these derivatives in turn by the derivatives of u and v with respect to x, and sum. This pattern is followed in all chain rules.

In particular, if x, y, and z are functions of a single variable t and $w = \phi(x, y, z)$, the appropriate chain rule is

$$\frac{dw}{dt} = \frac{\partial w}{\partial x}\frac{dx}{dt} + \frac{\partial w}{\partial y}\frac{dy}{dt} + \frac{\partial w}{\partial z}\frac{dz}{dt},$$

or

$$dw = \frac{\partial w}{\partial x}\,dx + \frac{\partial w}{\partial y}\,dy + \frac{\partial w}{\partial z}\,dz.$$

The latter formula is valid, then, whether one thinks of x, y, and z as independent with increments dx, dy, and dz, or as depending on t, with differentials dx, dy, and dz corresponding to an increment Δt.

E X A M P L E 4.3   Let $r = (x^2 + y^2)^{1/2}$, and let $x = 2t$, $y = t^2$. Then

$$\frac{dr}{dt} = \frac{\partial r}{\partial x}\frac{dx}{dt} + \frac{\partial r}{\partial y}\frac{dy}{dt}$$

$$= \frac{x}{(x^2 + y^2)^{1/2}}\cdot 2 + \frac{y}{(x^2 + y^2)^{1/2}}\cdot 2t$$

$$= \frac{4t + 2t^3}{(4t^2 + t^4)^{1/2}}.$$

Everyone is accustomed to "solving" an equation such as

$$2x - 4y + 6 = 0$$

for y, say, in order to obtain y as a function of x:

$$y = \tfrac{1}{2}(x + 3).$$

This function has the property that when substituted into the original equation an identity in x is obtained:

$$2x - 4[\tfrac{1}{2}(x + 3)] + 6 \equiv 0.$$

"Implicit function theorems" in calculus assert that the same kind of thing happens rather generally; if $f(x, y)$ has continuous first partial derivatives with $f_y \neq 0$ at (x_0, y_0) and $f(x_0, y_0) = 0$, then there is defined near x_0 a function $y = g(x)$ with the property that $f(x, g(x)) \equiv 0$. There are also theorems covering more complicated cases; one such theorem asserts the existence of $z = \psi(x, y)$ as defined by $\phi(x, y, z) = 0$, for instance. Another asserts that the simultaneous equations

$$\begin{cases} F(x, y, z, u, v) = 0 \\ G(x, y, z, u, v) = 0 \end{cases}$$

imply the existence of two functions

$$\begin{cases} u = h(x, y, z) \\ v = k(x, y, z), \end{cases}$$

which yield identities when substituted for u and v in F and G. The assumptions in these theorems are essentially the existence of continuous first derivatives and the nonvanishing of denominators in expressions for derivatives of the explicit functions obtained by using the chain rule as discussed below. The theorems will be used here very casually, without proof and without stopping to verify in each case their applicability. (Proofs may be found in any good text on advanced calculus.)

Derivatives of implicitly defined functions can be calculated by means of the chain rule without actually determining the functions explicitly— which is an important point, since it is often impossible to determine them explicitly (except perhaps numerically). The following examples illustrate the technique.

EXAMPLE 4.4   Consider the simultaneous equations

$$x^2 + y^2 + z^2 = 25,$$
$$z = 3.$$

Assuming that these two equations in three variables define y as a function of x, and differentiating each identity with respect to x, we obtain

$$2x + 2yy' + 2zz' = 0,$$
$$z' = 0,$$

from which it follows that $y' = -x/y$. In this example the explicit function can easily be found:

$$y = \pm (16 - x^2)^{1/2},$$

the sign used depending on whether one is operating near a point where y is positive or negative. (A point where $y = 0$ would be a point where the implicit function theorem would not apply.) The derivative y' can be computed from this explicit function and is found to agree with the derivative as determined above.

E X A M P L E 4.5   Assuming that two differentiable explicit functions of x, y, and z are actually defined by the simultaneous equations

$$F(x, y, z, u, v) = 0,$$
$$G(x, y, z, u, v) = 0,$$

and differentiating with respect to x the identities obtained on substitution of these explicit functions, we find (using the chain rule)

$$F_z \cdot 1 + F_y \cdot 0 + F_z \cdot 0 + F_u \cdot u_x + F_v \cdot v_x = 0,$$
$$G_z \cdot 1 + G_y \cdot 0 + G_z \cdot 0 + G_u \cdot u_x + G_v \cdot v_x = 0.$$

These linear equations in u_x and v_x are readily solved for the derivatives u_x and v_x. Observe that the denominators in the solutions are exactly the same, namely, $F_u G_v - F_v G_u$; this must be different from zero to apply the implicit function theorem.

Problems

4.1.   Show that for any r_0, $\lim_{r \to r_0} r^2 = r_0{}^2$ (that is, r^2 is an everywhere continuous function of $\mathbf{r}$).

4.2.   Compute the indicated partial derivatives:

(a) $\dfrac{\partial}{\partial x}(x^2 y - z/x)$.

(b) $\dfrac{\partial}{\partial y} \cos(xyz)$.

(c) $\dfrac{\partial}{\partial \theta}(r \cos \theta \, \cos \phi)$.

(d) $\dfrac{\partial}{\partial x}(x^2 + y^2 + z^2)^{1/2}$.

4.3.   Write differentials of the four functions differentiated in Problem 4.2.

4.4.   Approximately what volume of material is used to make a closed box 12 by 8 by 10 inches out of cardboard $\frac{1}{32}$ inch thick?

4.5.   Write out chain rules for

(a) $\dfrac{\partial w}{\partial x}$, if $w = g(r)$ and $r = f(x, y, z)$.

(b) $\dfrac{dw}{dt}$, if $w = f(x, y, z, u)$ and $x, y, z,$ and u depend on t.

(c) $\dfrac{\partial w}{\partial u}$, if $w = f(x, y, z)$ and $x = \xi(u, v)$, $y = \zeta(u, v)$, and $z = \eta(u, v)$.

4.6. Given $x^4 + y^4 + z^4 = 3$, compute z_x and z_y at $(1, -1, -1)$.

4.7. Given that $\phi(x, y, z) = C$ defines z as a differentiable function of x and y, compute expressions for z_x and z_y in terms of the derivatives of ϕ.

4.8. Given

$$x^4 + y^4 + z^4 = 3,$$
$$xy + z^2 = 0,$$

compute dy/dx and dz/dx at $(1, -1, -1)$.

4.9. Referring to Example 4.5, obtain formulas for u_x, v_y, and u_z, pursuing the attack begun there.

4.2 *Line integrals*

Let Γ denote a rectifiable curve extending from A to B, and let $\phi(\mathbf{r})$ denote a scalar function defined for each point P (with position vector $\mathbf{r}$) on the curve. Consider a partition Π defined by the points $A = P_0, P_1, \ldots,$ $P_n = B$ on the curve, in that order. Let $\mathbf{r}_k^*$ denote the position vector of an arbitrarily chosen point on the curve between P_{k-1} and P_k, and form the sum

$$S_\Pi = \sum_{i=1}^{n} \phi(\mathbf{r}_k^*)\,|\mathbf{r}_k - \mathbf{r}_{k-1}|.$$

If, given $\epsilon > 0$, there is a $\delta > 0$ such that $|I - S_\Pi| < \epsilon$ whenever the maximum diameter of the arcs $\overset{\frown}{P_{k-1}P}$ is less than δ, the number I is said to be the integral of $\phi(\mathbf{r})$ over Γ. This kind of integral is referred to as a *line integral*, and will be denoted by

$$\int_\Gamma \phi(\mathbf{r})\,ds.$$

It can be shown that if the path Γ over which the integration is performed is made up of a number of pieces, $\Gamma_1, \ldots, \Gamma_n$, laid end to end, then the integral over the composite path Γ is the sum of the integrals over the pieces which make it up:

$$\int_\Gamma \phi(\mathbf{r})\,ds = \int_{\Gamma_1} \phi(\mathbf{r})\,ds + \cdots + \int_{\Gamma_n} \phi(\mathbf{r})\,ds.$$

The line integral can be thought of as a generalization of the notions of arc length and of the ordinary definite integral. For, the line integral of the function $\phi(\mathbf{r}) \equiv 1$ is clearly the length of the path of integration.

If the path of integration of a line integral is a piece of the x-axis, the integral is just an ordinary definite integral with respect to x over that region of x-values.

E X A M P L E 4.6   A piece of stiff wire is situated with respect to a rectangular coordinate system so that its shape defines a curve Γ. Suppose that it is desired to determine the center of gravity, given that the density of the wire at the point $\mathbf{r}$ is $\phi(\mathbf{r})$. (The units of such a density would be mass per unit length.) The first moment of the wire with respect to each coordinate plane would be required. To compute these consider a partition Π of the curve Γ, and form the approximate first moments; for example, for the first moment with respect to the xy-plane, form the sum

$$\sum_{i=1}^{n} \phi(\mathbf{r}_k{}^{*}) z_k{}^{*} |\mathbf{r}_k - \mathbf{r}_{k-1}|.$$

The terms in this sum are first moments of the pieces of the partition, $|\mathbf{r}_k - \mathbf{r}_{k-1}|$ being the approximate length of the kth piece, $\phi(\mathbf{r}_k{}^{*})$ the approximately constant density on the kth piece, and $z_k{}^{*}$ the distance (approximately the same for all points on the kth piece) from the xy-plane. (The point $\mathbf{r}_k{}^{*}$ is, as above, an arbitrarily selected point on the kth piece, and $z_k{}^{*}$ is the z-component or coordinate of this point.) The desired first moment is then the limit of the above approximating sums, or the line integral

$$\int_{\Gamma} z\, \phi(\mathbf{r})\, ds.$$

When the path of integration of a line integral is continuously differentiable, or is made up of a finite number of continuously differentiable pieces, the integral can be computed as an ordinary definite integral with respect to the parameter giving the representation. If the curve Γ is defined, say, by $\mathbf{r} = \mathbf{f}(u)$, where $\mathbf{f}(u)$ has a continuous derivative, for $a \leq u \leq b$, then

$$|\mathbf{r}_k - \mathbf{r}_{k-1}| \doteq |\mathbf{f}'(u)|\, \Delta u_k,$$

in which the partition of Γ is induced by a partition of the u-interval $[a, b]$. The value u in the above approximation is some value on the kth u-interval, Δu_k. Without exhibiting the details, it can be shown that if $G(u) \equiv \phi(\mathbf{f}(u))$, then

$$\int_{\Gamma} \phi(\mathbf{r})\, ds = \int_{a}^{b} G(u)\, |\mathbf{f}'(u)|\, du.$$

The reasoning is similar to that used earlier to obtain the integral formula for arc length.

EXAMPLE 4.7   Consider a semicircular wire of constant density, situated so that it lies along the curve

$$\mathbf{r} = (a \cos \theta)\mathbf{i} + (a \sin \theta)\mathbf{j},$$

from $\theta = 0$ to $\theta = \pi$. The appropriate first moment needed for locating its center of gravity on the y-axis is the line integral

$$\int \rho y \, ds = \rho \int_0^{\pi} (a \sin \theta) a \, d\theta = 2\rho a^2.$$

Since the mass of the wire is $\pi \rho a$, the center of gravity is at

$$y = \frac{2\rho a^2}{\pi \rho a} = \frac{2a}{\pi}.$$

A kind of line integral frequently encountered is an *oriented* line integral, in which the path Γ is directed and the integrand function has a factor which is the cosine of the angle between a vector function and the tangent to the path. More specifically, the integrand function is of the form

$$F(\mathbf{r}) \cos \theta = \mathbf{F}(\mathbf{r}) \cdot \mathbf{t},$$

where $\mathbf{F}(\mathbf{r})$ is a vector function defined at each point of the path, and $\mathbf{t}$ is a specified one of the two unit tangents to the path. Since (if s increases in the direction of $\mathbf{t}$) $d\mathbf{r}/ds = \mathbf{t}$, or $\mathbf{t} \, ds = d\mathbf{r}$, the integral can be written as

$$\int_{\Gamma} \mathbf{F} \cdot \mathbf{t} \, ds \qquad \text{or} \qquad \int_{\Gamma} \mathbf{F} \cdot d\mathbf{r}.$$

Such an integral arises in the computation of work done on a particle by the variable force $\mathbf{F}$ as the particle is moved along the path Γ from one point to another. (Subdivide the path into small pieces, assume the force to be constant on each piece to compute the approximate work over that piece as $\mathbf{F} \cdot \Delta \mathbf{r}$, sum, and pass to the limit over successively finer subdivisions in the usual way.) When the force $\mathbf{F}$ is written in terms of components:

$$\mathbf{F}(\mathbf{r}) = L(x, y, z)\mathbf{i} + M(x, y, z)\mathbf{j} + N(x, y, z)\mathbf{k},$$

and because

$$\mathbf{t} = \frac{d\mathbf{r}}{ds} = \frac{dx}{ds}\mathbf{i} + \frac{dy}{ds}\mathbf{j} + \frac{dz}{ds}\mathbf{k},$$

there follows

$$\int \mathbf{F}(\mathbf{r}) \cdot \mathbf{t} \, ds = \int L(x, y, z) \frac{dx}{ds} \, ds + \int M(x, y, z) \frac{dy}{ds} \, ds + \int N(x, y, z) \frac{dz}{ds} \, ds,$$

which is usually written in the more economical notation

$$\int \mathbf{F} \cdot d\mathbf{r} = \int L \, dx + M \, dy + N \, dz.$$

If one of the rectangular coordinates, say x, can be used as the curve parameter, then

$$\int L(x, y, z)\frac{dx}{ds}\, ds = \int_a^b L(x, y(x), z(x))\, dx,$$

indicating that there is some justification in the notation $\int L\, dx$.

EXAMPLE 4.8   Consider the force

$$\mathbf{F} = \frac{Kx}{(x^2 + y^2)^{1/2}}\,\mathbf{i} + \frac{Ky}{(x^2 + y^2)^{1/2}}\,\mathbf{j}.$$

The work done in moving a particle from $(1, 0, 0)$ to $(4, 0, 9)$ along the curve Γ_1: $\mathbf{r} = (u + 1)\mathbf{i} + u^2\mathbf{k}$, is given by

$$\int_{\Gamma_1} \mathbf{F} \cdot d\mathbf{r} = \int_{\Gamma_1} \frac{K(x\, dx + y\, dy)}{(x^2 + y^2)^{1/2}}$$

$$= K\int_0^3 \frac{(u + 1) + 0}{[(u + 1)^2 + 0^2]^{1/2}}\, du = 3K.$$

The work done moving the particle once around the circle Γ_2,

$$\mathbf{r} = (a \cos \theta)\mathbf{i} + (a \sin \theta)\mathbf{j},$$

is given by

$$\int_{\Gamma_2} \mathbf{F} \cdot d\mathbf{r} = K\int_0^{2\pi} \frac{(a \cos \theta)(-\sin \theta) + (a \sin \theta)(\cos \theta)}{(\cos^2 \theta + \sin^2 \theta)^{1/2}}\, d\theta = 0.$$

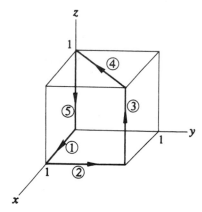

Figure 4.1.   (See Example 4.9.)

In this case the force is perpendicular to the path, so no work is involved, even in going part way around the circle.

EXAMPLE 4.9   Suppose that it is desired to compute the value of the line integral of $\mathbf{F} \cdot \mathbf{t}$, where $\mathbf{F} = x^2\mathbf{i} - xz\mathbf{j} + y^2\mathbf{k}$, and $\mathbf{t}$ is the unit tangent to the closed path shown in Fig. 4.1. The integration is performed in five parts, corresponding to the five pieces of the path which are numbered ① to ⑤ in the figure. Each piece is continuously differentiable. Along ①, $dy = dz = 0$, so that $\mathbf{F} \cdot d\mathbf{r} = x^2\, dx$, and x may be used as the parameter, varying from zero to one:

$$\int_① \mathbf{F} \cdot d\mathbf{r} = \int_0^1 x^2\, dx = \tfrac{1}{3}.$$

Along ②, $dx = dz = 0$, and $z = 0$, so the integral is zero. Along ③, $dx = dy = 0$, $x = y = 1$, so $\mathbf{F} \cdot d\mathbf{r} = dz$, and the integral ($z = 0$ to $z = 1$) has the value one. Along ④, $z = 1$, $dz = 0$, $x = y$, and

$$\int_{④} \mathbf{F} \cdot d\mathbf{r} = \int_{④} x^2 \, dx - x \, dy = \int_1^0 (x^2 - x) \, dx = \tfrac{1}{6}.$$

Along ⑤ the integrand and hence the integral are zero, so the desired result is

$$\int \mathbf{F} \cdot d\mathbf{r} = \tfrac{1}{3} + 0 + 1 + \tfrac{1}{6} + 0 = \tfrac{3}{2}.$$

Problems

4.10. Compute the center of gravity of a uniform, triangular-shaped wire whose vertices are at $(-1, 0, 0)$, $(1, 0, 0)$, and $(0, 1, 0)$.

4.11. Compute the line integral

$$\int_C \frac{-y\mathbf{i} + x\mathbf{j}}{x^2 + y^2} \cdot d\mathbf{r},$$

where C is a circle of radius a in the xy-plane, with center at the origin, traced out counterclockwise.

4.12. Let $\mathbf{F} = 2x\mathbf{i} + y\mathbf{j} + z\mathbf{k}$, and evaluate the integral of $\mathbf{F} \cdot d\mathbf{r}$ around the closed path traced out by

$$\mathbf{r} = (\cos u)\mathbf{i} + (\sin u)\mathbf{j} + (\cos u + \sin u)\mathbf{k},$$

as u varies from 0 to 2π.

4.13. Evaluate the integral of $\mathbf{F} \cdot d\mathbf{r}$, where $\mathbf{F} = (2y^2 + z)\mathbf{i} + 4xy\mathbf{j} + x\mathbf{k}$, from $(1, 0, 0)$ to $(1, 0, 2\pi)$, along:
  (a) the spiral $\mathbf{r} = (\cos \theta)\mathbf{i} + (\sin \theta)\mathbf{j} + \theta\mathbf{k}$;
  (b) the series of straight line segments from $(1, 0, 0)$ to $(0, 0, 0)$, to $(0, 0, 2\pi)$, to $(1, 0, 2\pi)$;
  (c) the straight line joining the two end points.

4.14. Evaluate the integral of $(x^2\mathbf{i} + y^2\mathbf{j} + [z^2 + 2xy]\mathbf{k}) \cdot d\mathbf{r}$ along the closed curve (either way) which is the intersection of $(x - 2)^2 + y^2 = 1$ with $z = x - 1$.

4.3 Surfaces

Surfaces can be specified in at least three ways, apparently different, but often equivalent: as the locus of points (x, y, z) or tips of position vectors $\mathbf{r}$ satisfying an equation of the form

(I) $$\phi(x, y, z) = C, \qquad \text{or} \qquad g(\mathbf{r}) = C;$$

as the graph of a scalar function of two variables,

$$\text{(II)} \qquad\qquad z = f(x, y);$$

or parametrically, as the image of a region in a two-dimensional parameter space under a transformation of the form

$$\text{(III)} \qquad \begin{cases} x = \lambda(u, v) \\ y = \mu(u, v) \\ z = \nu(u, v) \end{cases} \qquad \text{or} \qquad \mathbf{r} = \lambda(u, v)\mathbf{i} + \mu(u, v)\mathbf{j} + \nu(u, v)\mathbf{k}.$$

When $\phi(x, y, z)$ is sufficiently regular and $\phi_z \neq 0$, a function $z = f(x, y)$ is defined implicitly by (I), which can then be expressed in form (II); and form (II) can be put into form (I) simply by defining $\phi(x, y, z)$ to be $z - f(x, y)$. Also, if $\lambda(u, v)$ and $\mu(u, v)$ are sufficiently well behaved (say continuously differentiable, with $x_u y_v - x_v y_u \neq 0$), the equations $x = \lambda(u, v)$ and $y = \mu(u, v)$ can be solved simultaneously for u and v in terms of x and y: $u = \alpha(x, y)$, $v = \beta(x, y)$, which can be substituted into the third equation of (III) to yield a function of type (II): $z = \nu(\alpha(x, y), \beta(x, y)) = f(x, y)$. Form (II) can in turn be expressed in parametric form by using x and y as parameters:

$$\mathbf{r} = u\mathbf{i} + v\mathbf{j} + f(u, v)\mathbf{k}.$$

Form (I) arises naturally in studying scalar functions of position, defining loci (one for each choice of the constant C) on each of which ϕ has everywhere the same value; these are called *constant-value surfaces* (or, in the particular case in which ϕ is a potential, *equipotential* surfaces). This notion is perhaps familiar in the case of a function of position in a plane—a function of two variables; in this case the graph of $\psi(x, y) = C$ is a curve, called a contour line. Contour lines are useful in two-dimensional representations of functions $z = \psi(x, y)$, which really require three dimensions for a complete representation. On architects' drawings of land and navigational charts of lakes, elevation and depth are indicated by a series of contour lines, each contour line marked with the constant elevation or depth which defines it. Such a device avoids the need for three-dimensional graph paper. In the case of $w = \phi(x, y, z)$, four dimensions are needed for a complete representation, and the constant value surfaces, if not especially easy to draw, can at least be visualized.

Form (II), $z = f(x, y)$, is easy to visualize as something which the man on the street would want to call a surface. A point (x, y) in the xy-plane is chosen arbitrarily in the domain where the function is defined, and above this point [i.e., above $(x, y, 0)$] lies the point (x, y, z) on the locus—just one point covering each point of the xy-plane; and if the function f is smooth in the sense, say, of being continuously differentiable, the locus is smooth in the intuitive sense.

The parametric representation (III) is often the most mathematically convenient, taking more easily into account surfaces which double back or twist so that there is more than one z, say, corresponding to a given (x, y). It should be recognized, as in the case of the parametric representation of a curve, that many parametrizations are possible for a given surface.

Consider then a surface defined parametrically by the relation

$$\mathbf{r} = \mathbf{g}(u, v) = \lambda(u, v)\mathbf{i} + \mu(u, v)\mathbf{j} + \nu(u, v)\mathbf{k},$$

where $\mathbf{g}(u, v)$ is a differentiable function defined in a domain D of the uv-plane. Let D be a nonempty open set in the plane plus its boundary. (An open set in the plane is a set such that each point in it has a circular neighborhood contained in the set; its boundary consists of points not in the set D each of whose circular neighborhoods contains points of D.) Suppose further that $\mathbf{g}(u, v)$ has the property that for each $\mathbf{r}$ defining a point on the surface there is just one point (u, v) such that $\mathbf{r} = \mathbf{g}(u, v)$.

Let $\mathbf{r}_0 = \mathbf{g}(u_0, v_0)$ be an arbitrarily selected point on the surface, and consider the image of the line $u = u_0$. Holding u equal to u_0 reduces $\mathbf{r}$ to dependence on v alone, and the image is therefore a *curve*, the curve defined by

$$\mathbf{r} = \mathbf{g}(u_0, v).$$

This will be called a constant-u curve. There is similarly a constant-v curve through P_0:

$$\mathbf{r} = \mathbf{g}(u, v_0),$$

along which u is the parameter. Since $\mathbf{g}$ is differentiable, the partial derivatives exist:

$$\mathbf{r}_u = \frac{\partial \mathbf{g}}{\partial u} = \lambda_u(u_0, v_0)\mathbf{i} + \mu_u(u_0, v_0)\mathbf{j} + \nu_u(u_0, v_0)\mathbf{k}.$$

$$\mathbf{r}_v = \frac{\partial \mathbf{g}}{\partial v} = \lambda_v(u_0, v_0)\mathbf{i} + \mu_v(u_0, v_0)\mathbf{j} + \nu_v(u_0, v_0)\mathbf{k},$$

These are vectors tangent, respectively, to the constant-v and constant-u curves at P_0. If $\mathbf{r}_u \times \mathbf{r}_v \neq \mathbf{0}$, these tangent vectors define a *plane* through P_0, a plane whose normal direction is $\mathbf{r}_u \times \mathbf{r}_v$. This plane is the *tangent plane* to the surface at P_0, containing all tangent lines, as will be demonstrated next.

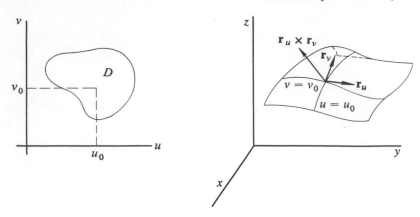

Figure 4.2

A curve through (u_0, v_0) in the uv-plane:

$$\begin{cases} u = \xi(\theta) \\ v = \zeta(\theta), \end{cases}$$

defines (as the image) a curve on the surface, through P_0:

$$\mathbf{r} = \mathbf{g}[\xi(\theta), \zeta(\theta)].$$

If the uv-curve is differentiable, so is its image, with tangent vector

$$\frac{d\mathbf{r}}{d\theta} = \mathbf{r}_u\, \xi'(\theta) + \mathbf{r}_v\, \zeta'(\theta).$$

But this is a linear combination of $\mathbf{r}_u$ and $\mathbf{r}_v$ and lies, therefore, in the plane determined by $\mathbf{r}_u$ and $\mathbf{r}_v$—the tangent plane.

E X A M P L E 4.10   A way of representing the surface of a sphere of radius b parametrically is by means of the equation

$$\mathbf{r} = (b \sin \theta \cos \phi)\mathbf{i} + (b \sin \theta \sin \phi)\mathbf{j} + (b \cos \theta)\mathbf{k}.$$

If (θ, ϕ) is restricted to the region $\pi/4 \leq \theta \leq \pi/2,\ 0 \leq \phi \leq \pi/2$, the image is a portion of the sphere in the first octant, as shown in Fig. 4.3. The tangent vectors along the constant-ϕ and constant-θ curves are

$$\mathbf{r}_\theta = (b \cos \theta \cos \phi)\mathbf{i} + (b \cos \theta \sin \phi)\mathbf{j} - (b \sin \theta)\mathbf{k},$$
$$\mathbf{r}_\phi = -(b \sin \theta \sin \phi)\mathbf{i} + (b \sin \theta \cos \phi)\mathbf{j},$$

with cross product

$$\mathbf{r}_\theta \times \mathbf{r}_\phi = (b\,\sin \theta)\mathbf{r}.$$

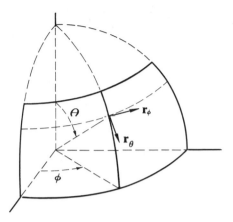

Figure 4.3.   (See Example 4.10.)

The unit normal is therefore

$$\mathbf{N} = \frac{\mathbf{r}_\theta \times \mathbf{r}_\phi}{|\mathbf{r}_\theta \times \mathbf{r}_\phi|} = \frac{\mathbf{r}}{b},$$

and the normal plane at $\mathbf{r}_0$ is

$$(\mathbf{r} - \mathbf{r}_0) \cdot \mathbf{r}_0 = 0.$$

The whole sphere is obtained as the image of the uv-region $0 \le \theta \le \pi$, $0 \le \phi < 2\pi$. At $\theta = 0$ the vector $\mathbf{r}_\theta \times \mathbf{r}_\phi = \mathbf{0}$ (its direction is undefined); the point $\theta = 0$, $\phi = \phi_0$ is just $\mathbf{r} = b\mathbf{k}$ for any ϕ_0, so this one $\mathbf{r}$ comes from many points $(0, \phi)$. Of course, since $\mathbf{N} = \mathbf{r}/b$, the unit normal tends to $\mathbf{k}$ as (θ, ϕ) tends to $(0, \phi)$ for *any* ϕ. Thus, a definition of $\mathbf{N}$ as $\mathbf{k}$ for $\mathbf{r} = b\mathbf{k}$ (and similarly as $-\mathbf{k}$ for $\mathbf{r} = -b\mathbf{k}$) would yield, with $\mathbf{N} = (\mathbf{r}_\theta \times \mathbf{r}_\phi)/|\mathbf{r}_\theta \times \mathbf{r}_\phi|$ when $\mathbf{r}_\theta \times \mathbf{r}_\phi \ne \mathbf{0}$, a continuous normal field—provided nothing goes wrong along $\phi = 0$. For such points one can use either $\phi = 0$ or $\phi = 2\pi$; but since $\mathbf{r}_\theta \times \mathbf{r}_\phi$ is dependent on ϕ only through the sine and cosine of ϕ, its value is the same for $\phi = 0$ as for $\phi = 2\pi$.

When a surface is specified as $z = f(x, y)$, a parametric equation for the same surface can be taken to be

$$\mathbf{r} = u\mathbf{i} + v\mathbf{j} + f(u, v)\mathbf{k}.$$

And then vectors tangent to the constant-v and constant-u curves are

$$\mathbf{r}_u = \mathbf{i} + f_u\mathbf{k},$$
$$\mathbf{r}_v = \mathbf{j} + f_v\mathbf{k},$$

with cross product

$$\mathbf{r}_u \times \mathbf{r}_v = -f_u\mathbf{i} - f_v\mathbf{j} + \mathbf{k}.$$

This is always nonzero and defined when $f(x, y)$ has partial derivatives. The equation of the plane tangent to $z = f(x, y)$ at (x_0, y_0) is clearly

$$f_x(x_0, y_0)(x - x_0) + f_y(x_0, y_0)(y - y_0) - (z - z_0) = 0.$$

Observe that for any point (x, y, z) on this tangent plane, z is given by

$$z = z_0 + dz,$$

where dz is the differential of $f(x, y)$ corresponding to increments $(x - x_0)$ and $(y - y_0)$. Thus, the differential can be interpreted as the approximation to the actual change in z obtained by using the tangent plane in place of the actual surface.

E X A M P L E 4.11   Consider the surface $z = x^2 + y^2$. The normal vector at (x, y, z) is $z_x \mathbf{i} + z_y \mathbf{j} - \mathbf{k} = 2x\mathbf{i} + 2y\mathbf{j} - \mathbf{k}$. The equation of the tangent plane at, say, $(1, -1, 2)$ is then

$$2(x - 1) - 2(y + 1) - (z - 2) = 0.$$

When a surface is specified as the locus of the equation $\phi(x, y, z) = C$ [or $g(\mathbf{r}) = C$], the tangent plane may be obtained by using the fact that *it's* ~~it is~~ normal ᶦˢ ⁿᵒʳᵐᵃˡ to every curve in the surface through the point of tangency. Consider a curve $\mathbf{r} = \mathbf{f}(u)$ in the surface:

$$g(\mathbf{f}(u)) = \phi[x(u), y(u), z(u)] = C.$$

The derivative with respect to u of this constant must be zero:

$$\frac{d}{du} g(\mathbf{f}(u)) = \phi_x x_u + \phi_y y_u + \phi_z z_u = 0, \qquad \phi_z = \frac{\partial \phi}{\partial z}; \ z_u = \frac{dz}{du}$$

or

$$(\phi_x \mathbf{i} + \phi_y \mathbf{j} + \phi_z \mathbf{k}) \cdot (x_u \mathbf{i} + y_u \mathbf{j} + z_u \mathbf{k}) = 0.$$

Since $x_u \mathbf{i} + y_u \mathbf{j} + z_u \mathbf{k}$ is a tangent vector (to the curve, and hence to the surface), the vector $\nabla \phi$ defined to be

$$\nabla \phi \equiv \phi_x \mathbf{i} + \phi_y \mathbf{j} + \phi_z \mathbf{k}$$

must be in the normal direction. (The symbol $\nabla \phi$ is read "del ϕ.")

E X A M P L E 4.12   A sphere of radius b is defined by the equation

$$\phi(x, y, z) \equiv x^2 + y^2 + z^2 = b^2.$$

The normal direction at a point (x, y, z) on the sphere is

$$\phi_x \mathbf{i} + \phi_y \mathbf{j} + \phi_z \mathbf{k} = 2x\mathbf{i} + 2y\mathbf{j} + 2z\mathbf{k},$$

and a unit normal is clearly $\mathbf{r}/b$, as found in Example 4.10, where the same sphere was defined parametrically.

Problems

4.15.   In each case determine the unit vector **N** normal to the surface and the equation of the tangent plane:

(a) $z = xy$, at $(1, -1, -1)$;

(b) $x^4 + y^4 + z^4 = 3$, at $(1, -1, -1)$;

(c) $\mathbf{r} = 2u\mathbf{i} + (u^2 + v)\mathbf{j} + v^2\mathbf{k}$, at $u = 0$, $v = 1$;

(d) $x^2 - 3xy + 2y^2 + yz + z^2 - 3x + 4y + 12z = 0$, at $(0, 0, 0)$.

4.16.   Obtain representations of the form $z = f(x, y)$ for (b) and (c) of Problem 4.15. Compute **N** from this form and reconcile with the earlier determination of **N**.

4.17.   Describe the surface $\mathbf{r} = (\cos u)\mathbf{i} + (\sin u)\mathbf{j} + v\mathbf{k}$, for $0 \le u \le 3\pi/2$, $0 \le v \le 1$. Determine **N** as a function of (u, v).

4.18.   Show that $\mathbf{r} = \mathbf{g}(u, v)$ represents a plane (for $-\infty < u, v < \infty$) if **g** is *linear* in u and v: $\mathbf{g}(u, v) = \mathbf{A}u + \mathbf{B}v + \mathbf{C}$. Express **N** in terms of **A**, **B**, and **C**. Compute **N** for the particular equation $\mathbf{r} = (u - v + 2)\mathbf{i} + (2u + v - 1)\mathbf{j} + (u - 2)\mathbf{k}$, and express this plane in the form $\phi(x, y, z) = C$.

4.19.   Consider the surface

$$\mathbf{r} = \frac{bu}{(u^2 + v^2)^{1/2}}\,\mathbf{i} + \frac{bv}{(u^2 + v^2)^{1/2}}\,\mathbf{j} + \sqrt{3}\left(\frac{b^2}{u^2 + v^2} - 1\right)^{1/2}\mathbf{k}.$$

Obtain an equation of the form $\phi(x, y, z) = C$ and from this identify the surface. What is the image of the region $b/2 < (u^2 + v^2)^{1/2} < b$? Express the surface parametrically using cylindrical coordinates, (ρ, θ, z). What is the normal direction?

4.4   Directional derivatives and the gradient

The variation of a scalar function of position, $g(\mathbf{r})$, is more complicated when that position is a point in three-dimensional space than it is when the position is a point on one axis. The rate of change in the values of the function at a given point is different in different directions. If only points on a constant value surface $g(\mathbf{r}) = C$ are considered, for instance, the rate of change is clearly zero, whereas from one such surface to another (with a different C) the rate is generally different from zero.

The *directional derivative* of $w = g(\mathbf{r})$ at the point $\mathbf{r}_0$ in the direction of **v**, a given *unit* vector, is defined to be

$$\frac{dw}{ds} \equiv \lim_{\Delta s \to 0+} \frac{g(\mathbf{r}_0 + \Delta s\,\mathbf{v}) - g(\mathbf{r}_0)}{\Delta s},$$

when this limit exists. The points $\mathbf{r}_0 + \Delta s\,\mathbf{v}$ (for $\Delta s \ge 0$) are the points on a ray extending from $\mathbf{r}_0$ in the direction $\mathbf{v}$, and the quantity Δs (being the length of $\Delta s\,\mathbf{v}$) measures distance from P_0 along this ray. Thus, the

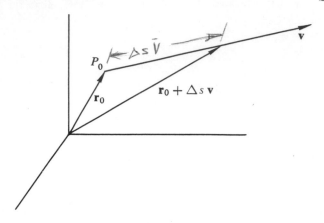

Figure 4.4

increment quotient in the above definition is the change in the function per unit length along the ray $\mathbf{f}(s) = \mathbf{r}_0 + s\mathbf{v}$ (where $s = 0$ corresponds to $\mathbf{r} = \mathbf{r}_0$):

$$\frac{dw}{ds} = \frac{d}{ds}\,g(\mathbf{r}_0 + s\mathbf{v}).$$

useful later

► EXAMPLE 4.13   Consider the function $g(\mathbf{r}) = |\mathbf{r}|$, the distance from the origin out to P. The directional derivative in a direction $\mathbf{v}$ which makes an angle θ

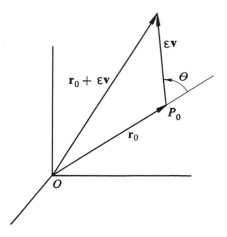

Figure 4.5.   (See Example 4.13).

with $\mathbf{r}$ (see Fig. 4.5) is

$$\frac{dw}{ds} = \lim_{\epsilon \to 0+} \frac{|\mathbf{r}_0 + \epsilon\mathbf{v}| - |\mathbf{r}_0|}{\epsilon}$$

$$= \lim_{\epsilon \to 0+} \frac{(r_0^2 + \epsilon^2 + 2r_0\epsilon \cos\theta)^{1/2} - r_0}{\epsilon} = \cos\theta.$$

(This follows from the law of cosines and from l'Hospital's rule.)

Thus the rate is 1 along $\mathbf{r}$, 0 normal to $\mathbf{r}$, and -1 along $-\mathbf{r}$. But it has been assumed that $\mathbf{r}_0 \neq \mathbf{0}$, so that θ is defined; if $\mathbf{r}_0 = \mathbf{0}$, the limit is even simpler to evaluate:

$$\frac{dw}{ds}\bigg|_{r=0} = \lim_{\epsilon \to 0+} \frac{|\epsilon\mathbf{v}| - 0}{\epsilon} = 1,$$

and so the directional derivative of $w = |\mathbf{r}|$ at $\mathbf{r} = \mathbf{0}$ is the same in all directions.

The directional derivative of a function in an arbitrary direction $\mathbf{v}$ can be expressed in terms of the directional derivative in a direction normal to the constant value surface. Consider a point $\mathbf{r}_0$, let $g(\mathbf{r}_0) = C$, and let $\mathbf{N}$ denote that unit vector normal to $g(\mathbf{r}) = C$ at $\mathbf{r} = \mathbf{r}_0$ which makes an acute

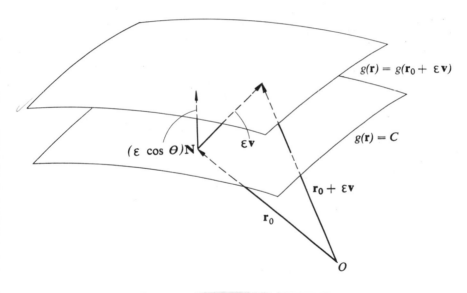

Figure 4.6

angle θ with the chosen direction $\mathbf{v}$. The directional derivative of $g(\mathbf{r})$ along $\mathbf{v}$ is

$$\frac{dw}{ds} = \lim_{\epsilon \to 0+} \frac{g(\mathbf{r}_0 + \epsilon\mathbf{v}) - g(\mathbf{r}_0)}{\epsilon}.$$

Since (see Fig. 4.6)

$$g(\mathbf{r}_0 + \epsilon \mathbf{v}) = g(\mathbf{r}_0 + \epsilon \cos \theta \, \mathbf{N}),$$

there follows

$$\frac{dw}{ds} = \lim_{\epsilon \to 0+} \frac{g(\mathbf{r}_0 + \epsilon \cos \theta \, \mathbf{N}) - g(\mathbf{r}_0)}{\epsilon \cos \theta} \cos \theta$$

$$= \lim_{\delta \to 0+} \frac{g(\mathbf{r}_0 + \delta \mathbf{N}) - g(\mathbf{r}_0)}{\delta} \cos \theta = \frac{dw}{dn} \cos \theta,$$

where dw/dn is a temporary notation for the directional derivative along $\mathbf{N}$. Writing the foregoing in the form

$$\frac{dw}{ds} = \left(\frac{dw}{dn} \mathbf{N} \right) \cdot \mathbf{v}$$

shows that dw/ds ranges in value between $|dw/dn|$ and $-|dw/dn|$, and that the maximum value dw/dn is achieved when $\mathbf{v}$ is in the direction of $(dw/dn)\mathbf{N}$. The vector $(dw/dn)\mathbf{N}$ is called the gradient of w, and the directional derivative of w in an arbitrary direction $\mathbf{v}$ is the component of the gradient along $\mathbf{v}$. The gradient is sometimes denoted by grad ϕ.

This discussion has been based on an approximation which was not really justified, though it seemed reasonable. It can be avoided, by using a rectangular coordinate representation, as follows. Let $g(\mathbf{r}) = \phi(x, y, z)$ and let

$$\mathbf{v} = \lambda \mathbf{i} + \mu \mathbf{j} + \nu \mathbf{k}$$

be a unit vector. Then

see eqn middle p112

$$\frac{dw}{ds} = \frac{d}{ds} g(s\lambda \mathbf{i} + s\mu \mathbf{j} + s\nu \mathbf{k})$$

$$= \frac{d}{ds} \phi(s\lambda, s\mu, s\nu)$$

$$= \phi_x \lambda + \phi_y \mu + \phi_z \nu = (\phi_x \mathbf{i} + \phi_y \mathbf{j} + \phi_z \mathbf{k}) \cdot \mathbf{v}.$$

This is the component of the vector

Same result as bottom p.110

$$\nabla \phi = \phi_x \mathbf{i} + \phi_y \mathbf{j} + \phi_z \mathbf{k}$$

in the direction $\mathbf{v}$. The maximum value of dw/ds is then $|\nabla \phi|$ and is achieved in the direction $\nabla \phi$. Thus, $\nabla \phi$ is the vector function called earlier the *gradient*:

$$\boxed{\nabla \phi = \text{grad } \phi.}$$

This is a definition of gradient which does not depend on the geometrical approximation of the earlier discussion.

E X A M P L E 4.14   The directional derivative of $w = z^2 + xy$ in the direction $\frac{1}{3}(\mathbf{i} + 2\mathbf{j} - 2\mathbf{k})$ is computed from the gradient

$$\nabla w = y\mathbf{i} + x\mathbf{j} + 2z\mathbf{k}$$

as the component

$$\frac{dw}{ds} = (y\mathbf{i} + x\mathbf{j} + 2z\mathbf{k}) \cdot \frac{\mathbf{i} + 2\mathbf{j} - 2\mathbf{k}}{3} = \frac{y + 2x - 4z}{3}.$$

At the point $(1, 2, -1)$, for instance,

$$\nabla w = 2\mathbf{i} + \mathbf{j} - 2\mathbf{k}, \qquad \text{and} \qquad \frac{dw}{ds} = \frac{8}{3}.$$

The maximum dw/ds at $(1, 2, -1)$ would be $\left| y\mathbf{i} + x\mathbf{j} + 2z\mathbf{k} \right| = 3$.

The directional derivative can be used to express the rate of change of a function $w = g(\mathbf{r})$ along a continuously differentiable path, $\mathbf{r} = \mathbf{f}(u)$. The rate of change with respect to arc length along the path is

$$\frac{dw}{ds} = \frac{d}{ds} g(\mathbf{r})$$

$$= \frac{d}{du} g(\mathbf{f}(u)) \frac{du}{ds}.$$

Using rectangular coordinates, with $\phi(x, y, z) = g(\mathbf{r})$, we find

$$\frac{dw}{ds} = \frac{d}{du} \phi(x, y, z) \frac{du}{ds}$$

$$= \left(\phi_x \frac{dx}{du} + \phi_y \frac{dy}{du} + \phi_z \frac{dz}{du} \right) \bigg/ \frac{ds}{du}$$

$$= \phi_x \frac{dx}{ds} + \phi_y \frac{dy}{ds} + \phi_z \frac{dz}{ds}$$

$$= (\text{grad } w) \cdot \frac{d\mathbf{r}}{ds}$$

$$= \nabla w \cdot \mathbf{t},$$

where $\mathbf{t}$ is a unit tangent to the curve in the direction of increasing s. Thus, the rate of change of w with respect to arc length along a smooth path is just the directional derivative in the direction of the tangent to the path. It is the same along all paths having the same tangent.

The differential of a scalar function is now conveniently represented in terms of the gradient:

$$dw = \frac{dw}{ds} ds = (\nabla \phi \cdot \mathbf{t}) ds$$

or

$$dw = \nabla \phi \cdot d\mathbf{r}.$$

The symbol ∇ (read "del") is used as a vector "operator" which creates a vector function (the gradient) from a scalar function:

$$\nabla\phi = \phi_x\mathbf{i} + \phi_y\mathbf{j} + \phi_z\mathbf{k}.$$

Formally, we write (in rectangular coordinates)

$$\nabla = \frac{\partial}{\partial x}\mathbf{i} + \frac{\partial}{\partial y}\mathbf{j} + \frac{\partial}{\partial z}\mathbf{k}.$$

The following computation formulas are easily derived:

$$\nabla(\phi\psi) = \phi\nabla\psi + \psi\nabla\phi,$$
$$\nabla r = \mathbf{r}/r = \mathbf{u_r},$$
$$\nabla(\phi + \psi) = \nabla\phi + \nabla\psi,$$
$$\nabla\left(\frac{\phi}{\psi}\right) = \frac{\psi\,\nabla\phi - (\nabla\psi)\phi}{\psi^2},$$
$$\nabla\phi^n = n\phi^{n-1}\,\nabla\phi \qquad (n \text{ is an integer}),$$
$$\nabla r^n = nr^{n-2}\,\mathbf{r} \qquad (n \text{ is an integer}),$$
$$\nabla(\mathbf{A}\cdot\mathbf{r}) = \mathbf{A} \qquad (\mathbf{A} \text{ is a constant vector}).$$

EXAMPLE 4.15   Consider again, as in Example 4.9, the relation

$$w = r = (x^2 + y^2 + z^2)^{1/2}.$$

The constant-w surfaces are spheres: $r = C$, and the gradient at $\mathbf{r}_0$ is normal to the sphere through the tip of $\mathbf{r}_0$; that is, along the radius vector $\mathbf{r}_0$. As a function of position $\mathbf{r}$ it is

$$\nabla w = \frac{x}{r}\mathbf{i} + \frac{y}{r}\mathbf{j} + \frac{z}{r}\mathbf{k} = \frac{\mathbf{r}}{r},$$

a unit vector along the radial direction. The directional derivative of w along $\mathbf{r} = \mathbf{f}(s)$ is then

$$\frac{dw}{ds} = \frac{\mathbf{r}}{r}\cdot\mathbf{f}'(s),$$

with maximum value $|\nabla w| = 1$ along a radius in the outward direction (and minimum value -1 in the inward direction).

Problems

4.20.   Given $w = x^2 + yz$, compute grad w, and dw/ds in the direction $3\mathbf{i} + 4\mathbf{j} + 12\mathbf{k}$ at $(2, -1, 1)$.

4.21.   Compute the directional derivative of $w = x^2 + y^2$:
(a) along $\mathbf{r} = (\cos u)\mathbf{i} + (\sin u)\mathbf{j} + u\mathbf{k}$;
(b) along $\mathbf{r} = r\mathbf{u}$, where $\mathbf{u}$ is a constant unit vector;

(c) along $\mathbf{r} = \theta\mathbf{i} + \theta^2\mathbf{j}$ at $\theta = \sqrt{2}$.
What are the constant-w surfaces?

4.22. Show that the directional derivative along a path with unit tangent vector $\mathbf{t}$:

(a) of a function $h(r)$ is $h'(r)(\mathbf{u_r} \cdot \mathbf{t})$, where $\mathbf{u_r} = \mathbf{r}/r$;

(b) of a function $k(z)$ is $k'(z)(\mathbf{k} \cdot \mathbf{t})$.

Describe the constant-w surfaces in each case.

4.23. Verify the computation formulas:

(a) $\nabla(\mathbf{A} \cdot \mathbf{r}) = \mathbf{A}$;

(b) $\nabla\phi^n = n\phi^{n-1}\nabla\phi$, and from it the formula for ∇r^n;

(c) $\nabla(\phi\psi) = \phi\,\nabla\psi + \psi\,\nabla\phi$.

4.24. (a) Discuss the directional derivative and gradient of a function $z = f(x, y)$; that is, of a function of position in the *plane*. Show that $f_x\mathbf{i} + f_y\mathbf{j}$ is normal to the curve $f(x, y) = C$.

(b) Compute $d(x^2 + y^2)/ds$ along the curve $y = x^2$.

4.25. Let (u, v, w) be rectangular coordinates with corresponding unit vectors $(\mathbf{i}', \mathbf{j}', \mathbf{k}')$, so that

$$\mathbf{r} = x\mathbf{i} + y\mathbf{j} + z\mathbf{k} = u\mathbf{i}' + v\mathbf{j}' + w\mathbf{k}' + \mathbf{A},$$

where $\mathbf{A}$ is a constant vector. Let ψ be defined by

$$\phi(x, y, z) = g(\mathbf{r}) = \psi(u, v, w).$$

Show directly that

$$\phi_x\mathbf{i} + \phi_y\mathbf{j} + \phi_z\mathbf{k} = \psi_u\mathbf{i}' + \psi_v\mathbf{j}' + \psi_w\mathbf{k}'.$$

[This follows indirectly from the fact that each side is the gradient of $g(\mathbf{r})$.]

4.5 Del applied to vector functions

Consider a vector field—a vector function of position, $\mathbf{F}(\mathbf{r})$—defined in some region of three-dimensional space. A related *scalar* function of position which is important in some applications of vector calculus is the *divergence* of $\mathbf{F}$, written div $\mathbf{F}$. This function can be given a definition which does not involve any particular coordinate system, but it will be defined here (at the outset, at least) in terms of specific coordinates: $\mathbf{r} = x\mathbf{i} + y\mathbf{j} + z\mathbf{k}$, where $(\mathbf{i}, \mathbf{j}, \mathbf{k})$ is a given orthonormal set. The function $\mathbf{F}(\mathbf{r})$ can be resolved into components along $\mathbf{i}$, $\mathbf{j}$, and $\mathbf{k}$, and these components will be scalar functions of position—position given now in terms of (x, y, z):

$$\mathbf{F}(\mathbf{r}) = P(x, y, z)\mathbf{i} + Q(x, y, z)\mathbf{j} + R(x, y, z)\mathbf{k}.$$

It is helpful to have in mind the application to steady-state fluid flow, in which $\mathbf{F}$ is the amount of flow per unit time per unit area normal to the flow—equal to the product of the density and the flow velocity vector at each point. If ΔA is a small plane area normal to the flow, the amount of flow through ΔA, one way or the other, is just $F\,\Delta A$. If a positive direction is chosen to one side of the area ΔA, the flow in that direction is positive if **F** is also in that direction, otherwise negative. If ΔA is not necessarily

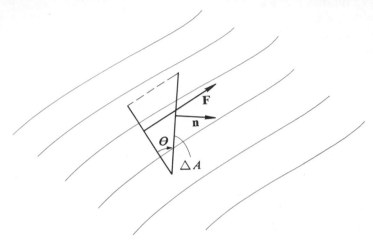

Figure 4.7

perpendicular to the flow, and has assigned to it a positive normal direction with unit vector **n**, the flow in that direction is (see Fig. 4.7.)

$$|\mathbf{F}|\,\Delta A \cos\theta = (\mathbf{F}\cdot\mathbf{n})\,\Delta A.$$

Consider now a little rectangular box defined by increments $(\Delta x,\ \Delta y,\ \Delta z)$ from $(x,\ y,\ z)$, shown in Fig. 4.8. Let unit normals be assigned to the faces

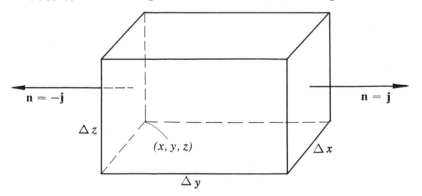

Figure 4.8

of the box pointing outward. The flow *out* from the box through the left-hand face ($\mathbf{n} = -\mathbf{j}$) is then

$$[\mathbf{F}\cdot(-\mathbf{j})]\,\Delta x\,\Delta z = -Q(x, y, z)\,\Delta x\,\Delta z,$$

and that through the right-hand face ($\mathbf{n} = \mathbf{j}$) is

$$(\mathbf{F}\cdot\mathbf{j})\,\Delta x\,\Delta z = Q(x, y + \Delta y, z)\,\Delta x\,\Delta z.$$

The total flow out through these two faces is then

$$[Q(x, y + \Delta y, z) - Q(x, y, z)]\,\Delta x\,\Delta z \doteq Q_y(x, y, z)\,\Delta x\,\Delta y\,\Delta z.$$

Similar treatment of the other faces and combination of the results yields as the total flow out from the box (approximately)

$$[P_x(x, y, z) + Q_y(x, y, z) + R_z(x, y, z)]\,\Delta x\,\Delta y\,\Delta z.$$

Dividing by the volume $\Delta x\,\Delta y\,\Delta z$ and passing to the limit as the dimensions of the box tend to zero yields (exactly, if first partials are continuous)

$$P_x(x, y, z) + Q_y(x, y, z) + R_z(x, y, z)$$

as the flow out from (x, y, z) per unit volume per unit time. It is this scalar function which is called the *divergence* of the flow $\mathbf{F}$:

$$\operatorname{div}\mathbf{F} = P_x + Q_y + R_z.$$

Treating the operator ∇ as though it were a vector we have formally

$$\operatorname{div}\mathbf{F} = \left(\frac{\partial}{\partial x}\mathbf{i} + \frac{\partial}{\partial y}\mathbf{j} + \frac{\partial}{\partial z}\mathbf{k}\right)\cdot(P\mathbf{i} + Q\mathbf{j} + R\mathbf{k})$$

$$= \nabla\cdot\mathbf{F}.$$

That the same function would result using some other choice of rectangular coordinates is of interest, and is seen as follows. Let ($\mathbf{i}', \mathbf{j}', \mathbf{k}'$) denote an orthonormal set, and (u, v, w) the corresponding coordinates, so that

$$\mathbf{F}(\mathbf{r}) = L(u, v, w)\mathbf{i}' + M(u, v, w)\mathbf{j}' + N(u, v, w)\mathbf{k}'.$$

Then

$$L(u, v, w) = \mathbf{F}\cdot\mathbf{i}' = P(\mathbf{i}\cdot\mathbf{i}') + Q(\mathbf{j}\cdot\mathbf{i}') + R(\mathbf{k}\cdot\mathbf{i}'),$$

with similar expressions for M and N. Differentiating, and using the fact that, for instance, $\partial P/\partial u = \nabla P \cdot \mathbf{i}'$ (as seen in Problem 4.25), we obtain

$$\frac{\partial L}{\partial u} = [(\nabla P \cdot \mathbf{i}')\mathbf{i}'] \cdot \mathbf{i} + [(\nabla Q \cdot \mathbf{i}')\mathbf{i}'] \cdot \mathbf{j} + [(\nabla R \cdot \mathbf{i}')\mathbf{i}'] \cdot \mathbf{k},$$

$$\frac{\partial M}{\partial v} = [(\nabla P \cdot \mathbf{j}')\mathbf{j}'] \cdot \mathbf{i} + [(\nabla Q \cdot \mathbf{j}')\mathbf{j}'] \cdot \mathbf{j} + [(\nabla R \cdot \mathbf{j}')\mathbf{j}'] \cdot \mathbf{k},$$

$$\frac{\partial N}{\partial w} = [(\nabla P \cdot \mathbf{k}')\mathbf{k}'] \cdot \mathbf{i} + [(\nabla Q \cdot \mathbf{k}')\mathbf{k}'] \cdot \mathbf{j} + [(\nabla R \cdot \mathbf{k}')\mathbf{k}'] \cdot \mathbf{k}.$$

After summation and collection of terms in $\mathbf{i}$, in $\mathbf{j}$, and in $\mathbf{k}$, there follows the desired relation:

$$\frac{\partial L}{\partial u} + \frac{\partial M}{\partial v} + \frac{\partial N}{\partial w} = (\nabla P) \cdot \mathbf{i} + (\nabla Q) \cdot \mathbf{j} + (\nabla R) \cdot \mathbf{k}$$

$$= \frac{\partial P}{\partial x} + \frac{\partial Q}{\partial y} + \frac{\partial R}{\partial z}.$$

The following computation formulas for the operation ∇ are readily derived:

$$\nabla \cdot (\mathbf{F} + \mathbf{G}) = \nabla \cdot \mathbf{F} + \nabla \cdot \mathbf{G},$$

$$\nabla \cdot (\phi \mathbf{F}) = \phi (\nabla \cdot \mathbf{F}) + \mathbf{F} \cdot (\nabla \phi),$$

$$\nabla \cdot \mathbf{r} = 3,$$

$$\nabla \cdot [h(r)\mathbf{u_r}] = \frac{1}{r^2} \frac{d}{dr} [r^2 h(r)],$$

$$\nabla \cdot (\nabla \phi) = \phi_{xx} + \phi_{yy} + \phi_{zz} \equiv \nabla^2 \phi,$$

EXAMPLE 4.16   Consider the following computation of the divergence of the vector function

$$\mathbf{F} = -\frac{\mathbf{r}}{r^3} = -\frac{x}{r^3}\mathbf{i} - \frac{y}{r^3}\mathbf{j} - \frac{z}{r^3}\mathbf{k} \cdot$$

The derivative of the $\mathbf{i}$ component with respect to x is

$$\frac{\partial}{\partial x}\left(-\frac{x}{r^3}\right) = -\frac{r^3 - 3r^2(x/r)x}{r^6} = \frac{3x^2 - r^2}{r^5}.$$

Summing this with the corresponding expressions for the derivatives of the $\mathbf{j}$- and $\mathbf{k}$-components with respect to y and z, we obtain

$$\nabla \cdot \left(\frac{-\mathbf{r}}{r^3}\right) = \frac{1}{r^5}(3x^2 + 3y^2 + 3z^2 - r^2 - r^2 - r^2) = 0.$$

This shows, incidentally, since $-\mathbf{r}/r^3 = \nabla(1/r)$, that the function $1/r$ satisfies "Laplace's equation," $\nabla \cdot \nabla w = 0$:

$$\nabla \cdot \nabla \frac{1}{r} = \left(\frac{\partial^2}{\partial x^2} + \frac{\partial^2}{\partial y^2} + \frac{\partial^2}{\partial z^2}\right)\frac{1}{r} = 0.$$

An important *vector function* of position derived from a given vector field **F** is called the *curl* of **F**, and written curl **F**. (The name stems from the fact that in fluid flow problems it is proportional to the instantaneous angular velocity of a fluid element.) As in the case of div **F**, it is possible to give a definition of curl **F** which does not involve the particular coordinate system being used, but again it seems simpler to define it in terms of a given rectangular coordinate system, say with coordinates (x, y, z):

$$\text{curl } \mathbf{F} = (R_y - Q_z)\mathbf{i} + (P_z - R_x)\mathbf{j} + (Q_x - P_y)\mathbf{k},$$

where as before $\mathbf{F} = P\mathbf{i} + Q\mathbf{j} + R\mathbf{k}$, and P, Q, and R are functions of (x, y, z). The definition is more easily remembered in the mnemonic form

$$\text{curl } \mathbf{F} = \begin{vmatrix} \mathbf{i} & \mathbf{j} & \mathbf{k} \\ \dfrac{\partial}{\partial x} & \dfrac{\partial}{\partial y} & \dfrac{\partial}{\partial z} \\ P & Q & R \end{vmatrix}.$$

Expanded formally in the way a determinant is evaluated, this yields the earlier definition. But now observe that the second row of the determinant contains the components of the vector operator ∇, so that carrying out formally the cross product of ∇ with **F** yields the curl:

$$\nabla \times \mathbf{F} = \text{curl } \mathbf{F}.$$

The vector function curl **F**, although defined in terms of a computation in a particular coordinate system, actually turns out to be the same when computed in terms of any other rectangular coordinate system. (This is easily shown in a way similar to that used to show the analogous fact about div **F**.)

The differential of a vector function can be defined, in an obvious way, as

$$d\mathbf{F} = \frac{\partial \mathbf{F}}{\partial x} dx + \frac{\partial \mathbf{F}}{\partial y} dy + \frac{\partial \mathbf{F}}{\partial z} dz,$$

where, for instance (with $\mathbf{F} = P\mathbf{i} + Q\mathbf{j} + R\mathbf{k}$),

$$\frac{\partial \mathbf{F}}{\partial x} = \frac{\partial P}{\partial x}\mathbf{i} + \frac{\partial Q}{\partial x}\mathbf{j} + \frac{\partial R}{\partial x}\mathbf{k}.$$

Putting $d\mathbf{F}$ in the equivalent form

$$d\mathbf{F} = dx \frac{\partial}{\partial x}\mathbf{F} + dy \frac{\partial}{\partial y}\mathbf{F} + dz \frac{\partial}{\partial z}\mathbf{F}$$

suggests the operational notation

$$d\mathbf{F} = \left(dx\,\frac{\partial}{\partial x} + dy\,\frac{\partial}{\partial y} + dz\,\frac{\partial}{\partial z} \right) \mathbf{F}$$

$$= (d\mathbf{r} \cdot \nabla)\, \mathbf{F} = d\mathbf{r} \cdot \nabla\, \mathbf{F},$$

the omission of the parentheses causing no confusion inasmuch as $\nabla \mathbf{F}$ is not defined. A *directional derivative* of the vector function $\mathbf{F}$ along a curve with unit tangent $\mathbf{t}$ would then be

$$\frac{d\mathbf{F}}{ds} = \frac{d\mathbf{r}}{ds} \cdot \nabla \mathbf{F} = \mathbf{t} \cdot \nabla \mathbf{F}.$$

The above notational convention is also useful when $\mathbf{t}$ is replaced by any vector function $\mathbf{G} = A\mathbf{i} + B\mathbf{j} + C\mathbf{k}$:

$$\mathbf{G} \cdot \nabla \mathbf{F} = (\mathbf{G} \cdot \nabla)\mathbf{F} = \left(A\,\frac{\partial}{\partial x} + B\,\frac{\partial}{\partial y} + C\,\frac{\partial}{\partial z} \right) \mathbf{F}.$$

Again a variety of computation formulas can be derived, including the following:

$$\nabla \times (\mathbf{F} + \mathbf{G}) = \nabla \times \mathbf{F} + \nabla \times \mathbf{G},$$
$$\nabla \times \nabla \phi = \mathbf{0},$$
$$\nabla \cdot \nabla \times \mathbf{F} = 0,$$
$$\nabla \times (\phi \mathbf{F}) = \phi \nabla \times \mathbf{F} + (\nabla \phi) \times \mathbf{F},$$
$$\nabla \times \mathbf{r} = \mathbf{0}.$$
$$\nabla(\mathbf{F} \cdot \mathbf{G}) = (\mathbf{F} \cdot \nabla)\mathbf{G} + (\mathbf{G} \cdot \nabla)\mathbf{F} + \mathbf{F} \times (\nabla \times \mathbf{G}) + \mathbf{G} \times (\nabla \times \mathbf{F})$$
$$\nabla \times (\mathbf{F} \times \mathbf{G}) = (\mathbf{G} \cdot \nabla)\mathbf{F} - (\mathbf{F} \cdot \nabla)\mathbf{G} + \mathbf{F}(\nabla \cdot \mathbf{G}) - \mathbf{G}(\nabla \cdot \mathbf{F})$$
$$\nabla \times (\nabla \times \mathbf{F}) = \nabla(\nabla \cdot \mathbf{F}) - (\nabla \cdot \nabla)\mathbf{F}.$$
$$\nabla \cdot (\mathbf{F} \times \mathbf{G}) = \mathbf{G} \cdot \nabla \times \mathbf{F} - \mathbf{F} \cdot \nabla \times \mathbf{G}.$$

These formulas, and the earlier computation formulas for the gradient and divergence, have been given without any concern for assumptions under which they are valid. In most cases they are valid when the quantities involved in the formula are defined; but in at least the case of $\nabla \times \nabla \phi = \mathbf{0}$, the derivation depends on the equality of the mixed second partial derivatives in the two possible orders. For instance, the equality $\phi_{xy} = \phi_{yx}$ is needed, and this requires somewhat more than just the mere existence of these second partial derivatives, namely, their continuity. Explicit verification of such conditions will be foregone; the functions which occur here will be sufficiently regular that the formulas can be used, except perhaps for obvious situations in which a denominator becomes zero, for instance.

E x a m p l e 4.17   Let **F** be given by $xyz(x\mathbf{i} + y\mathbf{j} + z\mathbf{k})$. The curl of **F** is then

$$\begin{vmatrix} \mathbf{i} & \mathbf{j} & \mathbf{k} \\ \dfrac{\partial}{\partial x} & \dfrac{\partial}{\partial y} & \dfrac{\partial}{\partial z} \\ x^2yz & xy^2z & xyz^2 \end{vmatrix} = (xz^2 - xy^2)\mathbf{i} + (x^2y - yz^2)\mathbf{j} + (y^2z - x^2z)\mathbf{k}.$$

The divergence of this function, in turn, is

$$\nabla\cdot\nabla\times\mathbf{F} = (z^2 - y^2) + (x^2 - z^2) + (y^2 - x^2) = 0.$$

Problems

4.26.   Let $\phi(x, y, z) = \arctan(x/y)$, and compute:
(a) $\nabla\phi$;
(b) $\nabla\times\nabla\phi$;
(c) $\nabla\cdot\nabla\phi$.
[Do (b) and (c) directly, without using general formulas for these particular combinations.]

4.27.   Let $h(r)$ be an arbitrary function of the magnitude r, and $\mathbf{u_r} = \mathbf{r}/r$.
(a) Compute $\nabla h(r)$.
(b) Show that $\nabla\times h(r)\mathbf{u_r} = [\nabla h(r)]\times\mathbf{r} = 0$.
(c) Show that $\nabla\cdot[h(r)\mathbf{u_r}] = \dfrac{1}{r^2}\dfrac{d}{dr}[r^2h(r)]$.

4.28.   Show that:
(a) $\nabla\cdot(f\mathbf{F}) = f(\nabla\cdot\mathbf{F}) + \mathbf{F}\cdot(\nabla f)$;
(b) $\nabla\times(\phi\mathbf{F}) = \phi\nabla\times\mathbf{F} + (\nabla\phi)\times\mathbf{F}$.

4.29.   Show that $\operatorname{curl}(\operatorname{grad}\phi) = 0$.

4.30.   Show that $\operatorname{div}(\operatorname{curl}\mathbf{F}) = 0$.

4.31.   Let (t, u, v) denote coordinates defined by

$$\mathbf{r} = at\mathbf{i} + bu\mathbf{j} + cv\mathbf{k},$$

where a, b, and c are given constants, and $(\mathbf{i}, \mathbf{j}, \mathbf{k})$ are unit vectors corresponding to (x, y, z). Let ψ be defined by

$$w = \phi(x, y, z) = \psi(t, u, v).$$

Show that ∇w is given by

$$\nabla w = \frac{1}{a}\psi_t\mathbf{i} + \frac{1}{b}\psi_u\mathbf{j} + \frac{1}{c}\psi_v\mathbf{k}.$$

4.32.   Show that $\nabla\cdot(\nabla\phi\times\nabla\psi) = 0$.

4.6   *Surface area and surface integrals*

Arc length was defined (in Sect. 2.3) by a limiting process using polygonal approximations; but the analogous approach to surface area turns out to be not so feasible. It seems expedient here to define surface area as an integral—a double integral in the parameter space over which the surface is defined. The intuitive derivation of this integral and the fact that it produces the correct results in simple cases (sphere, cylinder, plane) are perhaps justification enough for its use.

A background in the rigorous study of double integrals is not assumed, and it will be best, therefore, to impose some restrictions on the nature of the region of integration and on the integrand function in the double integrals to be considered. These restrictions are satisfied in the cases to be encountered here (and in practice generally), so they are not really burdensome. Double integrals of the form

$$\iint\limits_{D} g(u, v) \, dA$$

will be encountered, and it will be assumed that $g(u, v)$ is a continuous function. The region D will be assumed to be either of a certain simple type, called *u-simple*, or possibly a finite union of such simple regions. A

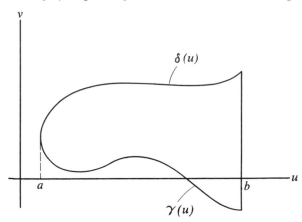

Figure 4.9.   A *u*-simple region.

u-simple region is bounded, lying between the vertical lines $u = a$ and $u = b$ and between curves of the form $v = \gamma(u)$ and $v = \delta(u)$, piecewise continuously differentiable, with $\gamma(u) \leq \delta(u)$ for $a \leq u \leq b$. For a *u*-simple region the double integral is expressible as a repeated (iterated) integral:

$$\iint_D g(u, v)\, dA = \int_{u=a}^{u=b} \int_{v=\gamma(u)}^{v=\delta(u)} g(u, v)\, dv\, du.$$

Such a region is shown in Fig. 4.9, and a region which can be expressed as a finite union of u-simple and v-simple regions is shown in Fig. 4.10.

A surface S is assumed to be represented by the parametric form

$$\mathbf{r} = \mathbf{F}(u, v),$$

where (u, v) is a point in a domain D of the type described above and $\mathbf{F}(u, v)$ is continuously differentiable in D. This region, being bounded, can be partitioned into a finite number of small pieces, mostly rectangles, by means of partitions of a u-interval and a v-interval containing D, as indicated in Fig. 4.11:

$$a = u_0 < u_1 < \cdots < u_m = b,$$
$$c = v_0 < v_1 < \cdots < v_n = d.$$

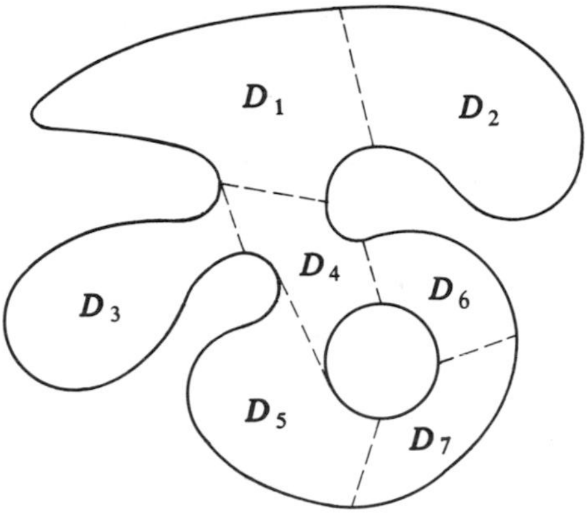

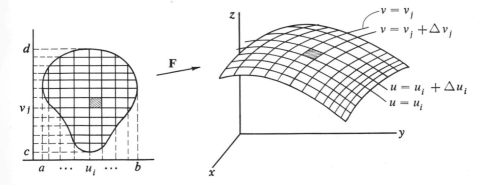

Figure 4.10.   Decomposition into u-simple regions.

Figure 4.11.   Partitioning a surface.

Since each line $u = u_i$ defines a constant u-curve and each line $v = v_j$ defines a constant v-curve, there is induced on the surface S a partition into small pieces ΔA_{ij} bounded by such curves. These small pieces are approximately plane parallelograms (except for edge pieces, which can be ignored) with sides given by the vectors

$$\Delta_u \mathbf{r} = \mathbf{r}(u_i + \Delta u_i, v_j) - \mathbf{r}(u_i, v_j) \doteq \mathbf{r}_u(u_i, v_j)\, \Delta u_i,$$
$$\Delta_v \mathbf{r} = \mathbf{r}(u_i, v_j + \Delta v_j) - \mathbf{r}(u_i, v_j) \doteq \mathbf{r}_v(u_i, v_j)\, \Delta v_j.$$

The area of a parallelogram with these sides is the magnitude of their cross product:

$$|\Delta_u \mathbf{r} \times \Delta_v \mathbf{r}| = |\mathbf{r}_u \times \mathbf{r}_v|\, \Delta u_i\, \Delta v_j,$$

and the various approximations become increasingly better as the maximum of the subdivision lengths Δu_i and Δv_j tends to zero. It is then natural to think of the area of S as a limit of approximating sums:

$$\lim \sum_{i,j} A_{ij} = \lim \sum_i \sum_j |\mathbf{r}_u \times \mathbf{r}_v|\, \Delta u_i\, \Delta v_j,$$

as the maximum subinterval width tends to zero. The limit on the right-hand side is a double integral, and it is this which is taken as *defining* the area of S:

$$\text{area of } S = \iint_D |\mathbf{r}_u \times \mathbf{r}_v|\, du\, dv.$$

The symbol $d\sigma$ will be used to denote the *area element:*

$$d\sigma = |\mathbf{r}_u \times \mathbf{r}_v|\, du\, dv.$$

EXAMPLE 4.18   Consider the sphere $x^2 + y^2 + z^2 = a^2$, represented parametrically by

$$\mathbf{r} = a[(\cos \phi \sin \theta)\mathbf{i} + (\sin \phi \sin \theta)\mathbf{j} + (\cos \theta)\mathbf{k}],$$

where $0 \le \theta \le \pi$, and $0 \le \phi < 2\pi$. These inequalities define D, a rectangle in the (θ, ϕ)-space. The vector $\mathbf{r}_\theta \times \mathbf{r}_\phi$ was computed in Example 4.10 and found to be $(a \sin \theta)\mathbf{r}$, with magnitude $a^2 \sin \theta$. Thus

$$d\sigma = a^2 \sin \theta\, d\theta\, d\phi,$$

and the area of the sphere is

$$\int_0^{2\pi} \int_0^{\pi} a^2 \sin \theta\, d\theta\, d\phi = 4\pi a^2,$$

which is the usual formula for the area of a sphere of radius a.

It is often convenient to take two of the rectangular coordinates as parameters, say (x, y):

$$\mathbf{r} = x\mathbf{i} + y\mathbf{j} + f(x, y)\mathbf{k}.$$

In this case,

$$\mathbf{r}_x \times \mathbf{r}_y = -f_x\mathbf{i} - f_y\mathbf{j} + \mathbf{k},$$

and

$$d\sigma = (f_x^2 + f_y^2 + 1)^{1/2}\, dx\, dy.$$

But then

$$dx\, dy = \frac{(-f_x\mathbf{i} - f_y\mathbf{j} + \mathbf{k})\cdot\mathbf{k}}{(f_x^2 + f_y^2 + 1)^{1/2}}\, d\sigma = \frac{d\sigma}{(f_x^2 + f_y^2 + 1)^{1/2}}.$$

That is, the element of area in the xy-plane is the element $d\sigma$ multiplied by the cosine of the angle between the normal to the surface and the normal to the xy-plane—the angle between $d\sigma$ and the xy-plane—which is certainly intuitively correct, since the rectangles of a partition in the xy-plane are just the projections of the corresponding pieces in the partition of the surface. (See Fig. 4.12.)

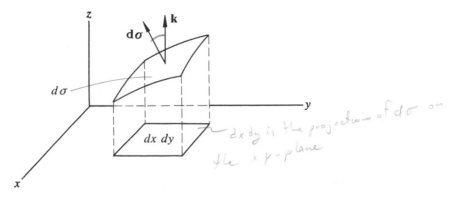

Figure 4.12

If the surface is given in the form $\phi(x, y, z) = C$, and if this can be solved, say, for z as a function of (x, y) defined over a suitable region, the expression for $d\sigma$ is

$$d\sigma = \frac{(\phi_x^2 + \phi_y^2 + \phi_z^2)^{1/2}}{|\phi_z|}\, dx\, dy = \left|\frac{\nabla\phi}{\nabla\phi\cdot\mathbf{k}}\right| dx\, dy.$$

Since the area of a surface has been defined here as an integral in a parameter space, involving a specific parametrization of the surface, it may be wondered whether a different parametrization would yield a

different number as the area. Fortunately this does not happen. For, suppose that a surface is given in terms of two sets of parameters:

$$\mathbf{r} = \mathbf{F}(u, v) = \mathbf{G}(s, t),$$

where

$$u = \xi(s, t), \qquad \text{and} \qquad v = \zeta(s, t),$$

the transformation from (u, v) to (s, t) being continuously differentiable. Suppose further that $u_s v_t - u_t v_s \neq 0$, so that the inverse transformation is defined, with $(u_s v_t - u_t v_s)^{-1} = (s_u t_v - s_v t_u)$. Then

$$\mathbf{r}_u = \frac{\partial \mathbf{G}}{\partial s} \frac{\partial s}{\partial u} + \frac{\partial \mathbf{G}}{\partial t} \frac{\partial t}{\partial u} = \mathbf{r}_s s_u + \mathbf{r}_t t_u,$$

$$\mathbf{r}_v = \frac{\partial \mathbf{G}}{\partial s} \frac{\partial s}{\partial v} + \frac{\partial \mathbf{G}}{\partial t} \frac{\partial t}{\partial v} = \mathbf{r}_s s_v + \mathbf{r}_t t_v,$$

and

$$|\mathbf{r}_u \times \mathbf{r}_v| = |\mathbf{r}_s \times \mathbf{r}_t| \cdot |s_u t_v - s_v t_u|.$$

Thus

$$\text{area} = \iint_S d\sigma = \iint_D |\mathbf{r}_u \times \mathbf{r}_v| \, du \, dv$$

$$= \iint_D |\mathbf{r}_s \times \mathbf{r}_t| \cdot |s_u t_v - s_v t_u| \, du \, dv$$

$$= \iint_{D'} |\mathbf{r}_s \times \mathbf{r}_t| \, ds \, dt,$$

where D' is the image of D in the st-plane. The last equality here follows from the standard method of changing variables in a double integral.

A *surface integral* is defined in terms of the area differential much as a line integral was defined from the arc length element. If $g(\mathbf{r})$ is a scalar function of position, the surface integral of this function over a surface S is defined to be the following uv-integral:

$$\iint_S g(\mathbf{r}) \, d\sigma = \iint_D g(\mathbf{F}(u, v)) \, |\mathbf{r}_u \times \mathbf{r}_v| \, du \, dv,$$

where of course $\mathbf{r} = \mathbf{F}(u, v)$ defines the surface, mapping the region D in the uv-plane into S. *

Observe that if the particular function $g(\mathbf{r}) = 1$ is used, the surface

and $|\mathbf{r}_u \times \mathbf{r}_v| \neq 0$ which means can have
2 sides ⇒ 2 normals; + § —.
Example of one sided surface is Mobius strip.
(non orientable surface)
⟶ Chapter 5

integral reduces to the integral which gives the area of S:

$$\iint_S 1 \, d\sigma = \iint_C 1 \, |\mathbf{r}_u \times \mathbf{r}_v| \, du \, dv = \text{area of } S.$$

E X A M P L E 4.19   A surface integral can be used (as was a line integral) for determining the center of gravity (or second moments) of a surface distribution of mass. For a thin hemispherical shell of constant density and radius a, for example, the computation is as follows:

$$\bar{z} = \frac{\iint_S z \, d\sigma}{\iint_S d\sigma} = \frac{1}{2\pi a^2} \int_0^{2\pi} \int_0^{\pi/2} (a \cos \theta) a^2 \sin \theta \, d\theta \, d\phi$$

$$= \frac{2\pi a^3}{2\pi a^2} \int_0^{\pi/2} \frac{\sin 2\theta}{2} \, d\theta = \frac{a}{2}.$$

(The z-axis was taken to be the axis of the hemisphere, and the center of gravity lies on the z-axis, with $\bar{x} = \bar{y} = 0$. But these values can be computed by similar integrations, as well as by symmetry.)

Problems

4.33.   Compute the area of that portion of the surface $z = 2x - y + 4$ bounded by the coordinate planes:

(a) using (x, y) as parameters;

(b) using (y, z) as parameters;

(c) using (u, v) as parameters, where $\mathbf{r} = (u + v)\mathbf{i} + (u - v)\mathbf{j} + (u + 3v + 4)\mathbf{k}$ on the surface.

4.34.   Compute the area of the lateral surface of the cylinder $x^2 + y^2 = a^2$ between $z = 0$ and $z = h$:

(a) using (x, z) as parameters;

(b) using (θ, z) as parameters, where $\mathbf{r} = a[(\cos \theta)\mathbf{i} + (\sin \theta)\mathbf{j}] + z\mathbf{k}$ on the cylinder.

4.35.   Compute the area of that portion of the surface $z = 4 - x^2 - y^2$ above the xy-plane.

4.36.   Determine the location of the center of gravity of a thin shell of constant density shaped like the surface whose area is computed in Problem 4.35.

4.37.   Give expressions for $d\sigma$ in terms of ϕ for a surface defined by $\phi(x, y, z) = C$, using (x, z) as parameters, and using (y, z) as parameters.

4.38.   Compute the moment of inertia of the parabolic shell in Problem 4.36 about the z-axis.

4.7   *Oriented surfaces and surface integrals*

The term *smooth surface element* will be used to denote the image of a region D of the simple type defined in the preceding section under a transformation $\mathbf{r} = \mathbf{F}(u, v)$ which is continuously differentiable on D, and which satisfies the additional properties

(i) $\mathbf{r}_u \times \mathbf{r}_v \neq 0$ on D;

(ii) $\mathbf{F}(u, v) = \mathbf{F}(u_0, v_0)$ implies that $(u, v) = (u_0, v_0)$.

(This second condition says that only one point in D maps into any given point on the surface element.)

Because of condition (ii), there are through each point on the surface (not on the boundary) a unique u-curve and v-curve in the surface, and corresponding unique vectors $\mathbf{r}_u$ and $\mathbf{r}_v$. Therefore, the vector

$$\mathbf{N} = \frac{\mathbf{r}_u \times \mathbf{r}_v}{|\mathbf{r}_u \times \mathbf{r}_v|}$$

defines a unique normal vector at each point—a normal field—and the vector $-\mathbf{N}$ defines another normal field. The surface element is then *oriented*, having two sides.

Saying that a surface has two sides may seem unnecessary, until one is exposed to the possibilities suggested by the example of a Möbius band, shown in Fig. 4.13, which is not a simple surface element. Such a surface

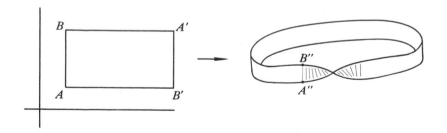

Figure 4.13.   Möbius band.

can be obtained as the image of a rectangle, in which the right edge is identified with the left edge, but in reverse order—the points A and A' both map into A'', and B and B' both map into B'' in Fig. 4.13. Along the seam $A''B''$ the image $\mathbf{r}$ moves one way on the surface as v increases along the right edge, and it moves the other way when v increases along the left edge; that is, the vector $\mathbf{r}_v$ is not uniquely defined.

A surface is said to be *piecewise-smooth* if it can be decomposed into a finite number of smooth surface elements. It is then orientable if orientations can be chosen for the pieces in a coherent manner. "Coherent" will not here be given a rigorous mathematical definition; it will be clear what is meant in the examples to be encountered. For instance, the strip in Fig. 4.13 can be expressed as the union of two smooth surface elements by cutting across in two places, but it is readily seen (upon trying to do it) that however orientations are chosen on the pieces, if they match at one seam, they will not match at the other. On the other hand, the surfaces of a tetrahedron, a parallelepiped, a sphere, and of finite portions of cones and cylinders are all orientable, piecewise-smooth surfaces.

A vector area differential is defined to be

$$\mathbf{d\sigma} = \mathbf{N}\, d\sigma,$$

where $\mathbf{N}$ is a unit normal field, given by either

$$\mathbf{N} = \frac{\mathbf{r}_u \times \mathbf{r}_v}{|\mathbf{r}_u \times \mathbf{r}_v|}$$

or its negative, depending on the orientation chosen. An oriented surface integral is then defined for any given continuous function of position, $\mathbf{G}(\mathbf{r})$, as follows:

$$\iint_S \mathbf{G}(\mathbf{r})\cdot \mathbf{d\sigma} = \iint_S \mathbf{G}(\mathbf{r})\cdot \mathbf{N}\, d\sigma$$

$$= \iint_D \mathbf{G}(\mathbf{F}(u,\,v))\cdot \mathbf{r}_u \times \mathbf{r}_v \, du\, dv,$$

where the smooth surface element S has the parametric representation $\mathbf{r} = \mathbf{F}(u,\,v)$ for $(u,\,v)$ on the domain D. If S is piecewise-smooth, made up of smooth surface elements $S_1,\ \ldots,\ S_k$, the integral over S is the sum of the integrals over $S_1,\ \ldots,$ and S_k, where the orientations of the pieces are chosen in a coherent manner.

EXAMPLE 4.20   Let $\mathbf{G}(\mathbf{r}) = \mathbf{r}$, and consider the following computation of the oriented surface integral $\int \mathbf{G}(\mathbf{r})\cdot \mathbf{d\sigma}$ over S, the entire surface of the wedge determined by the cylinder $x^2 + y^2 = 4$ and the planes $z = 0$ and $y + z = 2$. Let the orientation of S be given by the outer normal to the surface, and let S_1, S_2, and S_3 denote, respectively, the slant face, the lateral surface, and the bottom of the wedge, as shown in Fig. 4.14.

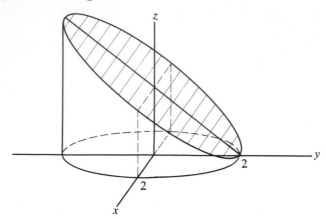

Figure 4.14.   (See Example 4.20.)

On S_3 the outer normal is $\mathbf{N} = -\mathbf{k}$, so that $\mathbf{G}(\mathbf{r}) \cdot \mathbf{N} = -z$; since $z = 0$ on the bottom of the wedge, the integral over S_3 is zero. On S_1, $y + z = 2$, and this plane can be represented parametrically in terms of polar coordinates in the xy-plane:

$$\mathbf{r} = x\mathbf{i} + y\mathbf{j} + (2 - y)\mathbf{k}$$
$$= (\rho \cos \theta)\mathbf{i} + (\rho \sin \theta)\mathbf{j} + (2 - \rho \sin \theta)\mathbf{k},$$

where $0 \leq \theta < 2\pi$ and $0 \leq \rho \leq 2$. Then

$$\mathbf{r}_\rho = (\cos \theta)\mathbf{i} + (\sin \theta)\mathbf{j} - (\sin \theta)\mathbf{k},$$
$$\mathbf{r}_\theta = (-\rho \sin \theta)\mathbf{i} + (\rho \cos \theta)\mathbf{j} - (\rho \cos \theta)\mathbf{k},$$

and

$$\mathbf{r}_\rho \times \mathbf{r}_\theta = \begin{vmatrix} \mathbf{i} & \mathbf{j} & \mathbf{k} \\ \cos \theta & \sin \theta & -\sin \theta \\ -\rho \sin \theta & \rho \cos \theta & -\rho \cos \theta \end{vmatrix} = \rho(\mathbf{j} + \mathbf{k})$$

so that

$$\mathbf{G}(\mathbf{r}) \cdot (\mathbf{r}_\rho \times \mathbf{r}_\theta) = \mathbf{r} \cdot [\rho(\mathbf{j} + \mathbf{k})] = \rho(y + z) = 2\rho.$$

The integral over S_1 is then

$$\iint_{S_1} \mathbf{G}(\mathbf{r}) \cdot d\boldsymbol{\sigma} = \int_0^{2\pi} \int_0^2 2\rho \, d\rho \, d\theta = 8\pi.$$

On S_2 let the parameters be (θ, z), where θ is the polar angle in the xy-plane. The equation of the cylinder in terms of these coordinates is

$$\mathbf{r} = (2 \cos \theta)\mathbf{i} + (2 \sin \theta)\mathbf{j} + z\mathbf{k},$$

so that

$$\mathbf{r}_\theta = (-2 \sin \theta)\mathbf{i} + (2 \cos \theta)\mathbf{j},$$
$$\mathbf{r}_z = \mathbf{k},$$

and

$$\mathbf{r}_\theta \times \mathbf{r}_z = (2 \sin \theta)\mathbf{j} + (2 \cos \theta)\mathbf{i}.$$

Then

$$\mathbf{G}(\mathbf{r}) \cdot (\mathbf{r}_\theta \times \mathbf{r}_z) = 4 \cos^2 \theta + 4 \sin^2 \theta = 4,$$

and

$$\iint_{S_2} \mathbf{G}(\mathbf{r}) \cdot (\mathbf{r}_\theta \times \mathbf{r}_z)\, dz\, d\theta = \int_0^{2\pi} \int_0^{2-2\sin\theta} 4\, dz\, d\theta$$

$$= 16\pi - 8\int_0^{2\pi} \sin\theta\, d\theta = 16\pi.$$

(The upper limit for z was obtained from the equation of the plane: $z = 2 - y$, where on the cylinder $y = 2 \sin \theta$.) The integral over the entire surface S is the sum of the integrals over S_1, S_2, and S_3:

$$\iint_S \mathbf{G}(\mathbf{r}) \cdot d\boldsymbol{\sigma} = 8\pi + 16\pi + 0 = 24\pi.$$

Problems

4.39.   Carry out the computation of Example 4.20, except let $\mathbf{G}(\mathbf{r}) = yz\mathbf{i} + xz\mathbf{j} + xy\mathbf{k}$.

4.40.   Compute the integral over S_2 in Example 4.20 using y and z as parameters.

4.41.   Compute the integral $\iint \mathbf{G}(\mathbf{r}) \cdot d\boldsymbol{\sigma}$ over the surface of the cube bounded by $x = 1$, $y = 1$, $z = 1$, and the coordinate planes, with $\mathbf{N} = $ the outer unit normal, where $\mathbf{G}(\mathbf{r}) = \mathbf{r}$.

4.42.   Compute the integral $\iint \mathbf{G}(\mathbf{r}) \cdot d\boldsymbol{\sigma}$ over the surface of the tetrahedron bounded by $x + y + z = 1$ and the coordinate planes using the $\mathbf{G}(\mathbf{r})$ of Problem 4.39. (Use the outer normal.)

4.43.   Compute the integral $\iint \mathbf{G}(\mathbf{r}) \cdot d\boldsymbol{\sigma}$ over the surface of the sphere $x^2 + y^2 + z^2 = 1$, using the outer normal, and
   (a) $\mathbf{G}(\mathbf{r}) = \nabla(1/r)$;
   (b) $\mathbf{G}(\mathbf{r}) = \mathbf{r}$;
   (c) $\mathbf{G}(\mathbf{r}) = yz\mathbf{i} + xz\mathbf{j} + xy\mathbf{k}$.

5 GREEN'S, STOKES', AND RELATED THEOREMS

THIS chapter deals with a variety of very closely related integral theorems which are quite useful in applications of vector calculus. In addition, the notation of potential function is introduced, first in two and then in three dimensions.

The degree of generality possible in stating the theorems of this chapter depends on the extent of one's knowledge of the geometry of surfaces and curves—regions over which integrations are to be performed. In practice it is usually only regions which are geometrically very simple that are encountered. The procedure to be followed here will be to establish theorems for the simplest kinds of regions and then to indicate how the theorems may be extended to somewhat more complicated regions.

5.1 Green's lemma in the plane

Consider first a rectangle S in the plane, bounded by the lines $x = a$, $x = b$, $y = c$, and $y = d$. The perimeter or boundary of the rectangle is a piecewise smooth curve, denoted by C. Let there be given a continuously differentiable vector function

$$\mathbf{F}(x, y) = P(x, y)\mathbf{i} + Q(x, y)\mathbf{j}$$

134

at each point of S. Then

$$\iint\limits_{S} \frac{\partial Q}{\partial x} \, dA = \int_{c}^{d} \left\{ \int_{a}^{b} \frac{\partial Q}{\partial x} \, dx \right\} dy$$

$$= \int_{c}^{d} Q(b, y) \, dy - \int_{c}^{d} Q(a, y) \, dy$$

$$= \int_{C} Q(x, y) \, dy,$$

where the last integral is a line integral taken counterclockwise around

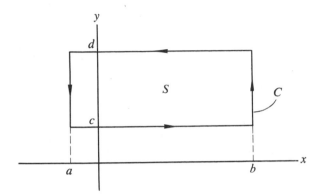

Figure 5.1

the rectangle. (The integral over the horizontal sides vanishes because $dy = 0$ there.) In exactly analogous fashion it follows that

$$\iint\limits_{S} \frac{\partial P}{\partial y} \, dA = - \int_{C} P(x, y) \, dx,$$

so that

$$\iint\limits_{S} \left(\frac{\partial Q}{\partial x} - \frac{\partial P}{\partial y} \right) dA = \int_{C} P \, dx + Q \, dy.$$

This is the result known (sometimes) as Green's lemma; in vector form it is

$$\int_{C} \mathbf{F} \cdot d\mathbf{r} = \iint\limits_{S} \nabla \times \mathbf{F} \cdot \mathbf{k} \, dA.$$

The above derivation works equally well for a region S which is simultaneously "x-simple" and "y-simple." [Recall that a region is x-*simple* which has the property that each ordinate $x = x_0$, $a \leq x_0 \leq b$, intersects the region in an interval (or in a single point) $\gamma(x_0) \le y \le \delta(x_0)$, such that $\gamma(x)$ and $\delta(x)$ are piecewise smooth curves.] In this case,

$$\iint_S \frac{\partial Q}{\partial x}\, dA = \int_a^b \left\{ \int_{\gamma(x)}^{\delta(x)} Q(x,\, y)\, dx \right\} dy,$$

which again reduces to $\int_C Q\, dy$. If the region is also y-simple, then

$$\iint_S \frac{\partial P}{\partial y}\, dA = -\int_C P(x,\, y)\, dx,$$

and Green's lemma follows on summation. Examples of regions which are both x-simple and y-simple are shown in Fig. 5.2.

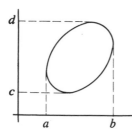 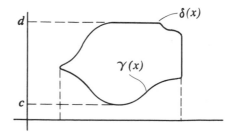

Figure 5.2.   Regions which are x-simple *and* y-simple.

If a region S is made up of two pieces S_1 and S_2 with boundaries C_1 and C_2, respectively, then

$$\iint_S \left(\frac{\partial Q}{\partial x} - \frac{\partial P}{\partial y} \right) dA = \iint_{S_1} \left(\frac{\partial Q}{\partial x} - \frac{\partial P}{\partial y} \right) dA + \iint_{S_2} \left(\frac{\partial Q}{\partial x} - \frac{\partial P}{\partial y} \right) dA$$

$$= \int_{C_1} P\, dx + Q\, dy + \int_{C_2} P\, dx + Q\, dy.$$

If the regions are contiguous, the boundary of the composite region S is not the whole curve C_1 plus the whole curve C_2, but is rather the union of the parts of C_1 and C_2 which are not common. Along the common part, however, the integral counterclockwise along C_1 cancels the integral counterclockwise along C_2, so that the sum of the two line integrals above reduces to the line integral around the boundary of S, and Green's lemma again holds—even though S is in general not both x-simple and y-simple.

Thus, by putting together a finite number of pieces each of which is both x-simple and y-simple, a region is obtained for which Green's lemma

$\iint_S \left(\frac{d Q}{\partial x} - \frac{\partial P}{\partial y} \right) ds = \int_C P\, dx + Q\, dy$

$\text{Let } P = y, \; Q = 0 \quad \text{the } \int_C (-y\, dx)$

$\text{Let } P = 0, \; Q = x \quad \text{then } \int_C x\, dy$

$= \iint dA = \frac{1}{2} \int x\, dy - y\, dx$

is valid; and this region may even have some holes in it, as shown in Fig. 5.3. Observe that for such a region, the direction to be used in traversing that part of the boundary which is the edge of the hole is the clockwise

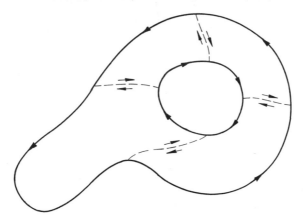

Figure 5.3

direction. The rule for the proper direction can be expressed by saying that it is the direction in which a man would walk so that the region S is at his left.

EXAMPLE 5.1   Consider the vector function

$$\mathbf{F}(x, y) = xy^2\mathbf{i} + (x^2 + y)\mathbf{j},$$

and the region S bounded by the line $x + y = 1$ and the coordinate axes. Here,

$$\frac{\partial Q}{\partial x} - \frac{\partial P}{\partial y} = 2x - 2xy,$$

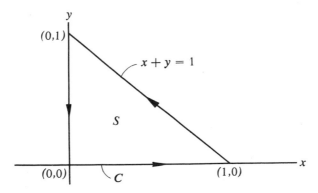

Figure 5.4.   (See Example 5.1.)

and

$$\iint_S \left(\frac{\partial Q}{\partial x} - \frac{\partial P}{\partial y}\right) dA = \int_0^1 \int_0^{1-y} 2x(1-y)\, dx\, dy$$

$$= \int_0^1 (1-y)(1-y)^2\, dy = \tfrac{1}{4}.$$

The line integral of $\mathbf{F}\cdot d\mathbf{r} = xy^2 dx + (x^2 + y)\, dy$ around the boundary C of the region S is computed in three parts. Along the x-axis from $(0,0)$ to $(1,0)$ both y and dy are zero, so the integral is zero. Along the straight line from $(1,0)$ to $(0,1)$, $y = 1 - x$, $dy = -dx$, and the line integral is

$$\int_1^0 [x(1-x)^2 - (x^2 + 1 - x)]\, dx = \tfrac{3}{4}.$$

Along the remaining portion of C, the straight line from $(0,1)$ to $(0,0)$, both x and dx are zero, and the line integral is

$$\int_1^0 y\, dy = -\tfrac{1}{2}.$$

The line integral over the complete boundary C is then the sum:

$$\int_C \mathbf{F}\cdot d\mathbf{r} = 0 + \tfrac{3}{4} - \tfrac{1}{2} = \tfrac{1}{4},$$

which agrees with the value of the double integral computed first, thus verifying Green's lemma in this instance.

Green's lemma has a number of useful consequences. Consider functions u and v which are twice continuously differentiable, so that, for instance,

$$\nabla\cdot\nabla v = v_{xx} + v_{yy}$$

exists and is integrable. This quantity is frequently denoted by Δv, and is called the *Laplacian* of v. Setting $P(x, y) = -uv_y$ and $Q(x, y) = uv_x$,

$$\iint_S \left\{\frac{\partial(uv_x)}{\partial x} - \frac{\partial(-uv_y)}{\partial y}\right\} dA$$

$$= \iint_S [u(v_{xx} + v_{yy}) + v_x u_x + v_y u_y]\, dA$$

$$= \iint_S (u\,\Delta v + \nabla u\cdot\nabla v)\, dA = -\int_C [uv_y\, dx - uv_x\, dy]$$

$$= \int_C u(\nabla v\cdot\mathbf{n})\, ds, \qquad = \int_C u\left(\frac{dv}{dn}\right) ds$$

$$\nabla u = u_x i + u_y j, \qquad \nabla v = v_x i + v_y j$$

$$\nabla u \cdot \nabla v$$

where

$$\mathbf{n} = \frac{dy}{ds}\,\mathbf{i} - \frac{dx}{ds}\,\mathbf{j} = \mathbf{t} \times \mathbf{k},$$

and $\mathbf{t}$ is the unit tangent to C in the positive sense. That is, $\mathbf{n}$ is a unit vector (since $dx^2 + dy^2 = ds^2$) in the outer normal direction (i.e., pointing outward from S). But then $\nabla v \cdot \mathbf{n}$ is the value of the directional derivative in the outer normal direction, denoted by $\partial v/\partial n$:

$$\iint_S (u \,\Delta v + \nabla u \cdot \nabla v) \, dA = \int_C u \, \frac{\partial v}{\partial n} \, ds.$$

Repetition of this derivation with u and v playing opposite roles yields (upon subtraction of the results)

$$\iint_S (u \,\Delta v - v \,\Delta u) \, dA = \int_C \left(u \frac{\partial v}{\partial n} - v \frac{\partial u}{\partial n} \right) ds,$$

a result which is often known as "Green's theorem."

Problems

5.1. Verify Green's lemma for $\mathbf{F} = -y\mathbf{i} + x\mathbf{j}$, where:
(a) S is the square bounded by $x = 1$, $y = 1$, $x = 0$, and $y = 0$;
(b) S is the interior of the unit circle, $x^2 + y^2 = 1$.

5.2. Show that when $\mathbf{F} = -y\mathbf{i} + x\mathbf{j}$, the line integral of $\mathbf{F} \cdot d\mathbf{r}$ around the boundary of a region S has a value which is twice the area of that region.

5.3. Verify Green's lemma for the triangle bounded by the lines $x + y = 1$, $-x + y = 1$, and $y = 0$, when
(a) $\mathbf{F} = (\sin y)\mathbf{i} + (x \cos y)\mathbf{j}$;
(b) $\mathbf{F} = y^2\mathbf{i} + x^2\mathbf{j}$.

5.4. By using an appropriate choice of P and Q in Green's lemma, show that

$$\iint_S \begin{vmatrix} u_x & v_x \\ u_y & v_y \end{vmatrix} dA = \int_C u \, dv.$$

5.5. Use Green's theorem to show the following:

$$\iint_S \Delta u \, dA = \int_C \frac{\partial u}{\partial n} \, ds.$$

5.6. Show that if $\Delta u = 0$ throughout a region S, then the integral of $u \, \dfrac{\partial u}{\partial n} \, ds$ around the boundary of S is non-negative.

5.2   *Potential functions in the plane*

It was seen in Chapter 4 that the curl operation applied to a gradient produces the zero vector:

$$\nabla \times \nabla \phi = \mathbf{0}.$$

It will be shown next that if $\nabla \times \mathbf{F} = \mathbf{0}$, then $\mathbf{F}$ can be expressed as the gradient of some function ϕ, called a *potential* function. $\mathbf{F} = P(x,y,z)\,\mathbf{i} + Q(x,y,z) + O\,\mathbf{k}$

A region U in the plane will here be called *connected* if each point of the region can be reached from every other point of the region by means of a *rectangular path*—a curve made up of at most a finite number of straight line segments parallel to the coordinate axes. It will be called *simply* connected if any two such rectangular paths joining a pair of points of the region enclose a set of points which lies entirely within the region (i.e., if every closed rectangular arc can be shrunk to a point without passing through points not in the region). Figure 5.5 shows a simply connected region and a region which is connected but not simply connected.

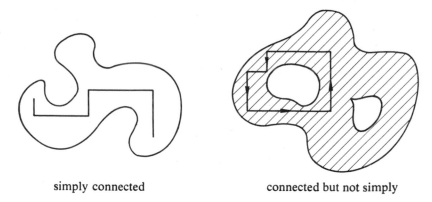

simply connected   connected but not simply

Figure 5.5.   Connected regions.

Suppose now that U is a simply connected region, and that at each point of the region, $\nabla \times \mathbf{F}$ vanishes:

$$\frac{\partial Q}{\partial x} - \frac{\partial P}{\partial y} = 0.$$

Consider then the line integral of $P\,dx + Q\,dy$ along a rectangular path (with sides parallel to the coordinate axes) from an arbitrary but fixed point A to a point (x, y) which is fixed for the integration but which will then be considered variable:

$$\int_A^{(x,y)} P(\xi, \varsigma)\, d\xi + Q(\xi, \varsigma)\, d\varsigma.$$

Suppose that C_1 and C_2 are two such rectangular paths from A to (x, y); let C_3 be any rectangular path in U from (x, y) to A which does

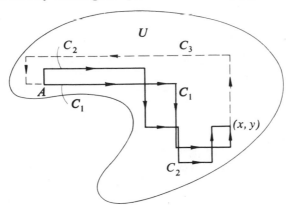

Figure 5.6

not cross either C_1 or C_2. Then C_1 and C_3 together form the boundary of a region S which lies in U, and Green's lemma applies:

$$\int_{C_1+C_3} P\, dx + Q\, dy = \int\int_S \left\{ \frac{\partial Q}{\partial x} - \frac{\partial P}{\partial y} \right\} dA = 0.$$

(This is written with the assumption that $C_1 + C_3$ is a counterclockwise path around S; if it is clockwise, a minus sign would be needed in Green's lemma, but the line integral would still vanish.) Similarly,

$$\int_{C_2+C_3} P\, dx + Q\, dy = 0,$$

and subtraction yields

$$\int_{C_1} P\, dx + Q\, dy = \int_{C_2} P\, dx + Q\, dy.$$

Thus, the integral does not depend on the particular rectangular path used, and depends then only on the terminal point (x, y); it defines a *function:*

$$\phi(x, y) = \int_A^{(x,y)} P(\xi, \varsigma)\, d\xi + Q(\xi, \varsigma)\, d\varsigma.$$

This is the *potential function.*

If the integral defining ϕ were started at another point, say B instead of A, its value would be the same function of (x, y) except for an additive constant—namely, the value of the integral along a rectangular path from B to A. (See Example 5.2 below.) So ϕ is not really unique; but the term *the potential function* will be used since the variable part of ϕ is unique.

E X A M P L E 5.2.   Consider the function $\mathbf{F} = 2xy^2\mathbf{i} + 2yx^2\mathbf{j}$, for which (at every point in the plane) $Q_x = P_y$:

$$\frac{\partial Q}{\partial x} - \frac{\partial P}{\partial y} = \frac{\partial(2x^2y)}{\partial x} - \frac{\partial(2y^2x)}{\partial y} = 4xy - 4xy = 0.$$

The corresponding potential function ϕ can then be defined by the integral

$$\int_{(0,0)}^{(x,y)} 2xy^2\, dx + 2yx^2\, dy$$

along any rectangular path. In particular, the path used can be that consisting of the horizontal line from $(0, 0)$ to $(x, 0)$ along the x-axis (along which $y = dy = 0$) and the vertical line from $(x, 0)$ up to (x, y) (along which $dx = 0$):

$$\phi(x, y) = \int_0^x 0\cdot d\xi + \int_0^y 2x^2\zeta\, d\zeta = 0 + x^2y^2.$$

Starting the integral at a different point gives the same function except for an additive constant. For instance,

$$\int_{(1,1)}^{(x,y)} 2xy^2\, dx + 2yx^2\, dy = \int_{(1,1)}^{(x,1)} \mathbf{F}\cdot d\mathbf{r} + \int_{(x,1)}^{(x,y)} \mathbf{F}\cdot d\mathbf{r}$$

$$= \int_1^x 2x\, dx + \int_1^y 2x^2y\, dy$$

$$= x^2y^2 - 1.$$

The constant -1 is the value of the integral of $\mathbf{F}\cdot d\mathbf{r}$ along a rectangular path from $(1, 1)$ to $(0, 0)$.

The potential function $\phi(x, y)$ which is defined at each point of the region U throughout which $Q_x = P_y$ has the interesting property that its gradient is $\mathbf{F}$:

$$\nabla\phi = P(x, y)\mathbf{i} + Q(x, y)\mathbf{j}.$$

To establish this is to show that the partial derivatives of ϕ with respect to x and y are, respectively, P and Q. Consider the increment from x to $x + \Delta x$; the value of ϕ at $(x + \Delta x, y)$ is

$$\phi(x + \Delta x, y) = \int_A^{(x+\Delta x, y)} \mathbf{F}\cdot d\mathbf{r},$$

where the path of integration can be any rectangular path from A to $(x + \Delta x, y)$. In particular, the path can be chosen to be that which is made up of the same path used in expressing $\phi(x, y)$ plus the horizontal path joining (x, y) to $(x + \Delta x, y)$, along which $dy = 0$:

$$\phi(x + \Delta x, y) = \phi(x, y) + \int_{x}^{x+\Delta x} P(\xi, y) \, d\xi.$$

Then

$$\frac{\partial \phi}{\partial x} = \lim_{\Delta x \to 0} \frac{\phi(x + \Delta x, y) - \phi(x, y)}{\Delta x}$$

$$= \lim_{\Delta x \to 0} \frac{1}{\Delta x} \int_{x}^{x+\Delta x} P(\xi, y) \, d\xi = P(x, y),$$

since P is differentiable and therefore certainly continuous in x. The demonstration that $\phi_y = Q$ is completely analogous.

The existence of a gradient function ϕ, such that $\nabla \phi = \mathbf{F}$, is then essentially equivalent to the condition $Q_x = P_y$, and is not a general property of vector fields. Since $\nabla \phi$ is normal to the level curves of ϕ, a field $\mathbf{F}$ which has a potential ϕ is such that at each point the field is normal to the curve $\phi = $ constant which passes through that point. The field is sometimes referred to as *lamellar*, since it divides the region where it has this property into layers or laminae; the field vectors are perpendicular to the layers. A more common term for such a field is *irrotational*. This will be justified in Sect. 5.5.

Another consequence of the property that a field $\mathbf{F}$ is a gradient field is that the quantity

$$\mathbf{F} \cdot d\mathbf{r} = P \, dx + Q \, dy$$

is an *exact* differential expression; that is, since

$$d\phi = \phi_x \, dx + \phi_y \, dy,$$

and since $\phi_x = P$ and $\phi_y = Q$, it follows that $\mathbf{F} \cdot d\mathbf{r} = d\phi$. The function ϕ can be found from its definition as a line integral, as in Example 5.2, or by "partial integrations," as in the following example.

E X A M P L E   5.3   Let $\mathbf{F} = (\log y)\mathbf{i} + (1 + x/y)\mathbf{j}$, a vector function which satisfies the condition $\nabla \times \mathbf{F} = \mathbf{0}$, or $P_y = Q_x$. Then there is a function $\phi(x, y)$ such that

$$d\phi = \mathbf{F} \cdot d\mathbf{r} = (\log y) \, dx + (1 + x/y) \, dy,$$

and clearly it must be the case that

$$\phi_x = \log y, \quad \text{and} \quad \phi_y = 1 + x/y.$$

From the first of these equations it follows that

$$\phi = x \log y + c(y) + K,$$

for some function $c(y)$ and some constant K. From the second equation,

$$\phi = y + x \log y + d(x) + K',$$

for some function $d(x)$ and constant K'. These determinations agree if $c(y) = y$, $d(x) = 0$, and $K = K'$. Thus,

$$\phi = y + x \log y + K.$$

The fact that $\mathbf{F} \cdot d\mathbf{r}$ is an exact differential makes it especially easy to integrate it along a path within a region where it has this property. Consider such a path C from the point A to the point B, the path being given parametrically by

$$\mathbf{r} = \mathbf{f}(u) = \xi(u)\mathbf{i} + \zeta(u)\mathbf{j},$$

where $\mathbf{f}(a) = \mathbf{r}_A$ and $\mathbf{f}(b) = \mathbf{r}_B$. Then $d\mathbf{r} = [\xi'(u)\mathbf{i} + \zeta'(u)\mathbf{j}]du$, and

$$\int_C \mathbf{F} \cdot d\mathbf{r} = \int_{u=a}^{u=b} [P(\xi, \zeta)\xi' + Q(\xi, \zeta)\zeta'] \, du$$

$$= \int_a^b \frac{d\phi}{du} \, du = \phi[\xi(u), \zeta(u)] \Big|_{u=a}^{u=b}$$

$$= \phi[\xi(b), \zeta(b)] - \phi[\xi(a), \zeta(a)].$$

Thus, the value of the integral is just the value of ϕ at the point B minus its value at the point A, independent of the choice of path along which the integration is carried out. (This had been observed previously for rectangular paths, and it is now seen to be the case for continuously differentiable paths.) This in turn implies that the integral of $\mathbf{F} \cdot d\mathbf{r}$ around a closed continuously differentiable path is zero—the value of the integral out to one point on the path from another point is equal and opposite in sign to the value along the return path.

Problems

5.7.   Evaluate the line integral

$$\int_C \nabla[x(y - 1)^{1/2}] \cdot d\mathbf{r},$$

where C is a path from $(1, 2)$ to $(2, 5)$ lying entirely above the line $y = 1$.

5.8. Determine functions ϕ such that:

(a) $d\phi = (y + 2x)\,dx + \left(\dfrac{1}{y} + x\right)dy;$

(b) $d\phi = \left(1 + \dfrac{2y}{x}\right)dy - \dfrac{y^2}{x^2}\,dx;$

(c) $d\phi = \dfrac{1}{x^2}[(x + y)\,dx - (x + x^2)\,dy].$

5.9. Let $P = y/r^2$ and $Q = -x/r^2$.

(a) Evaluate the line integral $\int P\,dx + Q\,dy$ clockwise around the circle $\mathbf{r} = (\cos\theta)\mathbf{i} + (\sin\theta)\mathbf{j}$.

(b) Verify that $P_y = Q_x$ wherever P and Q are defined.

(c) Explain why the answer to (a) is *not* zero.

(d) What is the value of the line integral $\int P\,dx + Q\,dy$ clockwise around the circle $\mathbf{r} = (2 + \cos\theta)\mathbf{i} + (\sin\theta)\mathbf{j}$?

(e) Determine the potential function ϕ such that $\nabla\phi\cdot d\mathbf{r} = P\,dx + Q\,dy$ holds throughout the region consisting of the whole plane with the negative x-axis deleted.

(f) Let C denote a path from $(-1, 1)$ to $(1, 1)$ which dips beneath the origin. Use the result of (a) and an integration along $y = 1$ to evaluate the integral along C.

5.10. Show that the line integral

$$\int \frac{y\,dx - x\,dy}{x^2 + y^2}$$

has the value zero around any closed path in the plane which does not enclose the origin, and has the value 2π (or -2π) around any closed path in the plane which goes around the origin once.

5.3   Stokes' theorem

The three-dimensional version of Green's lemma to be given now, called Stokes' theorem, is a generalization in that it includes Green's lemma as a special case; but it is also a consequence of Green's lemma, obtained by applying the lemma in the two-dimensional parameter space employed in defining a surface.

Let Σ denote an oriented surface with correspondingly oriented boundary curve Γ. (The "positive" normal to the surface and the "positive" direction around the boundary are related by the right-hand rule.) It is assumed that Σ is the image under $\mathbf{r} = \mathbf{G}(u, v)$ of a uv-region S which is both u-simple and v-simple, so that Green's lemma applies to S. The boundary C of the region S is mapped into the boundary Γ by $\mathbf{G}(u, v)$. The transformation $\mathbf{G}(u, v)$ will be assumed to have components which

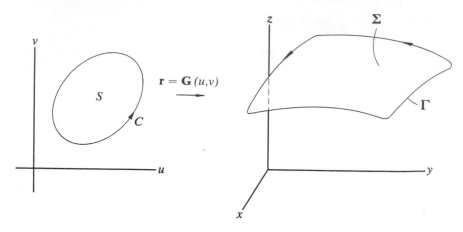

Figure 5.7

have continuous second derivatives; the derivatives of these components will be denoted by x_u, z_v, y_{uv}, x_{uu}, etc. It will be assumed further that $\mathbf{r}_u \times \mathbf{r}_v$ does not vanish in S, where $\mathbf{r}_u$ and $\mathbf{r}_v$ are (as in Chapter 4) tangents to the constant-v and constant-u curves on Σ (i.e., $\mathbf{r}_u = \partial\mathbf{G}/\partial u$ and $\mathbf{r}_v = \partial\mathbf{G}/\partial v$).

Consider the continuously differentiable vector field

$$\mathbf{F}(x, y, z) = P(x, y, z)\mathbf{i} + Q(x, y, z)\mathbf{j} + R(x, y, z)\mathbf{k}.$$

The relationship known as "Stokes' theorem" is then the following equality of an oriented surface integral over Σ and an oriented line integral around its boundary:

$$\iint_\Sigma \nabla \times \mathbf{F} \cdot d\boldsymbol{\sigma} = \int_\Gamma \mathbf{F} \cdot d\mathbf{r}.$$

This will be derived by expressing each side as an integral in the parameter space and there exploiting Green's lemma.

Since $r = x(u,r)\,i + y(u,r)j + z(u,v)k$

$$d\mathbf{r} = (x_u\mathbf{i} + y_u\mathbf{j} + z_u\mathbf{k})du + (x_v\mathbf{i} + y_v\mathbf{j} + z_v\mathbf{k})dv,$$

it follows that

$$\int_\Gamma \mathbf{F} \cdot d\mathbf{r} = \int_C (Px_u + Qy_u + Rz_u)\, du + (Px_v + Qy_v + Rz_v)\, dv,$$

where P, for instance, means $P[x(u, v), y(u, v), z(u, v)]$. Renaming the coefficients of du and dv, respectively, $\tilde{P}$ and $\tilde{Q}$ yields

$$\int_{\Gamma} \mathbf{F} \cdot d\mathbf{r} = \int_C \tilde{P}(u, v)\, du + \tilde{Q}(u, v)\, dv$$

$$= \int \int_S \left\{ \frac{\partial \tilde{Q}}{\partial u} - \frac{\partial \tilde{P}}{\partial v} \right\} dA_{uv},$$

left side of Fig 5.7

the last expression resulting from an application of Green's lemma in the uv-plane. Now

$$\frac{\partial \tilde{Q}}{\partial u} = P_u x_v + Q_u y_v + R_u z_v + P x_{vu} + Q y_{vu} + R z_{vu},$$

$$\frac{\partial \tilde{P}}{\partial v} = P_v x_u + Q_v y_u + R_v z_u + P x_{uv} + Q y_{uv} + R z_{uv},$$

so that

$$\int_{\Gamma} \mathbf{F} \cdot d\mathbf{r} = \int \int_S \{ (P_u x_v - P_v x_u) + (Q_u y_v - Q_v y_u) + (R_u z_v - R_v z_u) \}\, dA_{uv}.$$

Consider next an evaluation of the surface integral involved in Stokes' theorem:

$$\int \int_{\Sigma} \nabla \times \mathbf{F} \cdot d\boldsymbol{\sigma} = \int \int_S \nabla \times \mathbf{F} \cdot (\mathbf{r}_u \times \mathbf{r}_v)\, du\, dv.$$

Here,

$$\mathbf{r}_u \times \mathbf{r}_v = \begin{vmatrix} \mathbf{i} & \mathbf{j} & \mathbf{k} \\ x_u & y_u & z_u \\ x_v & y_v & z_v \end{vmatrix}$$

and

$$(\mathbf{r}_u \times \mathbf{r}_v) \cdot \nabla \times \mathbf{F} = \begin{vmatrix} R_y - Q_z & P_z - R_x & Q_x - P_y \\ x_u & y_u & z_u \\ x_v & y_v & z_v \end{vmatrix}$$

$$= (P_u x_v - P_v x_u) + (Q_u y_v - Q_v y_u) + (R_u z_v - R_v z_u).$$

The reduction to this last form follows from such formulas as $P_u = P_x x_u + P_y y_u + P_z z_u$ (i.e., the chain rule). Thus,

$$\int \int_{\Sigma} \nabla \times \mathbf{F} \cdot d\boldsymbol{\sigma} = \int \int_S [(P_u x_v - P_v x_u) + (Q_u y_v - Q_v y_u) + (R_u z_v - R_v z_u)]\, dA_{uv}.$$

This is precisely the expression found for the integral of $\mathbf{F} \cdot d\mathbf{r}$ around Γ, and so the relation in Stokes' theorem is established.

The class of regions to which Stokes' theorem applies is already quite broad, but it can clearly be extended, as was Green's lemma, to surfaces which can be thought of as composed of a finite number of the simpler surfaces, provided that orientability is not lost, as it would be for the Möbius band (Fig. 4.13), for instance.

EXAMPLE 5.4   Stokes' theorem will be verified here in a particular case: $\mathbf{F} = x\mathbf{i} + (2z - x)\mathbf{j} + y^2\mathbf{k}$, and $\nabla \times \mathbf{F} = (2y - 2)\mathbf{i} - \mathbf{k}$. Let Γ be the circle $x^2 + y^2 = 4$, $z = 1$, or $\mathbf{r} = (2 \cos t)\mathbf{i} + (2 \sin t)\mathbf{j} + \mathbf{k}$. Then

$$\int_\Gamma \mathbf{F} \cdot d\mathbf{r} = \int_0^{2\pi} [-2 \sin 2t + (2 - 2 \cos t)(2 \cos t) + 0]\, dt = -4\pi.$$

The curve Γ bounds any number of surfaces, for example, the portion of the para-

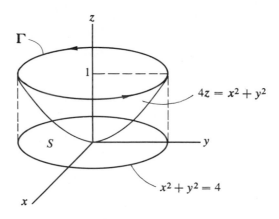

Figure 5.8.   (See Example 5.4.)

boloid $4z = x^2 + y^2$ beneath the plane $z = 1$. Since on this surface

$$\mathbf{r} = x\mathbf{i} + y\mathbf{j} + \frac{x^2 + y^2}{4}\,\mathbf{k},$$

with

$$\mathbf{r}_x = \mathbf{i} + \frac{x}{2}\mathbf{k}, \qquad \mathbf{r}_y = \mathbf{j} + \frac{y}{2}\mathbf{k},$$

$$\mathbf{r}_x \times \mathbf{r}_y = -\frac{x}{2}\mathbf{i} - \frac{y}{2}\mathbf{j} + \mathbf{k},$$

the appropriate surface integral is

$$\iint_\Sigma \nabla \times \mathbf{F} \cdot d\boldsymbol{\sigma} = \iint_S \nabla \times \mathbf{F} \cdot (\mathbf{r}_x \times \mathbf{r}_y)\, dx\, dy$$

$$= \iint_S [(2y - 2)(-x/2) - 1]\, dx\, dy,$$

where S is the region inside the circle $x^2 + y^2 = 4$ in the xy-plane. Carrying out the integration yields

$$\iint_S (-xy + x - 1)\, dx\, dy = 0 + 0 - (\text{area of circle}) = -4\pi.$$

The surface Γ could also have been taken to be the portion of the plane $z = 1$ within $x^2 + y^2 = 4$; on this surface $\mathbf{r}_x \times \mathbf{r}_y = \mathbf{k}$, and

$$\iint_\Sigma \nabla \times \mathbf{F} \cdot d\boldsymbol{\sigma} = \iint_S \nabla \times \mathbf{F} \cdot \mathbf{k}\, dx\, dy = -\iint_S dx\, dy = -4\pi.$$

With Stokes' theorem on hand to play the role played by Green's lemma in the plane, it is now possible to define a potential function for certain vector fields; the development parallels quite closely that followed for the case of the plane. Indeed, the parallel is so close that the details can almost be omitted, with a wave of the hand and a few mumbled words—except that there is one small detail which is a bit stubborn. The development is as follows. If $\nabla \times \mathbf{F} = \mathbf{0}$ in a region U which contains the line segments joining any two of its points, the value of the line integral along a rectangular path from a fixed point to (x, y, z) depends only on (x, y, z), and not on the rectangular path used; this integral then defines the potential function ϕ:

$$\phi(x, y, z) = \int_A^{(x, y, z)} P(\xi, \zeta, \eta)\, d\xi + Q(\xi, \zeta, \eta)\, d\zeta + R(\xi, \zeta, \eta)\, d\eta.$$

But to obtain this independence of the rectangular path used, it is necessary to assume that two given rectangular paths in U serve as the boundary of some surface Σ contained in U, so that an application of Stokes' theorem with $\nabla \times \mathbf{F} = \mathbf{0}$ yields a zero line integral around the boundary of Σ. In the plane it is obvious that two rectangular paths connecting two points in the region U serve as the boundary of a region contained in U; in three dimensions this is no longer obvious, and to show that it is still true is so involved as to be beyond our scope. It will be assumed to be valid. Then $\phi(x, y, z)$ is defined, with (as in the plane)

$$\nabla\phi = P\mathbf{i} + Q\mathbf{j} + R\mathbf{k} = \mathbf{F},$$

so that $\mathbf{F}$ is the gradient of a potential function, and is lammellar or irrotational. Further, $\mathbf{F} \cdot d\mathbf{r} = d\phi$, an exact differential, and the integral of $\mathbf{F} \cdot d\mathbf{r}$ from one point to another is the value of ϕ at one point minus the value at the other—independent of the path used.

EXAMPLE 5.5   Consider the vector field $\mathbf{F} = 2xy\mathbf{i} + (1 + x^2)\mathbf{j} + 3z^2\mathbf{k}$, which has everywhere the property that $\nabla \times \mathbf{F} = 0$. There then exists a potential function $\phi(x, y, z)$, such that $\nabla\phi = \mathbf{F}$, which can be obtained as the value of a line integral from a fixed point to (x, y, z):

$$\phi(x, y, z) = \int_{(0,0,0)}^{(x,y,z)} 2xy\, dx + (1 + x^2)dy + 3z^2\, dz,$$

taken along any convenient path between the end points. In particular, a rectangular path can be used, say along C_1, the straight line from $(0, 0, 0)$ to $(x, 0, 0)$; then along C_2, the straight line from $(x, 0, 0)$ to $(x, y, 0)$; and finally along C_3, the straight line from $(x, y, 0)$ to (x, y, z). Along C_1, $\mathbf{F} \cdot d\mathbf{r} = 0$; along C_2, $\mathbf{F} \cdot d\mathbf{r} = (1 + x^2)\, dy$ (with x constant); and along C_3, $\mathbf{F} \cdot d\mathbf{r} = 3z^2\, dz$. Thus

$$\int_{(0,0,0)}^{(x,y,z)} \mathbf{F} \cdot d\mathbf{r} = \int_{\zeta=0}^{y} (1 + x^2)\, d\zeta + \int_{\eta=0}^{z} 3\eta^2\, d\eta$$

$$= (1 + x^2)y + z^3.$$

This function (or this plus any arbitrary constant) is the desired potential function. It can also be obtained by partial integrations (as illustrated previously in two dimensions). Since $\phi_x = P$, $\phi_y = Q$, $\phi_z = R$, there are three ways of expressing ϕ:

$$\int 2xy\, dx = x^2y + K_1(y, z) = \phi(x, y, z),$$

$$\int (1 + x^2)\, dy = y + x^2y + K_2(x, z) = \phi(x, y, z),$$

$$\int 3z^2\, dz = z^3 + K_3(x, y) = \phi(x, y, z).$$

In order that these all be the same function ϕ, it is apparent that ϕ must be

$$\phi(x, y, z) = x^2y + y + z^3 + K.$$

The line integral between any two points is independent of the path used. The integral from, say, $(1, 0, 2)$ to $(0, -1, 1)$, along any path joining those points, is simply

$$\phi(0, -1, 1) - \phi(1, 0, 2) = -1 + 1 - 8 = -8.$$

Problems

5.11. Evaluate $\int \mathbf{F} \cdot d\mathbf{r}$ around the closed path Γ shown in the accompanying figure, where $\mathbf{F} = x\mathbf{i} - z\mathbf{j} + y\mathbf{k}$:

    (a) directly, as a line integral;
    (b) indirectly, using Stokes' theorem.

5.12. Verify Stokes' theorem for the case $\mathbf{F} = z\mathbf{i} + x\mathbf{j} + y\mathbf{k}$, where Σ is that portion of the plane $2x + y + 2z = 3$ which lies in the first octant (i.e., where x, y, and z are all positive).

5.13. Verify Stokes' theorem when Σ is the portion of the sphere $x^2 + y^2 + z^2 = 16$ which lies above the plane $z = 2$, with $\mathbf{F} = x^2\mathbf{i} - z^2\mathbf{j} + yz\mathbf{k}$.

5.14. Let $\mathbf{F} = (2y^2 + z)\mathbf{i} + 4xy\mathbf{j} + x\mathbf{k}$.

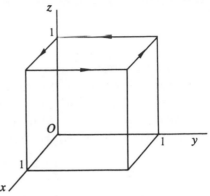

Problem 5.11

    (a) Determine $\nabla \times \mathbf{F}$.
    (b) Determine a function $\phi(x, y, z)$ such that $\nabla\phi = \mathbf{F}$ and such that $\phi(1, -1, 0) = 0$.
    (c) Determine the value of the line integral $\int \mathbf{F} \cdot d\mathbf{r}$ along the curve $\mathbf{r} = (\cos\theta)\mathbf{i} + (\sin\theta)\mathbf{j} + \theta\mathbf{k}$ from $(1, 0, 0)$ to $(-1, 0, \pi)$.
    (d) Determine the value of $\int \mathbf{F} \cdot d\mathbf{r}$ along the straight line from $(1, 0, 0)$ to $(-1, 0, \pi)$.

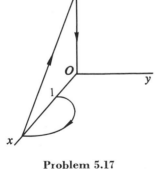

Problem 5.17

5.15. Given $\mathbf{F} = 2x\mathbf{i} + y\mathbf{j} + z\mathbf{k}$.
    (a) Determine $\phi(x, y, z)$ such that $\nabla\phi = \mathbf{F}$.
    (b) Compute $\int \mathbf{F} \cdot d\mathbf{r}$ around the closed path given by
$$\mathbf{r} = (\cos t)\mathbf{i} + (\sin t)\mathbf{j} + (\cos t + \sin t)\mathbf{k}.$$

5.16. Compute $\int x\,dx + 2z\,dy + y^2\,dz$ around the closed path defined by the simultaneous equations $x^2 + y^2 = 4$, $z = 1$,
    (a) as a line integral,
    (b) as a surface integral.

5.17. Compute $\int \nabla\phi \cdot d\mathbf{r}$ around the path shown in the accompanying figure from $(1, 0, 0)$ to $(0, 0, 0)$ where $\phi = z^2 + x$.

5.18. Determine a function $\phi(x, y, z)$ such that $\phi(0, 0, 0) = 0$ and $\nabla\phi = (x + y)\mathbf{i} + (x + y)\mathbf{j} + z\mathbf{k}$. Determine the integral of $\nabla\phi \cdot d\mathbf{r}$ along the path in Problem 5.17.

5.19.   Evaluate the line integral

$$\int \left(2x + \frac{z}{y}\right) dx - \frac{xz}{y^2} dy + \left(\frac{x}{y} + 1\right) dz$$

along the path $\mathbf{r} = (2 \sin t)\mathbf{i} + (\cos 4t)\mathbf{j} + (\cos 3t)\mathbf{k}$ from $t = 0$ to $t = \pi/2$.

5.4   *The divergence theorem*

Consider a region V (in three-dimensional space) which is *xy-simple:* each line $x = x_0$, $y = y_0$ intersects the region in an interval, with end points $z_1 = \eta_1(x_0, y_0)$ and $z_2 = \eta_2(x_0, y_0)$, such that $\eta_1 \leq \eta_2$, and such that $z = \eta_1(x, y)$ and $z = \eta_2(x, y)$ define piecewise smooth surfaces Σ_1 and Σ_2, respectively, each having the projection S in the xy-plane. (See Fig. 5.9).

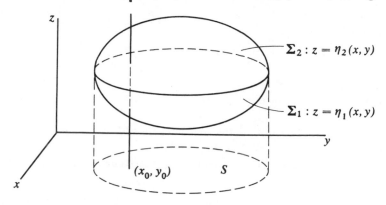

Figure 5.9.   An *xy*-simple region.

Let $\mathbf{F} = P(x, y, z)\mathbf{i} + Q(x, y, z)\mathbf{j} + R(x, y, z)\mathbf{k}$, and let the components of $\mathbf{F}$ have continuous partial derivatives, so that at least $\nabla \cdot \mathbf{F}$ is an integrable function. Then

$$\iiint_V \frac{\partial R}{\partial z} dV = \iint_S \int_{z = \eta_1(x,y)}^{\eta_2(x,y)} \frac{\partial R}{\partial z} dz \, dA_{xy}$$

$$= \iint_S \{R[x, y, \eta_2(x, y)] - R[x, y, \eta_1(x, y)]\} \, dA_{xy}$$

$$= \iint_{\Sigma_2} R(x, y, z)\mathbf{k} \cdot \mathbf{d\sigma} + \iint_{\Sigma_1} R(x, y, z)\mathbf{k} \cdot \mathbf{d\sigma}$$

$$= \iint_{\Sigma} R(x, y, z)\mathbf{k} \cdot \mathbf{d\sigma},$$

where Σ is the total boundary surface of V, namely, the union of Σ_1 and Σ_2, and $d\boldsymbol{\sigma}$ is the (oriented) surface element $\mathbf{n}\,d\sigma$, $\mathbf{n}$ denoting the unit normal pointing outward from V.

Similarly, it is clear that if V is also xz-simple and yz-simple, then

$$\iiint_V \frac{\partial Q}{\partial y}\,dV = \iint_\Sigma Q(x, y, z)\mathbf{j}\cdot d\boldsymbol{\sigma},$$

$$\iiint_V \frac{\partial P}{\partial x}\,dV = \iint_\Sigma P(x, y, z)\mathbf{i}\cdot d\boldsymbol{\sigma}.$$

A summation of these results yields

$$\iiint_V \nabla\cdot\mathbf{F}\,dV = \iint_\Sigma \mathbf{F}\cdot d\boldsymbol{\sigma},$$

which is the relationship known as the divergence theorem (or Gauss' theorem).

The divergence theorem holds also in cases where V, although not necessarily xy-, xz-, and yz-simple, is the union of finitely many such regions. For, if two subregions happen to be contiguous, sharing a part of their boundary surfaces, the boundary of the union is the union of the unshared portions; and the integrals of $\mathbf{F}\cdot d\boldsymbol{\sigma}$ over the shared portions would be equal and opposite in sign, thereby canceling, since the outer normal direction $d\boldsymbol{\sigma}$ on one boundary is the inner normal on the other.

EXAMPLE 5.6   Consider the vector field $\mathbf{F} = xy\mathbf{i} + z^2\mathbf{j} + 2yz\mathbf{k}$, defined in the tetrahedron V bounded by $x = 0$, $y = 0$, $z = 0$, and the plane $x + y + z = 1$. This region is xy-simple, xz-simple, and yz-simple, and its boundary surface

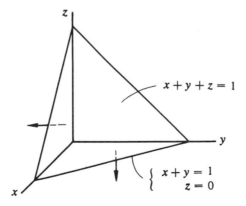

Figure 5.10.   (See Example 5.6.)

Σ consists of the four faces of the tetrahedron. The divergence of **F** is

$$\nabla \cdot \mathbf{F} = y + 0 + 2y = 3y,$$

with integral

$$\iiint_V 3y \, dV = 3 \int_0^1 \int_0^{1-y} \int_0^{1-x-y} y \, dz \, dx \, dy = \frac{3}{24}.$$

The integral of $\mathbf{F} \cdot \mathbf{d\sigma}$ over Σ is computed in four parts. On one back face, $x = 0$, $\mathbf{d\sigma} = -\mathbf{i} \, dy \, dz$, and the integral vanishes. On another, $y = 0$, $\mathbf{d\sigma} = -\mathbf{j} \, dx \, dz$, and

$$\iint \mathbf{F} \cdot \mathbf{d\sigma} = -\int_0^1 \int_0^{1-z} z^2 dx \, dz = -\frac{1}{12}.$$

On the bottom, $z = 0$, $\mathbf{d\sigma} = -\mathbf{k} \, dx \, dy$, and the integral vanishes. On the front face, given by $x + y + z = 1$, or $\mathbf{r} = x\mathbf{i} + y\mathbf{j} + (1 - x - y)\mathbf{k}$, one has $\mathbf{r}_x = \mathbf{i} - \mathbf{k}$, $\mathbf{r}_y = \mathbf{j} - \mathbf{k}$, and $\mathbf{r}_x \times \mathbf{r}_y = \mathbf{i} + \mathbf{j} + \mathbf{k}$; and so for that face,

$$\iint \mathbf{F} \cdot \mathbf{d\sigma} = \int_0^1 \int_0^{1-x} (xy\mathbf{i} + z^2\mathbf{j} + 2yz\mathbf{k}) \cdot (\mathbf{i} + \mathbf{j} + \mathbf{k}) \, dy \, dx$$

$$= \int_0^1 \int_0^{1-x} [xy + (1 - x - y)^2 + 2y(1 - x - y)] \, dy \, dx = \frac{5}{24}.$$

The integral over all of Σ is then $\frac{5}{24} - \frac{1}{12} = \frac{3}{24}$, which agrees (as it should, according to the divergence theorem) with the value of the volume integral of the divergence of **F** over V.

Several useful relations are obtainable from the divergence theorem. Consider two functions $u(x, y, z)$ and $v(x, y, z)$ which have continuous second partial derivatives, and let $\mathbf{F}(x, y, z) = u \, \nabla v$. Then with this **F**, and using a region V and corresponding boundary Σ such that the divergence theorem is valid, we have

$$\nabla \cdot \mathbf{F} = \nabla \cdot (u \nabla v) = u(\nabla \cdot \nabla v) + (\nabla v) \cdot (\nabla u),$$

and hence

$$\iiint_V [u \, \Delta v + (\nabla u) \cdot (\nabla v)] \, dV = \iint_\Sigma u \, \nabla v \cdot \mathbf{d\sigma}$$

(where Δv denotes the Laplacian of v, or $\nabla \cdot \nabla v = v_{xx} + v_{yy} + v_{zz}$). This relation is referred to as a form of Green's theorem; it can be written in terms of the "normal derivative"—the directional derivative of v in the direction of the outer normal to Σ, $\partial v / \partial n$:

$$\nabla v \cdot \mathbf{d\sigma} = \nabla v \cdot \mathbf{n} \, d\sigma = \frac{\partial v}{\partial n} \, d\sigma.$$

Thus,

$$\iiint_V [u\Delta v + (\nabla u)\cdot(\nabla v)]\, dV = \iint_\Sigma u\, \frac{\partial v}{\partial n}\, d\sigma.$$

Rewriting this with the roles of u and v interchanged and subtracting, one obtains the symmetric form known as Green's theorem:

$$\iiint_V (u\, \Delta v - v\, \Delta u)\, dV = \iint_\Sigma (u\, \nabla v - v\, \nabla u)\cdot \mathbf{d\sigma}$$

$$= \iint_\Sigma \left(u\, \frac{\partial v}{\partial n} - v\, \frac{\partial u}{\partial n} \right) d\sigma.$$

Other useful relations are obtained from the first form of Green's theorem using, respectively, $u = 1$ and $u = v$:

$$\iiint_V \Delta v\, dV = \iint_\Sigma \frac{\partial v}{\partial n}\, d\sigma,$$

$$\iiint_V [u\, \Delta u + |\nabla u|^2]\, dV = \iint_\Sigma u\, \frac{\partial u}{\partial n}\, d\sigma.$$

Problems

5.20.   Verify the divergence theorem for the $\mathbf{F}$ of Example 5.6, using as V the unit cube bounded by $x = 1$, $y = 1$, $z = 1$, and the coordinate planes.

5.21.   Verify the divergence theorem, using the V of Problem 5.20, for

$$\mathbf{F} = (x + y)\mathbf{i} + (y + z)\mathbf{j} + (z + x)\mathbf{k}.$$

5.22.   Evaluate the integral

$$\iint_\Sigma \nabla\phi\cdot \mathbf{d\sigma}$$

when $\phi = xy + yz$ and Σ is the surface of the region V of Example 5.6.

5.23.   Verify the divergence theorem for $\mathbf{F} = r\mathbf{r}$ and the region V bounded by the sphere $x^2 + y^2 + z^2 = 9$.

5.24.   Verify the divergence theorem for $\mathbf{F} = x\mathbf{i} + y\mathbf{j} + (z - 3)\mathbf{k}$, using as V the region bounded by $z = 1$ and the cone $x^2 + y^2 = (z - 3)^2$.

5.25.   Show that if $\Delta u = 0$ in V, then

$$\iint_\Sigma u \frac{\partial u}{\partial n}\, d\sigma \geq 0,$$

where Σ is the boundary of V.

5.5   *Interpretations and applications*

The *circulation* of a vector field $\mathbf{F}$ around a closed path Γ is defined to be the line integral

$$\int_\Gamma \mathbf{F}\cdot d\mathbf{r}.$$

If Γ is a plane path bounding a simply connected plane region R of area $A(R)$, the ratio

$$\frac{1}{A(R)} \int_\Gamma \mathbf{F}\cdot d\mathbf{r}$$

is the circulation per unit area. The limit of this ratio as the region R shrinks (in its plane) to a single point P_0 is a number associated with the point, the field, and the plane (or the normal direction). This limit, according to Stokes' theorem, is

$$\lim_{R\to P_0} \frac{1}{A(R)} \int_\Gamma \mathbf{F}\cdot d\mathbf{r} = \lim_{R\to P_0} \frac{1}{A(R)} \iint_R \nabla \times \mathbf{F}\cdot \mathbf{n}\, d\sigma$$

$$= \nabla \times \mathbf{F}\cdot \mathbf{n} \qquad (\text{at } P_0),$$

where $\mathbf{n}$ is the unit normal to R associated with the sense of Γ. This component of the curl is a maximum when R is perpendicular to $\nabla \times \mathbf{F}$, and the maximum value is $|\nabla \times \mathbf{F}|$. Thus, the curl of a vector field at a point is a vector whose magnitude is the maximum circulation per unit area at the point and whose direction is normal to the plane defining the maximum circulation. This interpretation makes it intuitively clear why the curl does not depend on the coordinate system employed.

(That the limit of the ratio of the double integral to the area of the region over which it is taken *is* the integrand function at the limiting point follows from a mean value theorem for double integrals, with appropriate hypotheses concerning the region as it shrinks and the integrand function. Since the relationship is presented here only as an aid to intuition and is not used as a definition of the curl [though it could be], the precise conditions under which the limiting operation produces the claimed result will not be considered.)

The *flux* (or flow) of a vector field $\mathbf{F}$ through a surface element Σ is defined to be the oriented surface integral See p. 118 also

$$\iint_{\Sigma} \mathbf{F} \cdot d\boldsymbol{\sigma}.$$

If Σ is a closed surface bounding a simply connected region V, the flux out through Σ per unit volume is

$$\frac{1}{V} \iint_{\Sigma} \mathbf{F} \cdot d\boldsymbol{\sigma} = \frac{1}{V} \iiint_{V} \nabla \cdot \mathbf{F} \, dV,$$

the last expression following from the divergence theorem. (The symbol V has been used both for the region V and for its volume.) If V is shrunk nicely to a single point, the right-hand side of the last equation becomes (again by a mean value theorem, for triple integrals) the integrand at that point:

$$\lim_{V \to 0} \frac{1}{V} \iint_{\Sigma} \mathbf{F} \cdot d\boldsymbol{\sigma} = \nabla \cdot \mathbf{F}.$$

The divergence thus can be interpreted as the flux per unit volume out from that point, an interpretation independent of any coordinate system. If the divergence is positive, the point is called a *source*, and if it is negative, the point is called a *sink*. If the divergence vanishes in a region, there are no sources or sinks there.

Suppose now that a fluid is in "steady state" motion, and in particular assume that this motion is a rotation $\boldsymbol{\omega}$ about some axis through the coordinate origin. The velocity vector at any point $\mathbf{r}$ is then just

$$\mathbf{v} = \boldsymbol{\omega} \times \mathbf{r}.$$

The divergence and curl of this field are computed as follows:

$$\nabla \cdot \mathbf{v} = \nabla \cdot (\boldsymbol{\omega} \times \mathbf{r}) = \mathbf{r} \cdot (\nabla \times \boldsymbol{\omega}) - \boldsymbol{\omega} \cdot (\nabla \times \mathbf{r}) = 0,$$
$$\nabla \times \mathbf{v} = \nabla \times (\boldsymbol{\omega} \times \mathbf{r}) = (\mathbf{r} \cdot \nabla)\boldsymbol{\omega} - (\boldsymbol{\omega} \cdot \nabla)\mathbf{r} + \boldsymbol{\omega}(\nabla \cdot \mathbf{r}) - \mathbf{r}(\nabla \cdot \boldsymbol{\omega})$$
$$= 0 - \boldsymbol{\omega} + 3\boldsymbol{\omega} - 0$$
$$= 2\boldsymbol{\omega}.$$

Thus, the divergence vanishes, and the curl is proportional to the angular velocity vector. The circulation per unit area at each point, normal to the axis of rotation, is $\nabla \times \mathbf{v} \cdot \mathbf{n} = 2\boldsymbol{\omega}$.

When $\nabla \times \mathbf{v} = \mathbf{0}$ the flow is said to be *irrotational*. If this is the case, and if $\nabla \cdot \mathbf{v} = 0$ (no sources or sinks) in a region, then there is a potential function ϕ such that

$$\mathbf{v} = \nabla \phi,$$

and

$$\nabla \cdot \nabla \phi = \Delta \phi = 0;$$

that is, the potential ϕ satisfies Laplace's equation:

$$\phi_{xx} + \phi_{yy} + \phi_{zz} = 0.$$

An important kind of vector field is that defined by an "inverse square" law. To be specific, consider the electric field $\mathbf{E}$ in the vicinity of a unit point charge:

$$\mathbf{E} = \frac{1}{r^3} \mathbf{r} = \frac{1}{r^2} \mathbf{u_r},$$

where the origin is taken at the charge. Then

$$\nabla \times \mathbf{E} = \frac{1}{r^3} \nabla \times \mathbf{r} + \nabla \left(\frac{1}{r^3} \right) \times \mathbf{r}$$

$$= \frac{1}{r^3} \mathbf{0} + \left(\frac{-3}{r^5} \right) (\mathbf{r} \times \mathbf{r}) = \mathbf{0}$$

(except when $r = 0$). Thus, $\mathbf{E}$ is irrotational and has a scalar potential ϕ such that

$$\nabla \phi = \frac{1}{r^3} \mathbf{r}.$$

Since

$$\phi_x = \frac{x}{r^{3/2}},$$

$$\phi_y = \frac{y}{r^{3/2}},$$

$$\phi_z = \frac{z}{r^{3/2}},$$

it follows that

$$\phi = \frac{1}{r} + (\text{const.}).$$

The *electric potential* at a point P is defined as the work done in bringing a unit charge from infinity to P:

$$V = - \int_{\infty}^{P} \mathbf{E} \cdot d\mathbf{r} = -\frac{1}{r}.$$

This is just $-\phi$, with the constant chosen so that the potential at infinity is zero.

The divergence of **E** is calculated as follows:

$$\nabla \cdot \mathbf{E} = \frac{1}{r^3}\nabla \cdot \mathbf{r} + \mathbf{r} \cdot \left(\nabla \frac{1}{r^3}\right)$$

$$= \frac{3}{r^3} + \mathbf{r} \cdot \left(-\frac{3}{r^5}\mathbf{r}\right) = 0$$

(except when $\mathbf{r} = \mathbf{0}$). Hence, if Σ is a closed, bounded surface not including the origin in its interior R,

$$\iint_{\Sigma} \mathbf{E} \cdot \mathbf{d\sigma} = \iiint_{R} \nabla \cdot \mathbf{E} \, dV = 0.$$

If Σ *does* include the origin in its interior, let Σ' denote a sphere containing Σ, say of radius a and center at the origin. Then if $\mathbf{d\sigma}$ refers to the outer normal of the boundary surface of the region between Σ and Σ', there follows

$$\iint_{\Sigma} \mathbf{E} \cdot \mathbf{d\sigma} - \iint_{\Sigma'} \mathbf{E} \cdot \mathbf{d\sigma} = 0,$$

so that

$$\iint_{\Sigma} \mathbf{E} \cdot \mathbf{d\sigma} = \iint_{\Sigma'} \mathbf{E} \cdot \mathbf{d\sigma} = \iint_{\Sigma'} \frac{1}{a^2} \mathbf{u_r} \cdot \mathbf{u_r} \, d\sigma$$

$$= \frac{1}{a^2} (\text{area of } \Sigma') = 4\pi.$$

If the charge at $\mathbf{r} = \mathbf{0}$ is of magnitude q, then

$$\iint_{\Sigma} \mathbf{E} \cdot \mathbf{d\sigma} = \begin{cases} 4\pi q, & \text{if } \Sigma \text{ includes } \mathbf{r} = \mathbf{0}, \\ 0, & \text{if } \Sigma \text{ does not include } \mathbf{r} = \mathbf{0}. \end{cases}$$

If there are charges q_1 at P_1, ..., and q_k at P_k, then adding the fields due to the individual charges to obtain the total field **E** we have the flux

$$\iint_{\Sigma} \mathbf{E} \cdot \mathbf{d\sigma} = 4\pi \sum_{P_i \text{ in } \Sigma} q_i.$$

The natural extension to a continuous charge distribution with density $\rho(x, y, z)$ results in the following formula for flux out of Σ:

$$\iint_{\Sigma} \mathbf{E} \cdot dV = \iiint_{R} 4\pi \rho \, dV,$$

where R is the region bounded by Σ. The divergence theorem then yields

$$\iiint_R \nabla \cdot \mathbf{E} \, dV = \iiint_R 4\pi\rho \, dV$$

for arbitrary regions R, with the conclusion

$$\nabla \cdot \mathbf{E} = 4\pi\rho,$$

or in terms of the electric potential defined above,

$$\nabla^2 V = -4\pi\rho.$$

(This is "Poisson's equation.")

6 CURVILINEAR COORDINATES

ALTHOUGH rectangular coordinates are often natural enough, there arise instances in which other kinds of coordinate systems are more convenient. A general coordinate system identifies and locates a point in space relative to a given origin or reference point by telling how to reach the point along certain members of families of curves; in the case of rectangular coordinates these curves are straight lines parallel to the coordinate axes, but in general they need not be straight. Hence the term *curvilinear coordinates*.

Rectangular coordinates are defined by three mutually perpendicular families of planes; curvilinear coordinates, by families of surfaces which are not necessarily plane surfaces. To describe such surfaces, however, it is convenient to use their representation by equations in the familiar rectangular coordinates. Thus, it will be pertinent to consider, in effect, the transformation from curvilinear to rectangular coordinates (and vice versa), and indeed to define curvilinear coordinate systems by means of such transformations.

It will be convenient to use (x_1, x_2, x_3) as rectangular coordinates in place of (x, y, z); the subscripts make it possible to use the Σ notation to indicate sums.

6.1 Definition by transformations

Consider now the transformation from (x_1, x_2, x_3) to (u_1, u_2, u_3) defined

161

by the equations

$$u_1 = f_1(x_1, x_2, x_3),$$
$$u_2 = f_2(x_1, x_2, x_3),$$
$$u_3 = f_3(x_1, x_2, x_3).$$

If there is (at least in some neighborhood of a given point) a unique inverse transformation:

$$x_1 = F_1(u_1, u_2, u_3),$$
$$x_2 = F_2(u_1, u_2, u_3),$$
$$x_3 = F_3(u_1, u_2, u_3),$$

then the label (u_1, u_2, u_3) serves to describe a given point P as well as its rectangular description (x_1, x_2, x_3).

The transformations from x's to u's and back can be viewed geometrically as providing a mapping from the x-space [the space in which the x's are rectangular coordinates and in which it is desired to use curvilinear coordinates] to the u-space [the set of points (u_1, u_2, u_3) obtained by interpreting the u's as rectangular coordinates] and back. In other words, the curvilinear coordinates (u_1, u_2, u_3) of a point in x-space whose rectangular coordinates are (x_1, x_2, x_3) can also be interpreted geometrically as rectangular coordinates of a point in a u-space. Indeed, the curvilinear coordinate curves and surfaces in the x-space are just the images of rectangular coordinate curves and surfaces in u-space.

To be specific, planes of the form $u_1 = a$, $u_2 = b$, and $u_3 = c$ in u-space define (as their images) surfaces in x-space. For, if $u = a$, for instance, then

$$x_1 = F_1(a, u_2, u_3),$$
$$x_2 = F_2(a, u_2, u_3),$$
$$x_3 = F_3(a, u_2, u_3),$$

and these equations define parametrically the surface $f(x_1, x_2, x_3) = a$ in x-space. This will be called a u_2u_3-surface†, and there are defined similarly a u_3u_1-surface and a u_1u_2-surface. The three surfaces through a given point in x-space intersect in three curves. If $u_1 = a$ and $u_2 = b$, the equations

$$x_1 = F_1(a, b, u_3),$$
$$x_2 = F_2(a, b, u_3),$$
$$x_3 = F_3(a, b, u_3)$$

---

†This surface is named according to the parameters which vary over it, just as the coordinate curves will be named (in this chapter) according to the parameters which vary along them. Some authors name the surfaces and curves according to what is held constant in defining them—the u_2u_3-surface would be a u_1-surface with that convention. Some authors use one convention for surfaces and the other for curves.

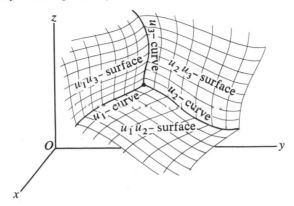

Figure 6.1

define parametrically a curve—called here a u_3-curve, which can also be
expressed as the intersection of the surfaces on which $u_1 = a$ and $u_2 = b$:

$$f_1(x_1, x_2, x_3) = a,$$
$$f_2(x_1, x_2, x_3) = b.$$

EXAMPLE 6.1   Consider again the transformation defining spherical coordinates (r, ϕ, θ):

$$x = r \cos \theta \cos \phi,$$
$$y = r \cos \theta \sin \phi,$$
$$z = r \sin \theta.$$

The $\theta\phi$-surfaces obtained by setting $r = r_0$ are spheres:

$$x^2 + y^2 + z^2 = r_0^2,$$

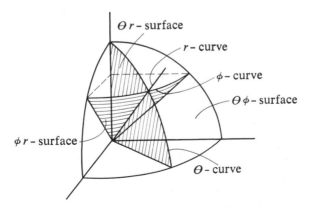

Figure 6.2.   (See Example 6.1.)

the ϕr-surfaces, with $\theta = \theta_0$, are cones:

$$x^2 + y^2 = (\cot \theta_0)z^2,$$

and the θr-surfaces $\phi = \phi_0$ are planes:

$$x = (\cot \phi_0)y.$$

The r-curves are rays from the origin, the θ-curves are great circles (longitude lines) on the sphere through the point in question, and the ϕ-curves are small circles (latitude lines) on the sphere.

According to an "implicit function theorem" of calculus a unique inverse of the transformation from u's to x's will exist (at least locally) if the functions f_1, f_2, and f_3 giving the x's in terms of the u's have continuous partial derivatives and are such that the *Jacobian* does not vanish:

$$\frac{\partial(u_1, u_2, u_3)}{\partial(x_1, x_2, x_3)} = \begin{vmatrix} \dfrac{\partial u_1}{\partial x_1} & \dfrac{\partial u_1}{\partial x_2} & \dfrac{\partial u_1}{\partial x_3} \\[2mm] \dfrac{\partial u_2}{\partial x_1} & \dfrac{\partial u_2}{\partial x_2} & \dfrac{\partial u_2}{\partial x_3} \\[2mm] \dfrac{\partial u_3}{\partial x_1} & \dfrac{\partial u_3}{\partial x_2} & \dfrac{\partial u_3}{\partial x_3} \end{vmatrix} = \nabla u_1 \cdot \nabla u_2 \times \nabla u_3 \neq 0.$$

Further, the inverse functions $x_j = F_j(u_1, u_2, u_3)$ are continuously differentiable, with Jacobian

$$\frac{\partial(x_1, x_2, x_3)}{\partial(u_1, u_2, u_3)} = \begin{vmatrix} \dfrac{\partial x_1}{\partial u_1} & \dfrac{\partial x_1}{\partial u_2} & \dfrac{\partial x_1}{\partial u_3} \\[2mm] \dfrac{\partial x_2}{\partial u_1} & \dfrac{\partial x_2}{\partial u_2} & \dfrac{\partial x_2}{\partial u_3} \\[2mm] \dfrac{\partial x_3}{\partial u_1} & \dfrac{\partial x_3}{\partial u_2} & \dfrac{\partial x_3}{\partial u_3} \end{vmatrix} = \mathbf{r}_{u_1} \cdot \mathbf{r}_{u_2} \times \mathbf{r}_{u_3} \neq 0.$$

Moreover, these Jacobians are reciprocals of one another

$$\frac{\partial(u_1, u_2, u_3)}{\partial(x_1, x_2, x_3)} \cdot \frac{\partial(x_1, x_2, x_3)}{\partial(u_1, u_2, u_3)} = 1.$$

This may be seen using the multiplication rule for determinants (which says that the element in the ith row and jth column of a product is the inner product of the ith row vector of the first factor and the jth column vector of the second). The element in the ith row and jth column of the product of the two Jacobians is (using the chain rule)

$$\sum_{k=1}^{3} \frac{\partial u_i}{\partial x_k} \frac{\partial x_k}{\partial u_j} = \frac{\partial u_i}{\partial u_j} = \begin{cases} 1, & \text{if } i = j, \\ 0, & \text{if } i \neq j; \end{cases}$$

that is, the product is a determinant with 1's on the main diagonal and zeros elsewhere, which has the value one, as claimed. Notice that these nine relations can be expressed as follows:

$$(\nabla u_i) \cdot (\mathbf{r}_{u_j}) = \begin{cases} 1, & i = j, \\ 0, & i \neq j. \end{cases}$$

The sets of vectors $(\nabla u_1, \nabla u_2, \nabla u_3)$ and $(\mathbf{r}_{u_1}, \mathbf{r}_{u_2}, \mathbf{r}_{u_3})$ are *reciprocal sets*, as defined in Sect. 1.9.

The vectors $(\mathbf{r}_{u_1}, \mathbf{r}_{u_2}, \mathbf{r}_{u_3})$ are tangents, respectively, to the u_1, u_2, and u_3-curves through a given point. If their scalar triple product is not zero, and only then, they are not coplanar. This is the geometrical significance of the assumption needed for the existence of a unique inverse transformation. If the vectors $\mathbf{r}_{u_1}, \mathbf{r}_{u_2}, \mathbf{r}_{u_3}$ are mutually perpendicular, the coordinate system (u_1, u_2, u_3) is said to be an *orthogonal* curvilinear coordinate system.

Let h_i denote the length of $\mathbf{r}_{u_i}$:

$$h_i = \left| \frac{\partial \mathbf{r}}{\partial u_i} \right| = \frac{ds_i}{du_i},$$

where s_i denotes arc length along the u_i-curve. Then

$$\frac{\partial \mathbf{r}}{\partial u_i} = h_i \frac{\partial \mathbf{r}}{\partial s_i} = h_i \mathbf{t}_i,$$

where $\mathbf{t}_i$ is a unit tangent to the u_i-curve. The lengths h_i will be seen to be crucial in expressing arc length and the vector operator ∇ in terms of curvilinear coordinates.

EXAMPLE 6.2   Consider the spherical coordinate system defined as in Example 6.1. Differentiation yields (with $\sin \theta = s\theta$, $\cos \phi = c\phi$, etc.):

$$\mathbf{r}_r = s\theta \, c\phi \, \mathbf{i} + s\theta \, s\phi \, \mathbf{j} + c\theta \, \mathbf{k},$$
$$\mathbf{r}_\theta = r \, c\theta \, c\phi \, \mathbf{i} + r \, c\theta \, s\phi \, \mathbf{j} - r \, s\theta \, \mathbf{k},$$
$$\mathbf{r}_\phi = -r \, s\theta \, s\phi \, \mathbf{i} + r \, s\theta \, c\phi \, \mathbf{j}.$$

Then

$$h_1 = 1, \qquad \mathbf{t}_1 = \mathbf{r},$$
$$h_2 = r, \qquad \mathbf{t}_2 = c\theta \, c\phi \, \mathbf{i} + c\theta \, s\phi \, \mathbf{j} - s\theta \, \mathbf{k},$$
$$h_3 = r \, s\theta, \quad \mathbf{t}_3 = -s\phi \, \mathbf{i} + c\phi \, \mathbf{j}.$$

(These unit tangents $(\mathbf{t}_1, \mathbf{t}_2, \mathbf{t}_3)$ are as given earlier in Sect. 2.5.) Notice that $\mathbf{r}_r \perp \mathbf{r}_\theta$, $\mathbf{r}_\theta \perp \mathbf{r}_\phi$, and $\mathbf{r}_r \perp \mathbf{r}_\phi$; the coordinates (r, θ, ϕ) are orthogonal. Since $\mathbf{t}_2 \times \mathbf{t}_3 = \mathbf{t}_1$, the set is right-handed, so that

$$\mathbf{r}_r \cdot \mathbf{r}_\theta \times \mathbf{r}_\phi = h_1 h_2 h_3 = r^2 \sin \theta.$$

Problems

6.1. Determine and sketch the reciprocal sets $(\nabla u, \nabla v)$, $(\mathbf{r}_u, \mathbf{r}_v)$ for the (plane) transformation $x = u$, $y = u + v$. Determine $\dfrac{\partial(u, v)}{\partial(x, y)}$ and $\dfrac{\partial(x, y)}{\partial(u, v)}$.

6.2. Consider the coordinates (u, v, w) defined by

$$x = u,$$
$$y = u + v,$$
$$z = u + v + w.$$

Determine h_u, h_v, h_w, where $h_u = \left| \dfrac{\partial \mathbf{r}}{\partial u} \right|$, etc. Is $h_u h_v h_w = \dfrac{\partial(x, y, z)}{\partial(u, v, w)}$? (Why not?)

6.3. Let cylindrical coordinates (ρ, θ, z) be defined by

$$x = \rho \cos \theta,$$
$$y = \rho \sin \theta,$$
$$z = z.$$

Determine h_ρ, h_θ, h_z, the unit tangents $\mathbf{t}_\rho$, $\mathbf{t}_\theta$, $\mathbf{t}_z$, and the Jacobian $\dfrac{\partial(\rho, \theta, z)}{\partial(x, y, z)}$. Show that the coordinates are orthogonal. What are the ρ-curves, θ-curves, and z-curves? What are the $\rho\theta$-surfaces, ρz-surfaces, θz-surfaces? Determine the reciprocal set $(\nabla \rho, \nabla \theta, \nabla z)$.

6.4. Study the (plane) transformation

$$x = \cosh u \cos v,$$
$$y = \sinh u \sin v.$$

(Determine h's, $\mathbf{t}$'s, and sketch u- and v-curves, etc. Are the (u, v) coordinates orthogonal?)

6.5. Study the transformation

$$x = a \sinh u \sin v \cos \theta,$$
$$y = a \sinh u \sin v \sin \theta,$$
$$z = a \cosh u \cos v.$$

6.2   *Volume and arc length elements*

A volume integral of a function of position over some region V in the (x_1, x_2, x_3)-space can often be more conveniently computed using curvilinear coordinates—as a volume integral over the corresponding region W in the (u_1, u_2, u_3)-space. Indeed, it is often useful to introduce curvilinear coordinates which are chosen so that the region W is especially simple.

Suppose that a rectangular grid is introduced in the region W, as is customary in defining a triple integral, and consider the image grid in the region V. A particular cell with edges Δu_1, Δu_2, and Δu_3 in W corresponds to a cell in V which is approximately a parallelepiped (see Fig. 6.3). The edges of this parallelepiped are approximately the vector differentials

$$\mathbf{r}_{u_1}\,\Delta u_1, \qquad \mathbf{r}_{u_2}\,\Delta u_2, \qquad \mathbf{r}_{u_3}\,\Delta u_3,$$

where, as before, $\mathbf{r}_{u_k} = \partial\mathbf{r}/\partial u_k$ is tangent to the u_k-curve. The volume of a

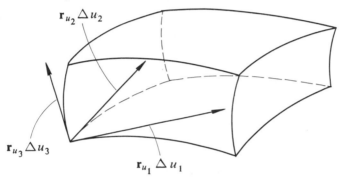

Figure 6.3. Volume element.

parallelepiped with three given vectors as adjacent edges is the magnitude of their scalar triple product:

$$dV = \left|\mathbf{r}_{u_1}\cdot\mathbf{r}_{u_2} \times \mathbf{r}_{u_3}\right| \Delta u_1\, \Delta u_2\, \Delta u_3,$$

$$= \left|\frac{\partial(x_1, x_2, x_3)}{\partial(u_1, u_2, u_3)}\right| \Delta u_1\, \Delta u_2\, \Delta u_3.$$

Thus,

$$\iiint_V f(x_1, x_2, x_3)\, dx_1\, dx_2\, dx_3 = \iiint_W f(x_1, x_2, x_3) \left|\frac{\partial(x_1, x_2, x_3)}{\partial(u_1, u_2, u_3)}\right| du_1\, du_2\, du_3.$$

The x's in $f(x_1, x_2, x_3)$ are of course to be replaced by their expressions in terms of the u's as given by the transformation which defines the curvilinear coordinates.

EXAMPLE 6.3   In spherical coordinates (see Examples 6.1 and 6.2) the Jacobian was found to be

$$\mathbf{r}_r\cdot\mathbf{r}_\theta \times \mathbf{r}_\phi = r^2 \sin\theta,$$

and so in transforming an integral in rectangular coordinates (x, y, z) into spherical coordinates one uses the substitution

$$dx\, dy\, dz \quad \rightarrow \quad r^2 \sin\theta\, dr\, d\theta\, d\phi.$$

(The region of integration must be determined, of course, in terms of the spherical coordinates.)

The length of arc in the (x_1, x_2, x_3)-space can be computed in the (u_1, u_2, u_3)-space once there is obtained an expression for the differential of arc length in terms of the curvilinear coordinates. The arc length differential is ds, where

$$ds^2 = d\mathbf{r} \cdot d\mathbf{r}.$$

Now,

$$d\mathbf{r} = \mathbf{r}_{u_1}\, du_1 + \mathbf{r}_{u_2}\, du_2 + \mathbf{r}_{u_3}\, du_3,$$

and therefore

$$ds^2 = \sum_m \mathbf{r}_{u_m}\, du_m \cdot \sum_n \mathbf{r}_{u_n}\, du_n$$

$$= \sum_n \sum_m g_{mn}\, du_m\, du_n,$$

where

$$g_{mn} = \mathbf{r}_{u_m} \cdot \mathbf{r}_{u_n}.$$

(The sums run from $m = 1$ to 3 and $n = 1$ to 3.) The matrix of g_{mn}'s has a determinant equal to the square of the Jacobian of the x's with respect to the u's:

$$\begin{vmatrix} g_{11} & g_{12} & g_{13} \\ g_{21} & g_{22} & g_{23} \\ g_{31} & g_{32} & g_{33} \end{vmatrix} = \left\{ \frac{\partial(x_1,\, x_2,\, x_3)}{\partial(u_1,\, u_2,\, u_3)} \right\}^2.$$

This follows from the fact that the Jacobian is itself a determinant with rows equal to the components of $\mathbf{r}_{u_m}$, $m = 1, 2, 3$. For, multiplying this determinant by itself (transposed, which doesn't alter its value), one obtains by the multiplication rule the quantity $\mathbf{r}_{u_m} \cdot \mathbf{r}_{u_n} = g_{mn}$ as the entry in the mth row and nth column.

It is to be observed that in the case of orthogonal curvilinear coordinates the $\mathbf{r}_u$ vectors are mutually orthogonal, so that all cross-product terms in ds^2 vanish. Further, with $\mathbf{r}_{u_m} = h_m$, the orthogonality of the $\mathbf{r}_u$'s implies that

$$\mathbf{r}_{u_1} \cdot \mathbf{r}_{u_2} \times \mathbf{r}_{u_3} = \pm h_1 h_2 h_3$$

with a plus sign $(+)$ if $(\mathbf{r}_{u_1}, \mathbf{r}_{u_2}, \mathbf{r}_{u_3})$ is a right-handed set, in that order, and a minus sign $(-)$ if it is a left-handed set. The quantities g_{mn} are

$$g_{mn} = \begin{cases} 0, & \text{if } m \neq n, \\ h_m{}^2, & \text{if } m = n, \end{cases}$$

and the determinant of the g's has the value

$$g_{11}g_{22}g_{33} = h_1{}^2 h_2{}^2 h_3{}^2.$$

EXAMPLE 6.4   Consider the oblique coordinates defined by the transformation

$$x_1 = u_1,$$
$$x_2 = u_1 + u_2,$$
$$x_3 = u_1 + u_2 + u_3.$$

Differentiation yields

$$\mathbf{r}_{u1} = \mathbf{i}_1 + \mathbf{i}_2 + \mathbf{i}_3,$$
$$\mathbf{r}_{u2} = \mathbf{i}_2 + \mathbf{i}_3,$$
$$\mathbf{r}_{u3} = \mathbf{i}_3,$$

and then

$$g_{11} = 3, \qquad g_{12} = 2, \qquad g_{13} = 1,$$
$$g_{22} = 2, \qquad g_{23} = 1, \qquad g_{33} = 1.$$

The arc length differential is then given by the relation

$$ds^2 = 3(du_1)^2 + 2(du_2)^2 + (du_3)^2 + 4du_1 du_2 + 2du_1 du_3 + 2du_2 du_3.$$

6.3   *The gradient in curvilinear coordinates*

It is assumed that the Jacobians of the transformation from (x) to (u) and back do not vanish in the regions being considered. Thus,

$$\frac{\partial(x_1, x_2, x_3)}{\partial(u_1, u_2, u_3)} = \mathbf{r}_{u_1} \cdot \mathbf{r}_{u_2} \times \mathbf{r}_{u_3} \neq 0,$$

and so the vectors $(\mathbf{r}_{u_1}, \mathbf{r}_{u_2}, \mathbf{r}_{u_3})$ are linearly independent. This means that any vector $\mathbf{V}$ can be expressed as a linear combination of those vectors:

$$\mathbf{V} = v_1 \mathbf{r}_{u_1} + v_2 \mathbf{r}_{u_2} + v_3 \mathbf{r}_{u_3},$$

using a unique set of coefficients v_1, v_2, v_3. These coefficients are readily determined using the reciprocal set. Taking the dot product on each side with ∇u_m we obtain

$$\mathbf{V} \cdot \nabla u_m = v_1(\mathbf{r}_{u_1} \cdot \nabla u_m) + v_2(\mathbf{r}_{u_2} \cdot \nabla u_m) + v_3(\mathbf{r}_{u_3} \cdot \nabla u_m) = v_m,$$

for $m = 1$, 2, and 3. Therefore

$$\mathbf{V} = \sum_{m=1}^{3} (\mathbf{V} \cdot \nabla u_m) \mathbf{r}_{u_m},$$

and in quite analagous fashion it is seen that $\mathbf{V}$ can also be written

$$\mathbf{V} = \sum_{m=1}^{3} (\mathbf{V} \cdot \mathbf{r}_{u_m}) \nabla u_m.$$

Unit vectors $(\mathbf{j}_1, \mathbf{j}_2, \mathbf{j}_3)$ along $(\mathbf{r}_{u_1}, \mathbf{r}_{u_2}, \mathbf{r}_{u_3})$ and $\mathbf{k}_1, \mathbf{k}_2, \mathbf{k}_3)$ along $(\nabla u_1, \nabla u_2, \nabla u_3)$ might be used; the length of $\mathbf{r}_{u_m}$ is $(\mathbf{r}_{u_m} \cdot \mathbf{r}_{u_m})^{1/2} = (g_{mm})^{1/2}$, and with $G_{mn} = \nabla u_m \cdot \nabla u_n$, the length of ∇u_m is $(G_{mm})^{1/2}$. Then

$$\mathbf{V} = \sum_{m=1}^{3} (\mathbf{V} \cdot \mathbf{k}_m) \mathbf{j}_m (g_{mm} G_{mm})^{1/2}$$

$$= \sum_{n=1}^{3} (\mathbf{V} \cdot \mathbf{j}_n) \mathbf{k}_n (g_{nn} G_{nn})^{1/2}.$$

In particular, if $w = f(\mathbf{r})$ is a given scalar function of position, the vector grad w can be expressed in terms of $(\nabla u_1, \nabla u_2, \nabla u_3)$:

$$\nabla w = \sum_{m=1}^{3} (\nabla w) \cdot \mathbf{r}_{u_m} \nabla u_m$$

$$= \sum_{m=1}^{3} \left\{ \frac{\partial w}{\partial x_1} \frac{\partial x_1}{\partial u_m} + \frac{\partial w}{\partial x_2} \frac{\partial x_2}{\partial u_m} + \frac{\partial w}{\partial x_3} \frac{\partial x_3}{\partial u_m} \right\} \nabla u_m$$

$$= \sum_{m=1}^{3} \frac{\partial w}{\partial u_m} \nabla u_m.$$

The quantities ∇u_m in this last formula for the gradient may be obtained directly by expressing the u's in terms of the x's, or indirectly, by determining the derivatives of the u's implicitly as solutions of some systems of equations. The following simple expressions for the ∇u's in terms of the $\mathbf{r}_u$'s, based on the fact that they are reciprocal sets (see Sect. 1.9), are convenient:

$$\nabla u_1 = \frac{1}{d} \mathbf{r}_{u_2} \times \mathbf{r}_{u_3},$$

$$\nabla u_2 = \frac{1}{d} \mathbf{r}_{u_3} \times \mathbf{r}_{u_1},$$

$$\nabla u_3 = \frac{1}{d} \mathbf{r}_{u_1} \times \mathbf{r}_{u_2},$$

where d is the Jacobian:

$$d = \mathbf{r}_{u_1} \cdot \mathbf{r}_{u_2} \times \mathbf{r}_{u_3}.$$

E X A M P L E 6.5   Consider again spherical coordinates (see Examples 6.2 and 6.3) with

$$\mathbf{r}_r = s\theta \, c\phi \, \mathbf{i} + s\theta \, s\phi \, \mathbf{j} + c\theta \, \mathbf{k},$$
$$\mathbf{r}_\theta = r \, c\theta \, c\phi \, \mathbf{i} + r \, c\theta \, s\phi \, \mathbf{j} - r \, s\theta \, \mathbf{k},$$
$$\mathbf{r}_\phi = -r \, s\theta \, s\phi \, \mathbf{i} + r \, s\theta \, c\phi \, \mathbf{j}.$$

Then (as found in Example 6.2)

$$d = \mathbf{r}_r \cdot \mathbf{r}_\theta \times \mathbf{r}_\phi = r^2 \sin \theta,$$

and

$$\nabla r = \frac{1}{d} \mathbf{r}_\theta \times \mathbf{r}_\phi = s\theta \, c\phi \, \mathbf{i} + s\theta \, s\phi \, \mathbf{j} + c\theta \, \mathbf{k} = \mathbf{r}_r,$$

$$\nabla \theta = \frac{1}{d} \mathbf{r}_\phi \times \mathbf{r}_r = \frac{1}{r}(c\theta \, c\phi \, \mathbf{i} + s\theta \, c\phi \, \mathbf{j} - s\theta \, \mathbf{k}) = \frac{1}{r} \mathbf{r}_\theta,$$

$$\nabla \phi = \frac{1}{d} \mathbf{r}_r \times \mathbf{r}_\theta = \frac{1}{r}(-s\phi \, s\theta \, \mathbf{i} + c\phi \, s\theta \, \mathbf{j}) = \frac{1}{r} \mathbf{r}_\phi.$$

If then

$$w = \psi(r, \theta, \phi),$$

its gradient is

$$\text{grad } w = \psi_r \nabla r + \psi_\theta \nabla \theta + \psi_\phi \nabla \phi$$

$$= \psi_r \mathbf{r}_r + \frac{1}{r} \psi_\theta \mathbf{r}_\theta + \frac{1}{r} \psi_\phi \mathbf{r}_\phi.$$

Notice that the unit vectors corresponding to the reciprocal sets $(\mathbf{r}_{u_m})$ and (∇u_m) in Example 6.5 are identical. This is because of the orthogonality of the curvilinear coordinates used there. For, when the curvilinear coordinates are orthogonal, the u_1-curve is normal to the $u_2 u_3$-surface, so that the tangent $\mathbf{r}_{u_1}$ is parallel to the normal ∇u_1, etc. So in the orthogonal case, the unit vectors along the $\mathbf{r}_u$'s are identical with those along the ∇u's: $\mathbf{j}_m = \mathbf{k}_m$, $m = 1, 2, 3$. Further,

$$\nabla u_1 = \frac{1}{d} \mathbf{r}_{u_2} \times \mathbf{r}_{u_3} = \frac{h_2 h_3}{h_1 h_2 h_3} \mathbf{j}_1 = \frac{1}{h_1} \mathbf{j}_1 = \frac{1}{h_1{}^2} \mathbf{r}_{u_1},$$

$$\nabla u_2 = \frac{1}{h_2} \mathbf{j}_2 = \frac{1}{h_2{}^2} \mathbf{r}_{u_2},$$

$$\nabla u_3 = \frac{1}{h_3} \mathbf{j}_3 = \frac{1}{h_3{}^2} \mathbf{r}_{u_3}.$$

The gradient, in the orthogonal case, can then be written

$$\text{grad } w = \sum_{m=1}^{3} \frac{\partial w}{\partial u_m} \frac{1}{h_m} \mathbf{j}_m.$$

Problems

6.6.   Consider the coordinates defined by

$$u_1 = x_3 - x_1,$$
$$u_2 = x_2 - x_3,$$
$$u_3 = x_1 + x_2 + x_3.$$

(a) Determine the u's, and from them the $\mathbf{r}_u$'s.

(b) Determine expressions for the elements of arc length and volume in the (x_1, x_2, x_3)-space in terms of the u's.

(c) Determine the expression for grad w in terms of the u's.

6.7.   Consider the plane curvilinear coordinates (u, v) defined by

$$x = u^2 + v,$$
$$y = u + v^2.$$

What are the constant-u and constant-v curves? Determine expressions in terms of u and v for the gradient and for the elements of arc length and area. (If you like, add the equation $z = w$ to make the problem three dimensional so that the discussion of the above section applies directly.)

6.8.   Let the "paraboloidal" coordinates (u, v, θ) be defined by

$$x = uv \cos \theta,$$
$$y = uv \sin \theta,$$
$$z = \tfrac{1}{2}(u^2 - v^2).$$

Obtain the gradient and the elements of arc length and volume in terms of (u, v, θ).

6.4   *Divergence and curl in curvilinear coordinates*

Consider a vector function $\mathbf{V}$, and let it be represented in terms of the basis $(\mathbf{r}_{u_1}, \mathbf{r}_{u_2}, \mathbf{r}_{u_3})$:

$$\begin{aligned}
\mathbf{V} &= V_1 \mathbf{r}_{u_1} + V_2 \mathbf{r}_{u_2} + V_3 \mathbf{r}_{u_3} \\
&= V_1 \, d \, \nabla u_2 \times \nabla u_3 + V_2 \, d \, \nabla u_3 \times \nabla u_1 + V_3 \, d \, \nabla u_1 \times \nabla u_2,
\end{aligned}$$

where as before

$$d = \mathbf{r}_{u_1} \cdot \mathbf{r}_{u_2} \times \mathbf{r}_{u_3}$$

Using the formula

$$\nabla \cdot \phi \mathbf{F} = \phi \nabla \cdot \mathbf{F} + \mathbf{F} \cdot \nabla \phi$$

(from Chapter 4) one can write, for instance,

$$\nabla \cdot (V_1 \, d \, \nabla u_2 \times \nabla u_3) = V_1 \, d \, \nabla \cdot (\nabla u_2 \times \nabla u_3) + (\nabla u_2 \times \nabla u_3) \cdot \nabla (V_1 \, d)$$

$$= 0 + \nabla u_2 \times \nabla u_3 \cdot \sum \frac{\partial (dV_1)}{\partial u_m} \nabla u_m$$

$$= \frac{1}{d} \frac{\partial (dV_1)}{\partial u_m}.$$

With similar computations for the other two terms, one has

$$\nabla \cdot \mathbf{V} = \frac{1}{d} \sum_{m=1}^{3} \frac{\partial (dV_m)}{\partial u_m}.$$

When the coordinates are orthogonal, this becomes

$$\nabla \cdot \mathbf{V} = \frac{1}{h_1 h_2 h_3} \sum_{m=1}^{3} \frac{\partial (h_1 h_2 h_3 V_m)}{\partial u_m},$$

where, as before, $h_m = |\mathbf{r}_{u_m}|$.

The Laplacian of a scalar function ψ can now be obtained in terms of the u's. First, write $\nabla \psi$ in the form

$$\nabla \psi = \sum (\nabla \psi \cdot \nabla u_m) \mathbf{r}_{u_m},$$

and use the $(\nabla \psi \cdot \nabla u_m)$ as the "V_m" in the divergence formula:

$$\nabla^2 \psi = \nabla \cdot \nabla \psi = \frac{1}{d} \sum_{m=1}^{3} \frac{\partial (d \nabla \psi \cdot \nabla u_m)}{\partial u_m}$$

$$= \frac{1}{d} \sum_{m=1}^{3} \frac{\partial}{\partial u_m} \left[d \sum_{n=1}^{3} \frac{\partial \psi}{\partial u_n} \nabla u_n \cdot \nabla u_m \right]$$

$$= \frac{1}{d} \sum_{m=1}^{3} \frac{\partial}{\partial u_m} \left[d \sum_{n=1}^{3} G_{mn} \frac{\partial \psi}{\partial u_n} \right],$$

where, as previously, $G_{mn} = \nabla u_m \cdot \nabla u_n$. In the case of *orthogonal* coordinates this reduces to

$$\nabla^2 \psi = \frac{1}{h_1 h_2 h_3} \sum_{m=1}^{3} \frac{\partial}{\partial u_m} \left(\frac{h_1 h_2 h_3}{h_m{}^2} \frac{\partial \psi}{\partial u_m} \right).$$

EXAMPLE 6.6   In the case of spherical coordinates (see Example 6.2),

$$h_1 = 1, \quad h_2 = r, \quad h_3 = r \sin \theta,$$

and

$$\nabla r = \mathbf{r}_r, \quad \nabla \theta = \frac{1}{r} \mathbf{r}_\theta, \quad \nabla \phi = \frac{1}{r} \mathbf{r}_\phi.$$

Thus,

$$\nabla \cdot \mathbf{V} = \frac{1}{r^2 \sin \theta} \left[\frac{\partial}{\partial r}(r^2 \sin \theta \, \mathbf{V} \cdot \nabla r) + \frac{\partial}{\partial \theta}(r^2 \sin \theta \, \mathbf{V} \cdot \nabla \theta) + \frac{\partial}{\partial \phi}(r^2 \sin \theta \, \mathbf{V} \cdot \nabla \phi) \right]$$

and

$$\nabla^2 \psi = \frac{1}{r^2 \sin \theta} \left[\frac{\partial}{\partial r}\left(r^2 \sin \theta \, \frac{\partial \psi}{\partial r}\right) + \frac{\partial}{\partial \theta}\left(\sin \theta \, \frac{\partial \psi}{\partial r}\right) + \frac{\partial}{\partial \phi}\left(\frac{1}{\sin \theta} \, \frac{\partial \psi}{\partial \phi}\right) \right].$$

To calculate the curl, let $\mathbf{V}$ be expressed in terms of ∇u_m:

$$\mathbf{V} = \sum_1^3 (\mathbf{V} \cdot \mathbf{r}_{u_m}) \, \nabla u_m.$$

Then

$$\nabla \times \mathbf{V} = \sum_1^3 (\mathbf{V} \cdot \mathbf{r}_{u_m}) \, \nabla \times \nabla u_m + \nabla(\mathbf{V} \cdot \mathbf{r}_{u_m}) \times \nabla u_m$$

$$= 0 + \sum_{m=1}^3 \sum_{n=1}^3 \frac{\partial}{\partial u_n}(\mathbf{V} \cdot \mathbf{r}_{u_m}) \, \nabla u_n \times \nabla u_m$$

$$= \frac{1}{d} \left\{ \frac{\partial}{\partial u_1}(\mathbf{V} \cdot \mathbf{r}_{u_2})\mathbf{r}_{u_3} - \frac{\partial}{\partial u_1}(\mathbf{V} \cdot \mathbf{r}_{u_3})\mathbf{r}_{u_2} \right.$$

$$+ \frac{\partial}{\partial u_2}(\mathbf{V} \cdot \mathbf{r}_{u_3})\mathbf{r}_{u_1} - \frac{\partial}{\partial u_2}(\mathbf{V} \cdot \mathbf{r}_{u_1})\mathbf{r}_{u_3}$$

$$+ \left. \frac{\partial}{\partial u_3}(\mathbf{V} \cdot \mathbf{r}_{u_1})\mathbf{r}_{u_2} - \frac{\partial}{\partial u_3}(\mathbf{V} \cdot \mathbf{r}_{u_2})\mathbf{r}_{u_1} \right\}$$

$$= \frac{1}{d} \begin{vmatrix} \mathbf{r}_{u_1} & \mathbf{r}_{u_2} & \mathbf{r}_{u_3} \\ \dfrac{\partial}{\partial u_1} & \dfrac{\partial}{\partial u_2} & \dfrac{\partial}{\partial u_3} \\ \mathbf{V} \cdot \mathbf{r}_{u_1} & \mathbf{V} \cdot \mathbf{r}_{u_2} & \mathbf{V} \cdot \mathbf{r}_{u_3} \end{vmatrix}.$$

Problems

6.9.   Determine the divergence and Laplacian in terms of the coordinates of Problem 6.6.

6.10.   Determine the Laplacian for the coordinates of Problem 6.8.

6.11.   Let (u_1, u_2, u_3) be related to (x_1, x_2, x_3) by an *orthogonal* transformation (i.e., a rotation)

$$\begin{aligned} x_1 &= a_{11}u_1 + a_{12}u_2 + a_{13}u_3, \\ x_2 &= a_{21}u_1 + a_{22}u_2 + a_{23}u_3, \\ x_3 &= a_{31}u_1 + a_{32}u_2 + a_{33}u_3, \end{aligned}$$

1.47. $2x + 2y + z = 5$.

1.48. $2\mathbf{i} + 8\mathbf{j} + 3\mathbf{k}$.

1.49. $2/\sqrt{77}, \quad 8/\sqrt{77}, \quad 3/\sqrt{77}$.

1.50. $\dfrac{x-1}{3} = \dfrac{y}{10} = \dfrac{z+3}{4}$

1.51. $3/\sqrt{2}$.

1.52. $7/\sqrt{6}$,   below.

1.53. $3x - 4y + 12z = 169$.

1.55. $-\mathbf{i} + 2\mathbf{j} - \mathbf{k}, \quad \mathbf{i} - \mathbf{j}, \quad \mathbf{i} - \mathbf{j} + \mathbf{k}$.

1.57.   No; since $\mathbf{B}_3$ is perpendicular to $\mathbf{A}_1$ and $\mathbf{A}_2$ it would also be perpendicular to $\mathbf{A}_3$, if $\mathbf{A}_3$ is in the plane of $\mathbf{A}_1$ and $\mathbf{A}_2$.

1.58. P: $(-637/259, 154/259, 553/259)$, Q: $(-385/259, 518/259, 637/259)$

CHAPTER 2

2.1.   (a) $4(x^3 - 2x)^3(3x^2 - 2)$;   (b) $3\cos(3x + 2)$;

   (c) $-2te^{-t^2}\dfrac{dt}{dx}$;   (d) $-\dfrac{4 + x^2}{x(x^2 - 4)}$.

2.2.   (a) $\mathbf{i} + 2t\mathbf{j} + 3t^2\mathbf{k}$;   (c) $\mathbf{V}(2) = 2\mathbf{i} + 4\mathbf{j} + 8\mathbf{k}$.

2.5.   (b) $.547$.

2.6.   (b) $\ddot{\mathbf{W}} = [(-\sin\theta)\mathbf{i} + (\cos\theta)\mathbf{j}]\,\ddot{\theta} + [-(\cos\theta)\mathbf{i} - (\sin\theta)\mathbf{j}]\dot{\theta}^2$.

2.8.   Use $\|\mathbf{V}(u)\| - |\mathbf{V}(u')| \| \leq |\mathbf{V}(u) - \mathbf{V}(u')|$.

2.10. $\sqrt{3}$.

2.11.   Line through tip of $\mathbf{j}$, parallel to $\mathbf{i} - \mathbf{j}$; $g(u)$ should range over $(-\infty, \infty)$.

2.12.   Ellipse, semi-axes 3 and 5; $s = \displaystyle\int_0^{2\pi} (25\sin^2\theta + 9\cos^2\theta)^{1/2}d\theta$.

2.13. $\frac{1}{4}[\sqrt{2} + \log(1 + \sqrt{2})]$.

2.14.   Elliptic spiral; $2\pi\sqrt{2}$.

2.15.   6.

2.16.   (b) $\mathbf{r} = u(\mathbf{i} + \mathbf{j}) + e^{-u}(\mathbf{j} + \mathbf{k})$,   plane curve.

2.17. $\frac{1}{2}\theta\sqrt{\theta^2 + 2} + \log\left(\dfrac{\theta + \sqrt{\theta^2 + 2}}{2}\right)$

2.19. $\kappa = \dfrac{(\theta^4 + 5\theta^2 + 8)^{1/2}}{(2 + \theta^2)^{3/2}}; \mathbf{b} = \dfrac{-\mathbf{i} + \mathbf{k}}{\sqrt{2}}$

2.20. $\tau = a/(1 + a^2)$.

2.21. $\mathbf{t} = [\mathbf{i} + 2u\mathbf{j} + 2\sqrt{u}\,\mathbf{k}]/(1 + 2u)$,

   $\kappa = [3\sqrt{u}(1 + 2u)^2]^{-1}$;

   $\mathbf{n} = [-2\sqrt{u}\,\mathbf{i} + 2\sqrt{u}\,\mathbf{j} + (1 - 2u)\mathbf{k}]/(1 + 2u)$.

2.22. $4x - 3z = 0$.

2.23. $\mathbf{r}_C = -6\mathbf{i} + 25\mathbf{j} - 8\mathbf{k}$.

2.24. $\mathbf{a} = \dfrac{g'(t)}{|g'(t)|}\,g''(t)\,\mathbf{t} + [g'(t)]^2\mathbf{n} = -\dot{\phi}^2\mathbf{u}_r + \ddot{\phi}\mathbf{u}_\phi$.

2.25. $\mathbf{a} = (t^2 + 2)^{-1/2}[t\mathbf{t} + (t^4 + 5t^2 + 8)^{1/2}\mathbf{n}]$
$= -(t/\sqrt{2})\mathbf{u}_r - (t/\sqrt{2})\mathbf{u}_\theta + 2\mathbf{u}_\phi.$

2.26. $\sqrt{2} + \log(\sqrt{2} + 1).$

CHAPTER 3

3.2. S/a, directed to the right along the axle (assuming zero ang. vel. of the car).

3.4.   (a) $q\mathbf{j} + r\mathbf{k}$;   (b) $p\mathbf{i} + r\mathbf{k}$;   (c) $A(p\mathbf{k} - r\mathbf{i})/2.$

3.5.   (a) Normal to the line of sight, perpendicular to each other;
(b) $u\mathbf{j} + v\mathbf{k}.$

3.6. $\dot{\theta}\mathbf{k}.$

3.7.   (a) W, N, S, E;   (b) E, S, N, W;
(c) normal to earth when wind is from W or E, zero when wind is from N or S.

3.8.   (a) $-S(r\mathbf{i} + 2\,v\mathbf{j})$, where $\mathbf{i}$ is along spoke and $\mathbf{k}$ is along axle.

3.9. $-A(q^2\mathbf{i} + \dot{q}\mathbf{k}).$

3.11. $\boldsymbol{\omega} + \dot{\theta}\mathbf{j}.$

3.12. $(p \sin \phi + q \cos \phi + \dot{\theta})\mathbf{j}'' +$
$(p \cos \phi \sin \theta - q \sin \phi \sin \theta + [r - \dot{\phi}]\cos \theta)\mathbf{k}''.$

3.13. $\delta\omega(\cos \omega t)\mathbf{j}'' - \dot{\phi}(\cos \theta)\mathbf{k}''.$

3.14. $H = (\sec E)(q \sin B + r \cos B),$
$B = p + (\tan E)(q \sin B + r \cos B),$
$E = q \cos B - r \sin B.$

3.15.   Axis is $\mathbf{i}.$

3.16.   Axis is $3\mathbf{i} + 3\mathbf{j} + \mathbf{k}$;
angle is $\arccos(-5/14).$

CHAPTER 4

4.2.   (a) $2xy + z/x^2$;   (b) $-xz \sin xyz$;
(c) $-r \sin \theta \cos \phi$;   (d) $x(x^2 + y^2 + z^2)^{-1/2}.$

4.3.   (a) $(2xy + z/x^2)\,dx + x^2\,dy - 1/x\;dz$;
(b) $-(\sin xyz)(yz\,dx + xz\,dy + xy\,dz)$;
(c) $(\cos \theta \cos \phi)\,dr - (r \sin \theta \cos \phi)\,d\theta - (r \cos \theta \sin \phi)\,d\phi$;
(d) $(x\,dx + y\,dy + z\,dz)(x^2 + y^2 + z^2)^{-1/2}.$

4.4. $(\frac{3.7}{2})$ in^3

4.5.   (a) $\dfrac{dw}{dr}\dfrac{\partial r}{\partial x}$;

(b) $\dfrac{\partial w}{\partial t} = f_x\dfrac{dx}{dt} + f_y\dfrac{dy}{dt} + f_z\dfrac{dz}{dt} + f_u\dfrac{du}{dt}$;

(c) $\dfrac{\partial w}{\partial u} = f_x\xi_u + f_y\varsigma_u + f_z\eta_u.$

4.6. $z_x = 1,\quad z_y = -1.$

4.7. $z_x = -\phi_x/\phi_z,\quad z_y = -\phi_y/\phi_z.$

4.8. $y' = 1, \quad z' = 0.$

4.9. $u_x = (F_v G_z - F_z G_v)/D, \quad v_y = (F_y G_u - F_u G_y)/D,$
$u_z = (F_v G_z - F_z G_v)/D, \quad \text{where} \quad D = F_u G_v - F_v G_u.$

4.10. $\bar{x} = 0, \quad \bar{y} = 1 - 1/\sqrt{2}, \quad \bar{z} = 0.$

4.11. $2\pi.$

4.12. $0.$

4.13. $2\pi.$

4.14. $\pm 4\pi.$

4.15. (a) $(\mathbf{i} - \mathbf{j} + \mathbf{k})/\sqrt{3}, \quad x - y + z = 1;$
(b) $(\mathbf{i} - \mathbf{j} - \mathbf{k})/\sqrt{3}, \quad x - y - z = 3;$
(c) $(2\mathbf{j} - \mathbf{k})/\sqrt{5}, \quad 2y - z = 1;$
(d) $(-3\mathbf{i} + 4\mathbf{j} + 12\mathbf{k})/13, \quad 3x - 4y - 12z = 0.$

4.16. (b) $z = \pm(3 - x^4 - y^4)^{1/4};$
(c) $z = (y - x^2/4)^2.$

4.17. Three quarters of a circular cylinder, one unit high;
$\mathbf{N} = (\cos u)\mathbf{i} + (\sin u)\mathbf{j}.$

4.18. (a) $\mathbf{N} = \mathbf{A} \times \mathbf{B}/|\mathbf{A} \times \mathbf{B}|;$
(b) $(\mathbf{i} + \mathbf{j} - 3\mathbf{k})/\sqrt{11}, \quad x + y - 3z = 7.$

4.19. Cylinder: $x^2 + y^2 = b^2;$ the portion between $z = 0$ and $z = 3;$
$\mathbf{r} = (b \cos \theta)\mathbf{i} + (b \sin \theta)\mathbf{j} + z\mathbf{k}; \quad \mathbf{N} = (x\mathbf{i} + y\mathbf{j})/b.$

4.20. $\frac{4}{13}.$

4.21. (a) $0;$ (b) $(2x\mathbf{i} + 2y\mathbf{j}) \cdot \mathbf{u};$
(c) $10\sqrt{2}/3;$ constant-w surfaces are cylinders.

4.24. $2x(1 + 2y)/(1 + 4y)^{1/2}.$

4.26. (a) $(y\mathbf{i} - x\mathbf{j})/(x^2 + y^2);$ (b) $0;$ (c) $0.$

4.27. $h'(r)\mathbf{u_r}.$

4.33. $4\sqrt{6}.$

4.34. $2\pi ah.$

4.35. $(17^{3/2} - 1)\pi/6.$

4.36. $\dfrac{17^{5/2} - 41}{10(17^{3/2} - 1)}.$

4.37. $d\sigma = \dfrac{|\nabla\phi|}{\nabla\phi \cdot \mathbf{j}} \, dx \, dz = \dfrac{|\nabla\phi|}{\nabla\phi \cdot \mathbf{i}} \, dy \, dz.$

4.38. $391\sqrt{17}\pi/60 + \pi/60.$

4.39. $0.$

4.41. $3.$

4.42. $0.$

4.43. (a) $-4\pi;$ (b) $4\pi;$ (c) $0.$

CHAPTER 5

5.1. (a) Common value is 2; (b) common value is $2\pi.$

5.3.   (a) 0;   (b) $-\frac{2}{3}$.

5.7.   3.

5.8.   (a) $xy + x^2 + \log y + C$;
            (b) $y + y^2/x + C$;
            (c) $\log x - y/x - y + C$.

5.9.   (a) 2π;   (c) **F** not defined at $r = 0$;
            (d) 0;   (e) $\arctan (x/y)$;
            (f) $3\pi/2$.

5.11.   0.

5.12. $\frac{45}{8}$.

5.13.   0.

5.14.   (a) 0;   (b) $2y^2x + xz - 2$;   (c) $-\pi$.

5.15.   (a) $x^2 + \frac{1}{2}(y^2 + z^2) + C$;   (b) 0.

5.16.   0.

5.17. -1.

5.18.   (a) $xy + \frac{1}{2}(x^2 + y^2 + z^2)$;   (b) $-\frac{1}{2}$.

5.19.   4.

5.20. $\frac{3}{2}$.

5.21.   3.

5.22.   0.

5.23. 324π.

5.24. 8π.

CHAPTER 6

6.1. $(\mathbf{i}, -\mathbf{i} + \mathbf{j})$, $(\mathbf{i} + \mathbf{j}, \mathbf{j})$,   1.

6.2. $h_u h_v h_w = \sqrt{6} \neq 1 = \dfrac{\partial(x, y, z)}{\partial(u, v, w)}$,   coordinates not orthogonal.

6.3. $h_\rho = h_z = 1$, $h_\theta = \rho$, $\nabla\rho = (x\mathbf{i} + y\mathbf{j})$, $\nabla\theta = (-y\mathbf{i} + x\mathbf{j})(x^2 + y^2)$,
            $\nabla z = \mathbf{k}$; z-curves are lines parallel to the z-axis, θz-surfaces are cylinders
            whose axes are the z-axis.

6.4. $h_u = (\cosh^2 u - \cos^2 v)^{1/2}$, $h_v = (\sinh^2 u + \sin^2 v)^{1/2}$;
            v-curves are ellipses, u-curves are hyperbolas;   coordinates
            are orthogonal.

6.5.   (*Partial ans.*) $h_u = a(\cosh^2 u - \cos^2 v)^{1/2}$, $h_\theta = a \sinh u \sin v$.

6.6.   (a) $-(2\mathbf{i} + \mathbf{j} - \mathbf{k})/3$, $(\mathbf{i} + 2\mathbf{j} + \mathbf{k})/3$, $(\mathbf{i} - \mathbf{j} + \mathbf{k})/3$;
            (b) $3ds^2 = 2du_1^2 + 2du_2^2 + du_3^2 - 2du_1\,du_2$.

6.9. $\nabla \cdot \mathbf{V} = \dfrac{\partial V_1}{\partial u_1} + \dfrac{\partial V_2}{\partial U_2} + \dfrac{\partial V_3}{\partial u_3}$

            $\nabla^2 \psi = \psi_{u_1 u_1} - 4\psi_{u_1 u_2} + 2\psi_{u_2 u_2} + 3\psi_{u_3 u_3}$.

6.10. $\nabla^2 \psi = \dfrac{1}{u^2 + v^2}\left\{\psi_{uu} + \psi_{vv} + \dfrac{1}{u}\psi_u + \dfrac{1}{v}\psi_v\right\} + \dfrac{1}{u^2 v^2}\psi_{\theta\theta}$.

INDEX